YOU AND HEREDITY

THESE PARENTS:

Can Have *ONLY*
Blond, Straight-Haired, Blue-Eyed Children

BUT THESE PARENTS:

May Have Various Types of Children,
Including

(For Results of Other Matings, See Text)

YOU *and* HEREDITY

by

AMRAM SCHEINFELD

assisted in the genetic sections by

MORTON D. SCHWEITZER, Ph.D.
RESEARCH GENETICIST, CORNELL UNIVERSITY
MEDICAL COLLEGE

ILLUSTRATED BY THE AUTHOR

With four color-plates and seventy-five drawings, maps and diagrams

Including an original study of The Inheritance
of Musical Talent

FREDERICK A. STOKES COMPANY

NEW YORK   MCMXXXIX

To
MY FATHER
AND
THE MEMORY OF
MY MOTHER

PREFACE

Most books on scientific subjects addressed to the general public are written from the *inside looking out*—that is to say, from the viewpoint of the scientist looking out, and not infrequently down, to the reader.

This book is written from the *outside looking in*—from the viewpoint of a layman peering into the laboratories of the scientists (in this case those concerned with the study of human heredity) and reporting back to others what he has seen, heard and learned.

The two viewpoints differ in many respects, and especially is this true of the subject here dealt with. The scientist studying heredity is preoccupied chiefly with the *processes* by which the findings in his field were achieved and which pave the way for future discoveries. When, and if, he stops to consider the practical aspects of his science in relation to human life, he is inclined to think in terms of broad averages, of large masses and many generations, and of individuals as mere fragments in a limitless mosaic.

But the layman is interested primarily in himself and in the immediate application of the scientific findings to his own life and to his own little world which will come to an end when he passes on.

The difference in viewpoints underlies the motivation and, I hope, the justification for this book. Had any scientist made easily available to me all the facts about human heredity which I wished to know, and which many years of writing for the general public have taught me that others wish to know, this book would never have been written, nor should I have had the temerity to think of writing it. When I began my study of the subject, it was solely with the practical purpose of utilizing some facts about human heredity in a projected work of fiction. Before very long I discovered that the findings in this field so completely shattered my own preconceived notions and the ideas held by all but an initiated few, as to obliterate my original plans. I became convinced that the most interestіng and important task before me was to acquire as thorough a knowledge of this subject as I could and then, in some way, to communicate what I had learned to others.

The subsequent steps included my enrolment (at a mature age) for a college course in genetics and the setting aside of all other activity for several years to devote myself to further study and research. The first fruits came with a series of articles on human heredity which I wrote for a popular magazine. These proved to my own satisfaction that the subject could be expounded to laymen without putting them through the technical mazes of meiosis and mitosis, the formation of spindle fibers and polar bodies, of linkage, cross-over, nondisjunction of chromosomes, tetraploidy, etc., all considered essentials in almost every college course and treatise on genetics.

From the articles grew the plan for a book, but even when the contract for it was signed with my publishers, nothing like the present work was contemplated. That it did grow to its present proportions was due to many factors, not the least of which was the quite unexpected aid and encouragement given it by the very scientists and other authorities who, I had feared, would look askance at such a project undertaken by one outside their fold.

Thus, well aware that a layman writing on a scientific subject must, like Caesar's wife, be—or try to be—above suspicion, I am heartened by the thought that in every phase of this book I have had expert counsel and guidance, and that, as a happy consequence, my acknowledgments of indebtedness are many.

In my toddling steps I was aided by Dr. Henry J. Fry of the New School For Social Research. Later, as the necessity for an active scientific associate grew imperative, through the friendly offices of Prof. Donald C. Lancefield, then of Columbia University and now of Queens College, I was brought in touch with Dr. Morton D. Schweitzer of the Cornell University Medical College.

Dr. Schweitzer's participation in this enterprise proved one of the happiest events that could have befallen it. To him fell the task of gathering most of the material for the chapters dealing with hereditary diseases and defects, and of preparing the data for the extensive "black" gene lists; of working out genetic ratios for the various "forecast" tables and other parts involving genetic predictions; and in general, of casting a trained eye over all the facts and statements in the book coming within the scope of his knowledge as a geneticist. I can say unreservedly that without his enthusiastic cooperation, painstaking research and meticulous editing, this book would have fallen short of such scientific validity as it may now possess.

Because human genetics is correlated with all other sciences dealing with human beings, it was necessary to seek further for information and counsel from physicians, sociologists, psychologists, anthropologists and various other experts. This aid was so graciously and generously given wherever sought that every part of this book can be said to have had the benefit in its preparation of careful reading, discussion, criticism or editing by some qualified expert. With both pride and gratitude I therefore acknowledge my great indebtedness to the following:

Prof. Lancefield, for reading all the first twenty chapters; Dr. George W. Henry, Associate Professor of Psychiatry at Cornell University Medical College, for reading and discussing "Sick Minds," "The Twilight Sexes" and "Sexual Behavior"; Dr. Walter Bromberg, Senior Psychiatrist, Bellevue Psychiatric Hospital, and Psychiatrist of the New York Criminal Courts, for editing the aforementioned three chapters and "Enter the Villain"; Dr. Alfred J. Lotka, of the Metropolitan Life Insurance Company, for editing and aiding, with members of his staff, in the preparation of charts for "How Long Will You Live?", and to Prof. Raymond Pearl, of Johns Hopkins University, for reading and discussing that chapter; Dr. Dwight F. Chapman, of the Department of Psychology, Columbia University, for helpful criticisms and suggestions regarding "The Battle of the IQ's" and "Personality"; Prof. Carl E. Seashore, of the University of Iowa, for reading "Musical Talent" and giving pertinent advice regarding the original study presented therein; Dr. Gene Weltfish, of the Department of Anthropology, Columbia University, for her suggestions regarding "Race" and her invaluable aid in the preparation of maps for that chapter; and to Frederick Osborn, Associate in Anthropology, American Museum of Natural History, for reading and discussing

"Ancestry," "The Giddy Stork," "Eugenics: Negative" and "Program for Tomorrow."

(In all of these acknowledgments no responsibility is implied on the part of the individuals named for any errors of fact or judgment that may still have survived in the text. The responsibility for any failings of commission or omission, or for any opinions expressed in this book, I accept fully as my own.)

On behalf of Dr. Schweitzer, as well as on my behalf, thanks are extended to the following who discussed with him special phases of disease inheritance: Dr. James Ewing, Director of the Memorial Hospital for the Treatment of Cancer; Dr. May Wilson, Associate Professor of Pediatrics at Cornell University Medical College (childhood rheumatism); Dr. Eugene Opie, Professor of Pathology at Cornell (tuberculosis); and also to Drs. William Schmidt, Harold Aaron, Emanuel Klein, Nathan Kaliss and Emil Smith.

Overseas our thanks go to Prof. J. B. S. Haldane of the University of London who, in editing this book for British publication, made many important suggestions by which we have profited. For several other corrections we may thank Prof. S. J. Holmes of the University of California.

For discussion of problems relating to intelligence I am indebted to Prof. Gertrude H. Hildreth of Teachers College, Columbia University; Dr. Beth L. Wellman of the University of Iowa; Dr. Donah B. Lithauer, Psychologist of the Hebrew Orphan Asylum, New York; and Dr. I. Newton Kugelmass.

Special thanks, which I am sure will be echoed by all music lovers, are due to the scores of musicians and singers who contributed data for the study of the Inheritance of Musical Talent, to their concert managements and personal representatives who aided in enlisting their cooperation, and to Ernest Hutcheson, President of the Juilliard Institute; also, for the auxiliary study of Voice Types, to Miss Rose Held and members of the Schola Cantorum.

To Prof. Gregory G. Pincus and to the Anatomical Record I am indebted for permission to reproduce the photograph of the human ovum; to Dr. Seymour F. Wilhelm, of Beth Israel and Montefiore Hospitals, New York City, for the slide from which the spermatozoa photograph was made; to Prof. Lewis M. Terman of Stanford University and to the McGraw-Hill Company, for permission to use material from "Sex and Personality"; and to the Macmillan Company for permission to quote from "Human Heredity," by Baur, Fischer and Lenz.

My memory has undoubtedly failed me with regard to others who have been of great help. Also, while I do not name them, members of my family and many friends know how deep is my gratitude for innumerable services and considerate acts which contributed toward the production of this book.

Finally, I wish to acknowledge my debt to all the many geneticists, scientists and research workers from whose painstaking studies I have gleaned, and in the conveyance of whose findings my rôle has been merely that of a reporter. It is my hope that the indebtedness will be repaid in some measure by such added interest as this book may stimulate in their work.

To acknowledge my great debt to my publishers would be superfluous, for the make-up of this book itself will speak for their faith in this enterprise and the unlimited support and encouragement which they gave it.

AMRAM SCHEINFELD

New York City,
June 1, 1939.

CONTENTS

LIST OF ILLUSTRATIONS

YOU AND HEREDITY

CHAPTER I

A NEW SCIENCE

STOP and think about yourself:

In all the history of the world there was never any one else exactly like you, and in all the infinity of time to come there will never be another.

Whether or not you attach any importance to that fact, undoubtedly you have often wondered what made you what you are; what it was that you got from your parents and your ancestors and how much of you resulted from your own efforts or the effects of environment; and finally, what of yourself you could pass on to your children.

Until comparatively recently, all this was a matter of theory and speculation. Not until the dawn of this century was anything definitely established about the mechanism of heredity, and for some years thereafter the most important points were bandied about like footballs among the biologists. Then, dramatically climaxing a series of some of the most remarkable experiments in all scientific history, the whole field of genetics (the study of heredity and variation among living things) became brilliantly illumined, and what had been theory became fact.

With American geneticists, led by the Nobel Prize winner, Thomas Hunt Morgan, in the vanguard, the work has been proceeding on many broad fronts throughout the world. New data are pouring in with increasing volume from geneticists, pathologists, and other scientists. Experiments are repeated countless times, statements checked and rechecked. If the reader is inclined to be skeptical regarding some of the conclusions, let him be advised that no greater skeptics can be found than the geneticists themselves. Their rigid determination to take nothing for granted, and to subject the reports of even their most brilliant colleagues to the severest tests, has made genetics one of the most exact of all biological sciences.

Thus it can be said with assurance that the mechanism of heredity—among humans as among other living and growing things—now stands clearly revealed. While all of its intricacies are by no means laid bare, the basic principles are as unmistakably clear as the workings of a watch. Problems of heredity that confounded the greatest thinkers and scientists of the past, from Aristotle to Darwin, have been solved. Long-standing mysteries about birth and development have been unraveled. Endless popular beliefs, theories and superstitions have been completely discredited. Existing social philosophies have been called into question and the way pointed to a reconstruction of humanity itself.

And yet, vitally important as all this is, very little of it has so far seeped through to the general public. If nobody believes in the stork any more, it is astonishing what people still do believe about heredity. The fault, however, is not that of the layman. Developments in the field of genetics have been too rapid and recent to reach widespread circulation, and most of the published reports have been of so technical a nature as to have little appeal for the average reader. Even where isolated phases of the subject are popularly treated in newspapers and magazines, the layman is generally left confused through lack of sufficient understanding of the basic principles.

So we come to the purpose of this book, which is:

1. To sift out from the genetics laboratories and research fields the outstanding facts about heredity directly applicable to human beings.

2. To present these facts in clear-cut, untechnical language, diagrams and illustrations.

3. To point out what their significance may be to the individual and to society, leaving the reader to draw his own conclusions.

The steps and processes by which these findings were arrived at will be largely omitted. It is assumed that you, the reader, do not care two raps about the love life of sea urchins or about the interaction of hereditary factors for coat colors in mice, or what happens when a yellow-bodied *Drosophila melanogaster* (fruit-fly) with double-bar eyes and vestigial wings is crossed with a gray-bodied, long-winged, normal red-eyed one. True, without laborious study of these lowlier creatures the geneticists could never have arrived at the facts about human beings, for not the least of their amazing discoveries has been that the mechanism of heredity is almost the same in all living things.

Nevertheless, the facts about the laboratory creatures can wait. What you probably wish to know, as directly as possible, are the answers to the innumerable questions about your own heredity and that of your fellow humans. These questions we hope have been anticipated and answered in the following pages.

The fact has not been overlooked that many readers may already know more or less about the subject of heredity; but for the sake of the many others to whom this is all quite new, it is our plan to presuppose no previous knowledge whatsoever. And so, in the vernacular, we are going to start from "scratch."

CHAPTER II

LIFE BEGINS AT ZERO

A SPERM and an egg: You, like every other human being and most other animals, began life as just that.

A single sperm enters a single egg and a new individual is started on its way.

Leaving aside for the present the part played by the mother, we know that a father's rôle in his child's heredity is fixed the moment that it is conceived. Whatever it is that the father passes on to his child must be contained within that single sperm.

But to find out exactly what that sperm contains has not been so simple a matter.

Consider, first, its size:

One hundred million sperms may be present in a single drop of seminal fluid. Two billion sperms—two thousand million, as many as were needed to father all the people in the world today—could be comfortably housed in the cap of a small-sized tube of toothpaste!

The microscope had to be well perfected before a sperm could be even seen. Then, in the first flush of discovery, carried away by their desire to believe, just as children and lovers imagine that they see a man in the moon, some scientists (*circa* 1700 A.D.) reported excitedly that every sperm contained a tiny embryonic being. With professional gravity they gave it the name of "homunculus" (little man), and scientific papers appeared showing careful drawings of the little being in the sperm—although there was some dispute as to whether it had its arms folded or pressed against its side, and whether or not its head had any features.

Presently, however, it became apparent that imagination had run away with scientific perspicacity. The head of the sperm—in which interest rightfully centered, as the tail was merely a means for

4

THE HUMAN EGG

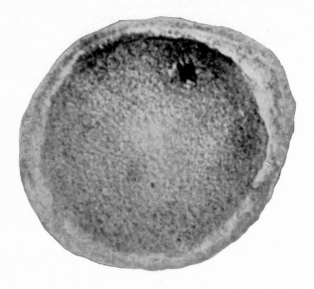

A two-day old un-
fertilized h u m a n
ovum, photograph-
ed by Dr. Gregory
G. Pincus.

Magnification and
enlargement about
600 diameters, or
millions of times by
volume.

The black spot at
upper center is the
region of the nu-
cleus.

HUMAN SPERMS

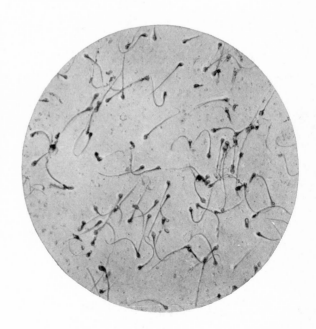

*Photographed from a
slide prepared by Dr.
Seymour F. Wilhelm.*

Magnification about
the s a m e as egg
above, showing rela-
tive size of a single
s p e r m c o m p a r e d
with the human egg.

propelling it—proved to be a solid little mass that defied all attempts at detailed study. Even the great Darwin, who was so right about many things, could never more than guess at what the sperm head comprised—and his guess was a wrong one. Many scientists thought it was hopeless to try to find out. Others concluded that if the sperm head itself could never be dissected and its contents examined, they might still find out what it carried if they could learn what happened *after* it entered the egg. And in this they were right.

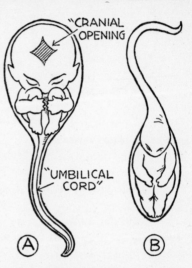

Crowning years of painstaking study, we know at last that what a human sperm carries— the precious load that it fights so desperately to deliver—*are twenty-four minute things called chromosomes.*

When the sperm enters the egg, and penetrates its substance, the head begins to unfold and reveal itself as having been made up of the twenty-four closely packed chromosomes. As they represent everything that enters the egg, we know beyond any doubt that *these chromo-somes must comprise all the hereditary material contributed by the father.*

THE HOMUNCULUS (or Manikin) which early scientists believed was contained in the sperm.

After drawings by

(a) Hartsoeker—1694

(b) Dalempatius—1699

What of the egg? Although many thousands of times larger than the sperm, the egg is yet smaller than a period on this page, barely visible to the naked eye. Under the microscope we see that it consists largely of foodstuffs with the exception of a tiny globule, or nucleus. What that contains we see when the sperm head enters the egg and releases its chromosomes. *Almost at the same time, the egg nucleus breaks up and releases its twenty-four similar chromosomes*—the contribution of the mother to the child's heredity.

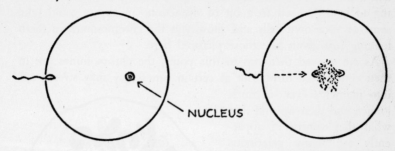

FERTILIZATION

(A) Sperm-head enters egg

(B) Sperm-head and nucleus of egg each release their chromosomes.

Thus, the new individual is started off with *forty-eight* chromosomes.

In order to reveal the otherwise colorless chromosomes special dyes have to be applied. When this is done, they appear as colored bodies. Hence their name "chromosomes" (color-bodies).

But almost immediately another remarkable fact becomes apparent. We find that the chromosomes are of twenty-four different kinds as to shape, size, etc., with one of each kind contributed by each parent. If we could arrange all the pairs in a line they would look like this:

A B C D E F G H I J K L M N O P Q R S T U V W X

How human chromosomes would look
if arranged in pairs.

These forty-eight chromosomes comprised all the physical heritage with which you began your life.

By a process of division and redivision, as we shall see in detail later, these initial forty-eight chromosomes are so multiplied that eventually every cell in the body contains an exact replica of each and every one of them. This is not mere theory. If you were willing to lend yourself to a bit of dissection, an expert could take some of your own cells and show you the chromosomes in them looking just about like those pictured here.

As we viewed them up to this point, the chromosomes are in their compressed form. But at certain times they may stretch out into filaments ever so much longer, and then we find that what they consist of apparently are many gelatinous beads closely strung together.

These beads either are, in themselves, or contain the *"genes,"* and *it is the genes which, so far as science can now establish, are the ultimate factors of heredity.* Under the most powerful magnification, differences are apparent among these chromosome sections in size, depth of shading, and patterns of striping. But whether or not

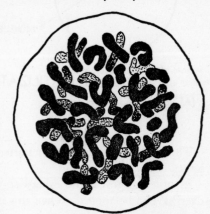

HUMAN CHROMOSOMES
As they look under the microscope.

differences are revealed to the eye, we *know* beyond any question that each gene has a definite function in the creation and development of the individual.

Of all the miraculous particles in the universe, one can hardly conceive of anything more amazing than these infinitesimally tiny units. We say again "infinitesimally tiny" for want of another and better expression. Think of the microscopic size of a sperm. Then recall that the head of a sperm alone contains twenty-four chromosomes. And now consider that strung in a single chromosome might be anywhere from scores to hundreds of genes—with a single gene, in some cases, able to change the whole life of an individual!

To grasp all this you must prepare yourself for a world in

which minuteness is carried to infinity. Contemplating the heavens, you already may have adjusted yourself to the idea of an infinity of bigness. You can readily believe that the sun is millions of miles away, that stars, mere specks of light, may be many times larger than the earth; that the light from a star which burned up six thousand years ago, is reaching us only now; that there are billions of stars in the space beyond space which our most power-

THE GENES

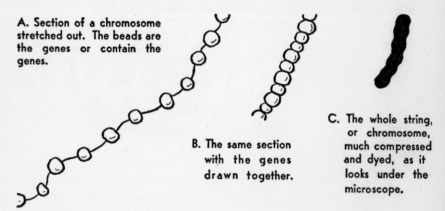

A. Section of a chromosome stretched out. The beads are the genes or contain the genes.

B. The same section with the genes drawn together.

C. The whole string, or chromosome, much compressed and dyed, as it looks under the microscope.

ful telescopes cannot yet reveal. This is the *infinity of bigness outside of you.*

Now turn to the world *inside* of you. Here there is an *infinity of smallness.* As we trace further and further inward we come to the last units of life that we can distinguish—the genes. And here with our limited microscopes, we must stop, just as we are stopped in our exploration of the stars by the limitations of our telescopes. But we can make some pretty good guesses about what the genes are from what we already know about what they can do.

You believe the astronomer when he tells you that, on October 26, in the year 2144, at thirty-four minutes and twelve seconds past twelve o'clock noon there will be a total eclipse of the sun. You believe this because time and again the predictions have come true.

You must now likewise prepare yourself to believe the geneticist when he tells you that a specific gene, which cannot yet be seen, will nevertheless at such and such a time do such and such things and create such and such effects—*under certain specified conditions.* The geneticist must make many more reservations than the astronomer, for genetics as a science is but a day-old infant compared to astronomy, and the genes are *living substances* whose action is complicated by innumerable factors. But despite all this, so much has already been established about our gene workings that we must stand in greater awe than ever at this latest revelation of how fearfully and wonderfully we are made.

THE HEREDITY PROCESS

EVERY MAN and EVERY WOMAN
At conception received
24 Chromosomes from each parent
or 48 in all

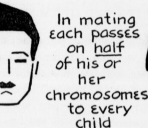

In mating
each passes
on <u>half</u>
of his or
her
chromosomes
to every
child

24   24

The FATHER'S rôle
is merely that of
passing on <u>half</u>
of his chromosomes
by way of a
sperm

These 48 chromo-
somes comprise
everything that
determines the
heredity of
the child

—The MOTHER,
although she also
acts as incubator
and nourisher for
the egg, con-
tributes no more
to the child's
heredity than
does the Father

CHAPTER III

THE ETERNAL GERM-PLASM

No less important than knowing what heredity is, is knowing what it *is not*. Before we examine the chromosomes and their genes in detail, let us first find out how the sperms or eggs which carry them are produced in the parent. That in itself will clear away much of the deadwood of the past with innumerable false theories, beliefs and superstitions about the life processes.

Not so long ago the most learned of scientists believed that whatever it was that the sperms or eggs contained, these were *products* of the individual, in which were incorporated in some way *extracts* of themselves. That is to say, that each organ or part of a person's body contributed something to the sperm or egg. Darwin, a proponent of that theory, called these somethings "gemmules."

By the "gemmule" theory, all the characteristics of both parents could be transmitted to the child, to be blended in some mysterious way within the egg and reproduced during development. A child would therefore be the result of what its parents were at the time it was conceived. As the parents changed through life, so would their eggs or sperms, and the chromosomes in them, also change. All that is what scientists believed not so long ago, and what the vast majority of people today still believe—erroneously.

The theory that sperms or eggs change as the individual changes has now been upset. Because we have learned finally that the chromosomes which they contain are *not new products of the individual* and are most certainly not made up of "gemmules" or contributions from the various parts of the body.

As we have seen, a human being starts life as just a single cell containing forty-eight chromosomes. That initial cell must be multiplied countless times to produce a fully developed person,

HOW A FERTILIZED EGG-CELL MULTIPLIES

(1) Original cell. (Only four chromosomes shown, for simplification)

(2) Each chromosome splits in half, lengthwise

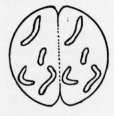

(3) The halved chromosomes go to opposite sides and wall forms between them as cell begins to divide

(4) The halved chromosomes grow to full size, resulting in two cells, each a replica of the original

and this is accomplished by a process of division and redivision, as shown in the accompanying illustration.

Continuing in the same way, the two cells become four, the four eight, and this goes on into the billions—the material with which to make the cells, after that in the egg is exhausted, coming from the mother.

But the cells do not all remain the same, by any means. After the earliest stages, when they are still very limited in number, they begin "specializing." Some give rise to muscle cells, some to skin, blood, brain, bone and other cells, to form different parts of the body. But a certain number of cells remain aloof. They take no part in building the body proper, and at all odds preserve their chromosomes unchanged and unaffected by anything that happens outside of them—short of death itself.

These "reserve" cells are the germ cells, dedicated to posterity. *It is from these cells that the sperms or eggs are derived.*

When a boy is born, he already has in his testes all the germ cells out of which sperms will eventually be produced. When he reaches puberty, a process is inaugurated that will continue throughout his life—or most of his life, at any rate. In the same way that billions of cells grew from one, millions of more germ cells are manufactured from time to time by division and re-division. Up to a certain point the process is the same as that previously explained—but just before the sperms themselves are to be formed, something different occurs. The chromosomes in the germ cell remain intact and the cell merely splits in half, *each half getting only twenty-four chromosomes, or one of every pair.*

The process of forming the sperms is illustrated on the following page (several stages omitted for simplification). This should make clear how, from a parent germ cell with the regular quota of forty-eight chromosomes, two sperms are formed, each carrying only twenty-four chromosomes. The reason and necessity for this "reduction division" will be explained presently.

Before we go on, let us stop to answer a question which has undoubtedly caused concern to many a man:

"Is it true that the number of sperms in a man is limited, and that if he is wasteful with them in early life, the supply will run out later?"

No, for as we have seen, the sperms are made out of germ cells thrown off without decreasing the "reserve" stock. Endless billions of sperms can continue to be discharged from a man's body (200,000,000 to 500,000,000 in a single ejaculation) and the original quota of germ cells will be there to provide more—so long as the reproductive machinery functions and the body can supply the material out of which to make them. (However, dissipation to an extreme point which might injure or weaken the body—and similarly, disease, accident, or old age—can curtail the production of sperms, or greatly reduce the number of those that are virile.)

HOW SPERMS ARE PRODUCED

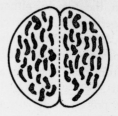

(1) Germ cell, containing forty-eight chromosomes

(2) The paired chromosomes separate, going to opposite sides of the cell, and the cell divides

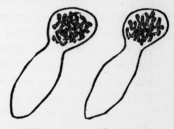

(3) There are now two half-cells, with only twenty-four single chromosomes in each

(4) The chromosomes mass together, and part of the cell contents forms a sheath around them

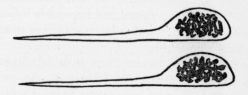

(5) The sheath shapes the chromosomes into a tightly packed mass forming the head. The rest of the cell contents is squeezed out behind to form the tail

In the female, although the eggs are also manufactured out of germ cells, the process does not provide for an endless number, running into billions, as in the case of the sperms. The female, when she reaches puberty, will be required normally to mature only one egg a month, for a period of about thirty-five years. So, when a girl baby is born, the fundamental steps in the process have already been taken, and the germ cells have already been turned into eggs. In other words, her ovaries at birth contain tiny clusters of all the eggs (in rudimentary form) which will mature years later. The chromosomes which she will pass on to her future children are, however, already present and will not be changed in any way. The maturing process will merely increase the size of the egg by loading it with a store of food material with which to start a new individual on its way.

Although we can ignore the complicated details of the egg-formation process, it may be pointed out that before the eggs are formed from the germ cells there is a "reduction" division, just as there is in the case of the sperms. This gives each egg, like each sperm, only *half* of the parent's quota of the chromosomes. But when the sperm, with its twenty-four *single* chromosomes, unites with the egg, with its twenty-four corresponding *single* chromosomes, the result is an individual with two each of every chromosome—twenty-four *pairs,* or forty-eight, the required quota for a human being.

If that reduction process hadn't taken place, each sperm or egg would carry 48 chromosomes; on uniting they would start off an individual with 96 chromosomes; the next generation would begin with 192, and so on to an absurd and impossible infinity. However, this reduction division, it will soon be seen, has much more than a mathematical significance.

One fact should be constantly kept in mind: Regardless of the differences in their processes of formation, *the sperms or eggs receive chromosomes which are replicas of those which the parents themselves received when they were conceived*. Nothing that happened to the *body cells* of the parents throughout their lives could have been communicated to their germ cells so as to alter the genes, or hereditary factors, which their child would receive.

Does this mean that a gene can *never* change? No, for as we shall see in a later chapter, a change ("mutation") might take place at rare intervals in any given human gene, either spontaneously or through some *outside influence* about which we know very little. *But nothing that we ourselves do can change the make-up of our germ cells.*

It is as if, when Nature creates an individual, she hands over to him billions of body cells to do with as he wishes, and in addition, wrapped up separately, a small number of special germ cells whose contents are to be passed on to the next generation. And, because Nature apparently does not trust the individual, she sees to it that the hereditary factors in those germ cells are so sealed that he cannot tamper with them or alter them in the slightest degree.

CHAPTER IV

WHAT WE *DON'T* INHERIT

MEN since the world began have taken comfort in the thought that they could pass on to their children not merely the possessions they had acquired, but also the physical and mental attributes they had developed.

To both types of inheritance, as previously conceived, serious blows have been dealt within recent years. The passing on of worldly goods has been greatly limited by huge inheritance taxes in most countries, and abolished (almost) entirely in Russia. As for physical heredity, all preexisting conceptions have been shaken by the finding we have just dealt with:

The chromosomes in our germ cells are not affected by any change that takes place within our body cells.

What this means is that no change that we make in ourselves or that is made in us in our lifetimes, for better or for worse, can be passed on to our children through the process of physical heredity. Such changes—made in a person by what he does, or what happens to him—are called *acquired characteristics.* Whether such characteristics could be passed on has provided one of the most bitter controversies in the study of heredity. It has been waged by means of thousands of experiments, and is still being carried on by a valiant few. But now that the smoke of battle has cleared away, there remains standing no verified evidence to prove that any acquired characteristic can be inherited.

Reluctantly we must abandon the belief that what we in one generation do to improve ourselves, physically and mentally, can be passed on through our germ-plasm to the next generation. It may not be comforting to think that all such improvements will go to the grave with us. And yet the same conclusion holds for the defects developed in us, of the things we may do in our life-

17

times to weaken or harm ourselves. If we cannot pass on the good, we cannot likewise pass on the bad.

Why we can't should now be obvious. Knowing that all that we transmit to our children, physically, are the chromosomes, it means that in order to pass on any change in ourselves, every such change as it occurred would have to be communicated to the germ cells and accompanied by some corresponding change in every specific gene in every specific chromosome concerned with the characteristic involved.

Just imagine that you had a life-sized, plastic statue of yourself and that inside of it was a small, hermetically sealed container filled with millions of microscopic replicas of this statue. Suppose now that you pulled out of shape and enlarged the nose of the big statue. Could that, by any means you could conceive, automatically enlarge all the noses on all the millions of little statues inside? Yet that is about what would have to happen if a change in any feature or characteristic of a parent were to be communicated to the germ cells, and thence to the child. It applies to the binding of feet by the Chinese, to circumcision among the Jews, to facial mutilation and distortion among savages, to all the artificial changes made by people on their bodies throughout generations, which have not produced any effect on their offspring. And it applies to the *mind* as well.

Nature performs many seeming miracles in the process of heredity. But it would be too much to ask that every time you took a correspondence course or deepened a furrow in your brain, every gene in your germ cells concerned with the mental mechanism would brighten up accordingly. Or that, with every hour you spent in a gymnasium, the genes concerned with the muscle-building processes would increase their vigor.

Thinking back to your father, you will see that what he was, or what he made of himself in his lifetime, might have little relation to the hereditary factors he passed on to you.

Remember, first, that your father gave you only *half* of his chromosomes—and which ones he gave you depended entirely on chance. It may be possible that you didn't receive a single one of the chromosomes which gave your father his outstanding characteristics.

Aside from this fact, what your father was or is may not at all indicate what hereditary factors were in him. The genes, as we shall see presently, do not necessarily *determine* characteristics. What they determine are the *possibilities* for a person's development under given circumstances.

Thus, your father may have been a distinguished citizen or a derelict, a success or a failure, and yet this may provide no clear indication of what chromosomes were in him. But whether or not the nature of his chromosomes did reveal themselves through his characteristics, you can make only a guess as to which of them came to you by studying unusual traits that your father and you have in common.

You may already be thinking, "What about my children? How much of *myself* did I, or can I, pass on to them?"

Let us first see what you *can't* pass on.

You may have started life with genes that tended to make you a brilliant person, but sickness, poverty, hard luck or laziness kept you from getting an education. *Your children would be born with exactly the same mental equipment as if you had acquired a string of degrees from Yale to Oxford.*

Suppose you are a woman who had been beautiful in girlhood, but through accident, suffering or hardship, had lost your looks. *The children born to you at your homeliest period would be not one whit different than had you developed into a movie queen.*

Suppose you are a World War veteran who was shell-shocked, blinded, crippled and permanently invalided. *If you had a child today his heredity would be basically the same as in one you might have fathered in your fullest vigor when you marched off to the Front.*

Suppose you are old.

The sperms of a man of ninety-five, if he is still capable of producing virile sperms (and there are records of men who were) would be the same in their hereditary factors as when he was sixteen. And although the span of reproductive life in a woman is far shorter than in a man, the eggs of a woman of forty-five would similarly be no different in their genes than when she was a young girl.

Nevertheless, there may be considerable difference in the off-spring born to parents under different conditions. But not because of *heredity*.

Let us take the case of drunkenness. On this point alone endless controversy raged in previous years. Certain experiments were reported as proving that drunkenness, and other dangerous habits, could be passed on by heredity. All these "findings" have since been discredited. But you may ask: "If drunkenness is not inherited, how explain that children of drunkards are so often drunkards themselves?"

The most likely and obvious explanation would be, "through precept and example."

As often as not, similarities between child and parent (mother as well as father), which are ascribed to heredity are really the effects of similar influences and conditions to which they have been exposed. In fact, *so interrelated and so dependent on each other are the forces of environment and heredity in making us what we are that they cannot be considered apart, and at every stage in this book will be discussed together.*

Thus where heredity may fall down, environment may be there to carry on. And if you ask, "Can I pass on to my child any of the accomplishments or improvements I have made in myself?" the answer may be, "Yes! You can pass on a great deal—not by heredity, but by training and environment!"

The successful, educated, decent-living father can give his son a better start in life. The athletic father can, by example and training, insure his child a better physique. The healthy, intelligent, alert mother can insure her child a more favorable entry into the world, and after it is born, can influence it for the better in innumerable ways.

There are, however, limits to what environment can accomplish. Exaggerated claims made for it in previous years have been refuted by the findings in genetics. The theory of the extreme "behaviorists" that any kind of person could be produced out of any stock by the proper training, has been deflated. On the other hand, the extreme "hereditarians" who in the first flush of discovering the mechanism of heredity attributed everything to its workings, have also been given a setback.

All that we can do here is to present the facts about heredity and environment. As to their relative influence on your own life, on that of your children or others, you will be left to draw your own conclusions.

CHAPTER V

MYTHS OF MATING

OF the various myths about mating and parenthood, one that has been most ardently cherished is that which many loving couples cling to about "putting themselves in the right state for the conception of a child." To disillusion them may be almost as bad as telling children there is no Santa Claus. But what we have just learned should convince us of the sad, unromantic fact that whether a child is conceived during a glamorous sojourn on sunny strands, or in the depressing air of a dingy tenement, whether in the height of passion or when its parents are barely on speaking terms with one another, the hereditary factors transmitted to it will be not one whit different.

What, then, of a *"love child"*? Popular belief is that a child born out of wedlock is in some ways different from a legitimate child —that it is likely to be more delicate, more sensitive, developing to extremes—often a criminal or a genius. It need hardly be stated that Nature takes no note of marriage certificates. Yet, strangely enough, an illegitimate child, as such, may well be different from a legitimate child. Not, however, because of any *genetic* difference, but again because of *environment*.

The worry of the unmarried mother, the improper care she generally receives and the furtiveness often preceding and following the birth may leave their mark on the illegitimate child. Subsequently the bad start may be overcome, but too often adverse conditions, both physical and psychological, attend the development of the illegitimate child and continue through life, strongly influencing its constitution and character, and sometimes giving it that queer twist which may lead it to great depths or great heights. Here we have a clear case of where environmental effects may be confused with those of heredity; for under the same conditions as stated, a legitimate child might be expected to turn out exactly like the illegitimate one.

The *age of parents* is also believed to affect the nature of the child, but where it does, it is only through environmental influences. A "child of old age," born, let us say, when a mother is in mid-forty and the father in his sixties, frequently appears to be frailer and sicklier than others. The explanation will be found not in any weakness in the parent's sperm or egg, but (1) in the less favorable intra-uterine environment provided by the older mother; (2) in the greater opportunity she has had to become affected by disease over the years; and (3) in the fact that such late births are generally unwanted and occur mostly where conditions for childbearing are bad. Following birth other factors enter. The "child of old age," surrounded as is often the case by mature brothers, sisters and their friends, in addition to the older parents, is frequently pampered and spoiled, and may quite understandably become high-strung and precocious.

In children born to very young mothers (under seventeen), both the intra-uterine and post-natal conditions are also likely to be unfavorable.

It should be hardly necessary now to dwell long on certain other erroneous beliefs associated with mating and parenthood, which, while prevalent largely among breeders of domestic animals, are also applied to human beings:

"Telegony" is the theory that if a female is mated with two or more successive males, the influence of an earlier sire may carry over to offspring of a later father.

Similarly, by "infection," that a male mated first with an undesirable female (a blooded bull with a scrub cow) may communicate some of her characteristics to offspring of the next female with whom he is mated.

Or that continued mating together may cause a male and female to resemble each other, and that by "saturation" the oftener a female is mated with the same male, the more the successive offspring will resemble him.

In the last two cases, the explanation which should readily occur is that individuals who live together for a long time, whether lower animals or humans, may show common effects of the same environment, diet, habits and other living conditions. Husbands and wives sometimes may get to look alike in the same way that any persons living in the same environment may develop similarities of physique and appearance. One often hears it said of a couple, "You'd think they were brother and sister!" The same environmental influence also tends to increase the resemblance between children and parents.

The myths and superstitions associated with mating and parenthood could fill a book by themselves. Back of all of them lie sometimes coincidences, sometimes mistaken assumptions of paternity, and most often the cropping out of hidden factors (recessive genes) which will be dealt with more fully further along.

One common question regarding mating may deserve special attention:

"Can there be such a thing as 'conflict' between the chromosomes of one person and another—a genetic incompatibility that would seriously affect or prevent birth of children?"

Yes, but only as applied to certain individuals, not to "races," groups or "types" of human beings. This is an important distinction. Later we shall see how in given persons there may be specific "dangerous" genes or other genetic factors which may seriously affect their having children if mated with each other. But one should not jump to the conclusion that this would single out persons of radically different "surface types." For the fact is that *all* human beings, regardless of "race," "type," "color" or any other classification in which they are placed, are, as members of the same species, sexually and genetically compatible with one another.

No such chromosome incompatibility exists between any two kinds of humans as there does between animals of different species —a cat and a dog, a chicken and a goose, etc. The tallest, blondest "Nordic" could mate with the smallest, blackest pigmy and produce children perfectly normal in the eyes of Nature. This, however, has certain qualifications, for if a tall, big-boned European mated with a pigmy woman, the child might be too large for her to bear without danger to it or to herself. The same, however, would apply to the mating of any extremely large man with

MATING
A Cat and a Dog

Cannot mate and have offspring together because they are of different species,

—and their chromosomes differing in kind and number are not compatible.

A Horse and a Donkey

Although of different species can mate and produce MULE offspring.
But these are sterile because

   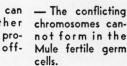

A HORSE

produces eggs or sperms containing one kind of chromosomes.

A DONKEY

produces eggs or sperms with another kind of chromosomes.

—While these can work together somehow to produce MULE offspring

— The conflicting chromosomes cannot form in the Mule fertile germ cells.

BUT All Varieties of Human Beings Are Fertile With One Another

Because
—All humans are of the same species with the same kind of chromosomes. Thus, the smallest pygmy

—and the tallest Nordic could mate and produce a child perfectly normal in the eyes of Nature.

a very small woman, even of the same "race," where sometimes a Caesarian operation is required to deliver the child.

The theory has been advanced that in the mating of parents of radically different types, serious disharmonies may result in the bodily structure and features of their offspring. The evidence on that score is far from conclusive, and until proved otherwise, must be placed among "beliefs" rather than facts, with which we are dealing.

As matters stand "incompatibility" of chromosomes or of their genetic make-up need hardly be a bogey to any except relatively few prospective parents.

CHAPTER VI

THE MIRACLE OF *YOU*

WHAT was the most thrilling, perilous, extraordinary adventure in your life?

Whatever you might answer, you are almost certain to be wrong. For the most remarkable and dramatic series of events that could possibly have befallen you took place before you were born.

In fact, it was virtually a miracle that YOU were born at all!

Consider what had to happen:

First, YOU—that very special person who is YOU and no one else in this universe—could have been the child of only *two specific parents* out of all the untold billions past and present. Assuming that YOU had been ordered up in advance by some capricious Power, it was an amazing enough coincidence that your parents came together. But taking that for granted, what were the chances of their having had YOU as a child? In other words, how many different kinds of children could they have had, or could any couple have, theoretically, if the number were unlimited?

This is not an impossible question. It can be answered by calculating how many different combinations of chromosomes any two parents can produce in their eggs or sperms. For what every parent gives to a child is just half of his or her chromosomes—one representative of every pair taken at random. In that fact you will find the explanation of why YOU are different from your brothers and sisters, why no two children (except "identical" twins) can ever be the same in their heredity.

Putting yourself in the rôle of parent, think for a moment of your fingers (thumbs excluded) as if they were four pairs of chromosomes, of which one set had come to you from your father, one set from your mother. (To distinguish between the two, we've

Representing chromosomes
received from one's
MOTHER

Representing chromosomes
received from one's
FATHER

made the paternal set black in the diagram, the maternal set white.)

Now suppose that these "chromosomes" were detachable and that you had countless duplicates of them. If you could give a set of four to every child, and it didn't make any difference whether any "chromosome" was a right- or left-hand one—in other words, whether it had come from your father or your mother—how many different combinations would be possible?

Sixteen (see the diagram opposite), in which every combination differs from any other in from one to four "chromosomes."

But this is with just *four pairs* involved. If now you put the thumb of each hand into play, representing a *fifth* pair of chromosomes, you could produce twice the number of combinations, or 32. In short, as our mathematician friends can quickly see, with every added pair of factors the number of possible combinations is doubled. So in the case of the actual chromosomes, with *twenty-four pairs* involved—where one from each pair is taken at random—every parent can theoretically produce 16,777,216 combinations of hereditary factors, each different from any other in anywhere from one to *all twenty-four chromosomes*.

Whether we are dealing with the millions of sperms released by a male at one time, or the single egg matured by a woman, the chance of any specific combination occurring would be that once in 16,777,216 times.

But to produce a given individual, *both* a specific sperm and a

Illustrating combinations of chromosomes
produced with four pair

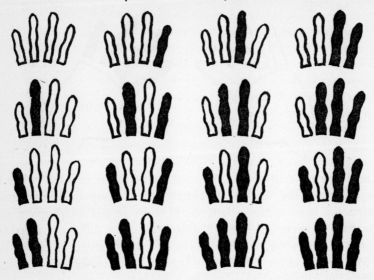

specific egg must come together. So think now what had to happen for you to have been born:

At exactly the right instant, the one out of 16,777,216 sperms which represented the *potential half* of you had to meet the one specific egg which held the *other potential half* of you. That could happen only once in some 300,000,000,000,000 times! Adding to this all the other factors involved (as we shall presently see), the chance of there having been or ever being another person exactly like you is virtually nil.

At this point you might say, with modesty or cynicism, *"So what?"*

Well, perhaps it wasn't worth all the fuss, or perhaps it wouldn't have made any difference whether or not you were born. But it was on just such a miraculous coincidence—the meeting of a specific sperm with a specific egg at a specific time—that the birth of a Lincoln, or a Shakespeare, or an Edison, or any other individual in history, depended. And it is by the same infinitesimal sway of chance that a child of yours might perhaps be a genius or a numb-skull, a beauty or an ugly duckling!

However, that first great coincidence was only the beginning.

The lucky sperm, which has won out in the spectacular race against millions of others, enters the chosen egg which has been waiting in the fallopian tube of the mother. Immediately, as we previously learned, the sperm and the nucleus in the egg each re-leases its quota of chromosomes, and thus the fertilized egg starts off on its career.

Already, from this first instant, the fertilized egg is an individual with all its inherent capacities mapped out—so far as the hereditary factors can decide. Will the baby have blue eyes or brown eyes? Dark hair or blond hair? Will it have six fingers or a tendency to diabetes? Will it live to nineteen or to ninety? These and thousands of other characteristics are already largely predetermined by genes in its particular chromosomes.

But as yet the individual consists of only one cell, like the most elemental of living things (i.e., the ameba). To develop it into a full-fledged human being, trillions of cells will be required. How this multiplication is effected we have seen in a previous chapter: The chromosomes split in half and separate, then the cell divides, mak-ing *two* cells, each with exact replicas of the forty-eight chromo-somes that there were in the original whole. Again the process is repeated, and the two cells become four. Again, and the four cells become eight. So it continues, and as you could figure out if you wished, the doubling process would have to be repeated only forty-five times to provide the twenty-six trillion cells which, it is estimated, constitute a fully developed baby.

However, as the cells go on to "specialize," some divide and multiply much more slowly than others. But regardless of how they multiply or what they turn into, to the very last cell, each one will still carry in its nucleus descendants of each of the original forty-eight chromosomes.

CHAPTER VII

THE PERILOUS ROAD TO BIRTH

W<small>E</small> have followed the first stage in Your Greatest Adventure—the remarkable coincidence by which you were conceived. But conception is a long way from birth. The beginnings of life, as science has now disclosed them, are beset with far more hazards than any one has ever imagined.

In the first days after fertilization, while all the cell-division and activity has been going on inside the egg, it has been slowly making its way down the fallopian tube toward the mother's uterus. Within a few more days the egg finds itself at the entrance of what—to this tiny droplet of substance, smaller than a period on this page—must be a vast, foreboding universe. If you can think of Y<small>OURSELF</small> at that stage, your life hung precariously in the balance. Innumerable adverse forces confronted you. At any moment you might be swept away to destruction. In short, the odds were most heavily against your survival.

But to become impersonal once more, the immediate concern of the human egg at this stage is to take root somewhere. Already it has prepared itself for this by developing microscopic little "tendrils" from its outer surface, so that it somewhat resembles a tiny thistle. Thus it can attach itself to the mother's membrane, assuming—which is not always the case—that that membrane is receptive. If luck is with the egg, it is hospitably received—a hungry and thirsty little egg that has almost exhausted the store of food with which it started out. Immediately, with the maternal tissues cooperating, arrangements are begun for its food, oxygen and water supply through the development of a receiving surface—the *placenta* —which grows into the mother's membrane *but does not become part of it*. And so, about nine days from the start of its existence—

CONCEPTION

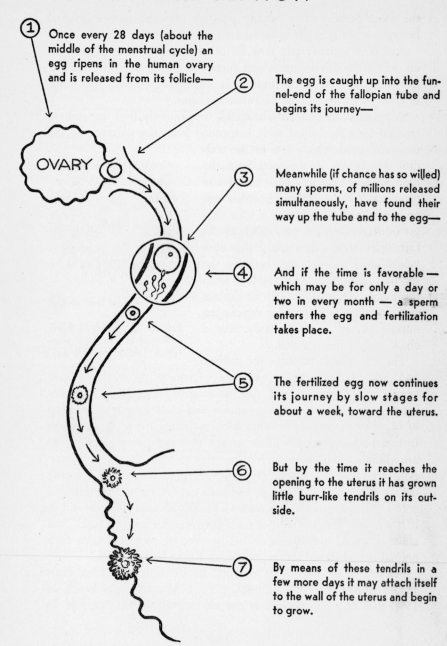

① Once every 28 days (about the middle of the menstrual cycle) an egg ripens in the human ovary and is released from its follicle—

OVARY

② The egg is caught up into the funnel-end of the fallopian tube and begins its journey—

③ Meanwhile (if chance has so willed) many sperms, of millions released simultaneously, have found their way up the tube and to the egg—

④ And if the time is favorable — which may be for only a day or two in every month — a sperm enters the egg and fertilization takes place.

⑤ The fertilized egg now continues its journey by slow stages for about a week, toward the uterus.

⑥ But by the time it reaches the opening to the uterus it has grown little burr-like tendrils on its outside.

⑦ By means of these tendrils in a few more days it may attach itself to the wall of the uterus and begin to grow.

NOTE: *The "rhythm" theory for women is based on the facts presented above.*

the most perilous days in any person's life—the new individual becomes what is really a parasite on its mother.

And now we may ask, how far can the mother, from this point on, affect the development and future of the child? The answer, as revealed by the latest findings in embryology, should do much to clear away many popular misconceptions.

Skipping some of the early stages, we presently find the embryo encased in a fluid-filled sack, suspended from the placenta by the umbilical cord which acts as the conduit that brings in the food from the mother and carries out the waste products. But the umbilical cord is not, as is commonly supposed, a tube that goes directly into the mother's body. In fact, there is no direct connection anywhere, and at any time, between the mother and child. The child is from the earliest stage until birth as distinct an individual as if it were developing outside of the mother's body, like a chick within the eggshell.

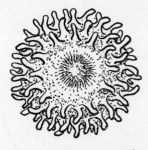

Actual Size →

Exterior of HUMAN EGG (embryo) at time of implantation (about twelfth day)

There is a wall between the mother and child. On one side, the *open ends* of some of the mother's blood vessels empty into the wall. *But the mother's blood, as such, never reaches the child, nor do any mother and child have a single drop of blood in common.* For what happens is that the food substances in the mother's blood—chiefly sugars, fats and protein elements—are strained out by *osmosis,* like moisture soaking through a blotter. And it is these which are drawn into the placenta pressed hungrily on the other side of the wall, and then conducted by the umbilical cord to the embryo. As Professor C. H. Waddington has phrased it, if it were not for that wall or filter between mother and child, "the embryo would actually be killed by foreign proteins, since each animal is a chemical individual which has to be respected."

Science, by the way, now overrules the decision by the late great Justice Oliver Wendell Holmes, from a Massachusetts bench in 1884, that an unborn child is not an individual, but "part of its

RELATIONSHIP BETWEEN MOTHER AND CHILD

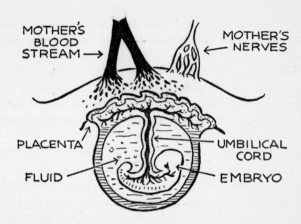

mother's bowels." The decision, used only recently in a Chicago court as a precedent, will, we feel sure, eventually be nullified.

Not only is there no direct blood connection between mother and child, but there is, moreover, no nerve connection, and hence no such mental or psychological relationship as mothers have always liked to believe exists between them and the little one they are carrying. In the light of all this, another batch of myths, about prenatal influences and maternal impressions, about "strawberry marks" or other marks and deformities in the child resulting from the mother's having seen or done this or that vanish into thin air. (We say "vanish" with reservations, for myths die hard, and even some of the most enlightened mothers still cherish a few of them.)

If the mother goes to concerts while she is carrying the child, that will not make it one whit more musical. Thinking pure thoughts, reading elevating books, doing kind deeds, can have their effect only in relaxing the mother and improving her physical condition. And, as already noted, if she is ardently in love with her husband—as sharply contrasted to hating him—the only difference it could make to her child would be to put her in a happier frame of mind and condition for bearing it.

Adversely, however, the effect of the mother may be great. First, of course, she is its food provider and if her supply is inadequate, the baby, being a voracious little parasite, will suffer malnutrition. Then, in her rôle as nurse—a nurse who is inseparably linked with the child throughout the crucial prenatal period—she may even unwittingly do it great injury. If her physical condition is bad, or if she suffers any great shock, severe chill or strong emotional reaction, the life of the potential child may be snuffed out. But there are other hazards, for we find that the wall between the embryo and the mother is, unfortunately, *not a barrier against everything*.

First, various drugs may pass from the mother to the embryo. If she smokes or drinks to excess, the nicotine or alcohol in her system may reach the child with harmful, or even disastrous effects. A large amount of alcohol penetrating to the child may result in its death or malformation. "Monsters" are often supposedly due to such prenatal alcoholization. Another serious result might be deafness in the child, which can also be caused by the mother's excessive use of quinine.

Among other substances which may pass from the mother to the embryo are lead and arsenic (the fumes of which may be inhaled in certain industrial operations) and—especially dangerous—narcotics. If the mother is addicted to the use of morphine or opium to the point where her tissues are saturated with the drug, *the child may actually come into the world as a drug addict*.

Certain disease germs, notably those of diphtheria, typhoid, influenza and syphilis, may also penetrate to the child. And whether through germs or through her condition, where the mother suffers from typhoid fever, scarlet fever, cholera, smallpox, erysipelas, pneumonia, sleeping sickness or malaria, in a great many cases the child will be killed before birth.

The birth of babies with syphilis has given rise to the belief (widely but erroneously promulgated through Ibsen's "Ghosts") that the disease can be inherited. Actually, no sperm and—so far as we have record—no human egg could carry a disease germ of any kind and function. What has happened when a child is born with syphilis is that the mother has been infected, and that she has then transmitted it to the child before or during the process of birth.

Here, in the prenatal period, we have our first clear-cut examples of what is due to heredity, and what to environment.

From the very first instant—we might say even before conception—both heredity and environment are at work.

An egg might start off with one or more defective chromosomes —or *bad heredity*—which might under average conditions destine it to be killed off. But if the mother's condition is unusually good, in other words if the *environment* is extremely favorable, the "weak" egg may develop through to birth and the individual may survive.

On the other hand, an egg might start off with the finest of chromosomes—the best of heredity. But through bad environment or influences (the poor condition of the mother, an accident or one of innumerable circumstances) the individual might be killed off or be permanently impaired. Under the same conditions, however, the egg with the better heredity will have a much brighter future.

In the nine months before birth every human being faces the severest test that he will ever undergo. With ruthlessness Nature exercises her "Law of Selection," killing off the weak more relentlessly than ever the ancient Greeks ventured to do. Undoubtedly, many worthy individuals are sacrificed in the effort to weed out the defectives. In fact, so stringent is the initial ordeal that experts believe the children who are born represent only a *portion of all the eggs fertilized*. In other words, in innumerable instances —perhaps a majority of cases—women conceive and the egg is killed off without their even knowing it. What frequently are described as "false alarms" may have been actual conceptions.

On the whole, however, parents should be grateful for this rigid pre-selection, for without it the world might be overrun with some pretty bad specimens. As it is, plenty of them do survive, but these are fortunately in the great minority. Where birth is achieved, it can generally be taken as a stamp of approval by Nature, qualifying the individual to face life. From that point on it is "up" to his parents, to himself and to the environment created by society.

CHAPTER VIII

"BOY OR GIRL?"

Next to being born, the most important single fact attending your coming into the world was whether you were to be a male or a female. Undoubtedly, that is the first question that occurs to prospective parents. Before you read this chapter, you may find it of interest to test your present knowledge as to what determines sex. Which of these statements would you say is right, which wrong?

1. The sex of an unborn child can be influenced before or during conception by (a) the stars, (b) the climate, (c) the mother's diet.
2. It can be influenced by other factors within two months after conception.
3. It is the mother who determines the sex of the child.
4. More boys are born than girls because boys are stronger.
5. On an average, as many boys are conceived as girls.
6. A mother's age or condition has no effect on her chances of giving birth to a boy or a girl.
7. Whether mothers are White or Negro the chances of their baby being a boy are exactly the same.

Every one of the foregoing statements, you will presently find, is wrong!

The scene is a regally furnished bedchamber, in medieval times.

A beautiful young woman is lying in a luxurious, canopied bed. She is to become a mother, but although this will not occur for many months, already there is much to do.

A midwife carefully adjusts her so that she lies on her right side, her hands held with thumbs out. Over her now a bearded necromancer swings with precise up-and-down motions a tiny incense-burner. (Heaven forfend that it be allowed to describe a circle!) At the foot of the bed an abbot kneels in prayer. In one corner an astrologer mumbles incantations as he studies an almanac. In another corner an alchemist prepares a potion in which are boiled the wattles of a rooster, some heart-blood of a lion, the head of an eagle and certain parts of a bull—the essence of all these will be blended with thrice-blessed wine and given to the young woman to drink. And meanwhile, surrounded by high counselors, the young woman's noble spouse—none other than the mighty Sovereign of the Realm—looks anxiously on.

By this time you have probably guessed that all the ceremonial and hocus-pocus was for a single purpose: To make sure that the expected child would be a son and heir to the throne.

Synthetic as this particular scene might be, in effect it occurred many times in history. But if it were only a matter of dim history we would not be dealing with it here. The fact is, however, that to this very present day, throughout the world and in our own country, a fascinating variety of potions, prayers, midwives' formulas, "thought applications," diets, drugs or quasi-medical treatments is still being employed by expectant mothers to influence the sex of the future child. Most often, undoubtedly, the objective is a boy. But an ample list could also be compiled of the "what-to-do's" to make it a girl.

Alas then, whatever the methods employed, primitive or supposedly enlightened, all are now equally dismissed by science with this definite and disillusioning answer:

The sex of every child is fixed at the instant of conception—and *it is not the mother, but the father, who is the determiner.*

The moment that the father's sperm enters the mother's egg, the child is started on its way to being a boy or a girl. Subsequent events or influences may possibly affect the *degree* of "maleness" or "femaleness," or thwart normal development, but *nothing within our power from that first instant on can change what is to be a girl into a boy, or vice versa.*

The solution of the mystery of sex-determination came about through this discovery:

That the only difference between the chromosomes of a man and a woman lies in just one of the pairs—in fact, in a single chromosome of this pair.

Of the twenty-four pairs of chromosomes, twenty-three pairs—which we could number from A to W, inclusive—are alike in both men and women. That is to say, any one of them could just as readily be in either sex. But when we come to the twenty-fourth pair, there is a difference. For, as we see in the accompanying diagram, every woman has in her cells two of what we call the "X" chromosome, but a man has just one "X"—its mate being the tiny "Y." It is the presence of that "Mutt and Jeff" pair of chromosomes in the male (the "XY" combination) and the "XX" in the female that sets the machinery of sex development in motion and results later in all the differences that there are between a man and a woman.

We have already seen how when human beings form eggs or sperms, each gets just *half* the respective parent's quota of chromosomes. When the female, then, forms eggs and gives to each egg one chromosome of every pair, as she has two X's, *each egg gets an X.* But when the male forms sperms and the different pairs of chromosomes split up, one chromosome to go into this sperm, the other into that sperm, *one of every two sperms will get an X, the other a Y.*

We find, then, with regard to the sex factor, that the female produces only one kind of egg, every egg containing an X. But the male produces *two* kinds of sperm—in exactly equal numbers. (Which is to say, that of the 200,000,000 to 500,000,000 sperms released by a man each time, exactly half would be X-bearers, half Y-bearers.)

Science having established that only one sperm fertilizes an egg (as a wall forms about the egg the instant it enters, shutting out all others), the result should be self-evident. If a sperm with an X gets to the egg first, it pairs up with the X already there, an XX individual is started on its way and eventually a girl baby is produced. But should a Y-bearing sperm win the race, the result will be an XY individual, or a boy.

Here at last is the comparatively simple answer to what was long considered an unfathomable mystery!

HOW SEX IS DETERMINED

This is what makes all the differences there are between a woman and a man:

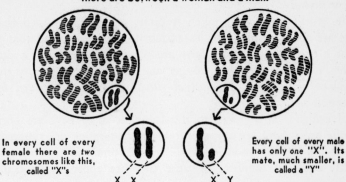

In every cell of every female there are *two* chromosomes like this, called "X"s

Every cell of every male has only one "X". Its mate, much smaller, is called a "Y"

X   X

X   Y

For reproduction, a female forms *eggs,* a male *sperms,* to each of which they contribute only HALF their quota of chromosomes, or *just one from every pair·*

Since a female has TWO "X"s, each egg gets one "X", so in this respect every egg is the same:

But as the male has only ONE "X", paired with a "Y", he forms TWO kinds of sperms:

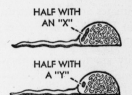

HALF WITH AN "X"

HALF WITH A "Y"

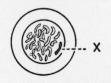

---- X

Thus: If an "X"-bearing sperm enters the egg, the result is an individual with TWO "X"s

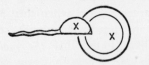

A GIRL

...If a "Y"-bearing sperm enters the egg, the result is an "XY" individual, or

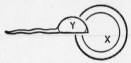

A BOY

But hardly have we solved this when we are confronted with a new mystery:

The world has always taken it pretty much for granted that there are about as many males as females *conceived,* and that if about 5 or 6 percent more boys are born than girls this is due to the "fact" that boys are stronger and better able to survive the ordeal of being born. *The actual situation, as now revealed by science, is radically different.*

All evidence now points to the fact that more boys are born *because more boys are conceived.* Why should this be, you may ask, if the "male"-producing and "female"-producing sperms are exactly equal in number? Because they are apparently not the same in character. The assumption follows that the sperm containing the small Y has some advantage over the one with the X, so that, on an average, it gets to the mark oftener—so much oftener, various scientists have stated, that the ratio at conception may be as high as *20 to 50 percent more males.*

(The most recent investigator, however, believes these previous estimates are exaggerated, but that, nevertheless, the excess of males over females *conceived* is still greater than the ratio at birth.)

On what are these estimates based? On the fact that the mortality among male embryos averages about 50 percent higher than among female embryos—completely contradicting the old belief that boys are better able to survive the ordeal of birth.

About one-quarter of the *known* pregnancies result in still-births. Great numbers of these aborted babies have been examined, and some surprising data obtained. In embryos aborted when they are about three months old, specialists can already distinguish sex, and in these early mortalities they have found that *the males outnumber the females almost four to one.* These, however, are but a small percentage of the total still-births. In those in the fourth month, aborted males are double those of females, in the fifth month, 145 males to 100 females, in the next few months the proportion drops further, but just before birth there is a rise to almost 140 males aborted to every 100 females.

All this leads to another conclusion: That before birth, certainly, *males as a class are not only not stronger than females, but, quite on the contrary, are weaker.* If we look beyond birth, we find, moreover, that at almost every stage of life, males drop out at a higher rate than females. It may very well be, then, that a canny Nature enters more males than females at the start of life's race in order to counterbalance the difference in mortality.

The theory as to *why* males are less able to survive will be brought out in a later chapter. For the present, assuming that the male embryo is the likeliest to be carried off under adverse conditions, we might gather that where the condition of a mother is more unfavorable, the possibility of a son being born will be lessened.

Some evidence has been advanced to support this. Among mothers who have had a considerable number of previous pregnancies the later children show a drop in percentage of sons. Among colored mothers, in general, perhaps because they may receive inferior care during pregnancy, there is a markedly smaller percentage of sons born than among white women. It has also been reported, from other countries, that births among unmarried mothers show a lower than average ratio of sons, but recent figures for the United States do not seem to bear this out.

A popular question is whether a tendency to bear sons may not run in certain families or individuals. Quite possibly, yes, although researches are not yet sufficiently adequate to permit a definite answer. One might guess that exceptionally active or virile sperms on the part of males, or exceptionally favorable conditions for motherhood on the part of women, would lead to an above-average ratio of male births. But a "run" of either sons or daughters in any given family may be as much a matter of chance as a run of "sevens" in a dice game.

Other questions you might ask, "What about the influence of hormones and glands on sex after birth? What part does heredity play in 'masculine women' and 'feminine men'?" etc., will be discussed in a later chapter. One question, however, might be answered here:

Knowing that an X-bearing sperm produces a girl, a Y-bearing sperm a boy, might not a way be found of separating the two kinds and then, by artificial insemination, producing boys and girls at will?

Yes—it seems only a matter of time before this will be possible. Already, in a number of laboratories, geneticists are working toward this goal. The distinct differences between the X sperm and Y sperm have provided a basis for their experiments. Definite affirmative results are already reported at this writing, and it is considered likely that in a not too distant future many persons— or those, at least, to whom the laboratory facilities will be available—will be able to have a boy or girl baby, as they wish.

For the time being the matter of "boy or girl?" remains one of chance, with this qualification, as we have seen: The better prepared a woman is for motherhood, the slightly greater will be the odds that as the anxious father paces the hospital corridor, the nurse will report,

"It's a boy!"

CHAPTER IX

SUPER CHAIN-GANGS

Sex is but one of the myriad characteristics potentially determined by your genes at the instant of conception.

But how, and by what processes, do the genes do their work during that long dark interval between conception and birth?

Recall that a single gene is millions of times smaller than the smallest speck you could see with your naked eye. How can such minute bits of substance do such astounding things as molding the shape of your nose, determining the color of your eyes or hair, actually making you sane or insane?

What, to begin with, *is* a gene?

At the present stage of our knowledge (and it is only yesterday, as science computes it, that we even knew about genes) no one can answer definitely, because it has so far not been possible to isolate a gene and to analyze it. But geneticists know a great deal of what genes do and how they do it. They are convinced (most of them) that a gene acts like an enzyme, a substance which produces a certain chemical change in a compound without in itself being affected.

Every housewife knows that a bit of yeast will make dough rise and that a pellet of rennet will turn milk into "junket." Home brewers of the prohibition era remember the potent effects of a few raisins in their jug of mash. Manufacturers are familiar with hundreds of substances (small pieces of platinum, for instance) used in various processes to bring about desired chemical changes.

And finally, if one is still puzzled by the smallness of the gene and the bigness of its effect, one has only to think of how a droplet of deadly poison, such as cobra venom, can speedily bring about chemical changes which will convert a hulking, roaring giant of a man into a lifeless mass of flesh and bone.

44

In creating an individual, the genes work first upon the raw material in the egg, then upon the materials which are sent in by the mother, converting these into various products. These, in turn, react again with the genes, leading to the formation of new products. So the process goes on, meanwhile specific materials being sorted out to go into and construct the various cells of the body.

Where the genes are unique is that they are *alive* and able to reproduce themselves. It is not impossible that genes may be made up of smaller particles, but so far as science can trace back today the *gene is the ultimate unit of life.*

We cannot therefore regard genes as mere chemical substances. When we consider what they do, we may well think of them as workers endowed with personalities. No factory, no industrial organization, has so varied an aggregation of workers and specialists as the genes in a single individual, and no army of workers can do more amazing things. Architects, engineers, plumbers, decorators, chemists, artists, sculptors, doctors, dieticians, masons, carpenters, common laborers—all these and many others will be found among the genes. In their linked-together form (the chromosomes) we can think of them as "chain-gangs" twenty-four of these gangs of workers sent along by each parent to construct the individual.

Turn back to the moment of conception. The chain-gangs contributed by your mother are packed together closely in a shell (the nucleus) suspended in the sea of nutrient material which constitutes the egg. Suddenly, into that sea, is plunged a similar shell (the sperm) filled with the chain-gangs sent by your father. Its entrance causes both shells to break, and out come the chain-gangs with their workers, stirred to activity.

The first impulse of the workers, after their long confinement, is to eat (which seems natural enough). They gorge themselves on the sea of materials around them, and as we have already noted before, they double in size, split in half, and form two of themselves. The one-cell egg divides into two cells, the two into four, the four into eight, etc.—a replica of *each original chain-gang going into each cell.*

Up to this point the genes have all been doing ordinary construction work. But now, while the process of multiplying themselves

OUR "CHAIN-GANGS"

The CHROMOSOMES may be thought of as "Chain-Gangs," twenty-four of which are sent along by each parent to create the child. Every "gang" consists of many linked-together workers, each assigned to given tasks.

Chemist, etc.
Colorist
Sculptor
Plumber
Carpenter
Mason
Engineer
Architect

CHAIN "A" FROM **FATHER**

Chemist, etc.
Colorist
Sculptor
Plumber
Carpenter
Mason
Engineer
Architect

CHAIN "A" FROM **MOTHER**

NOTE that in each of these "mated" chains, the workers ("genes") at corresponding points, are assigned to exactly the same type of work.

and the cells continues, the specialists get into action and begin constructing *different kinds of cells at different locations.*

The details of how this is done—such details as are known or surmised—fill tens of thousands of pages in scientific treatises. Briefly stated, we can assume that on set cues the different genes step out for their special tasks, snatching at this bit of material or element, combining it with other stuffs, fashioning a product, setting it in place, etc., all the time working in cooperation with the other genes.

Throughout one's lifetime the genes are in a constant ferment of activity, carrying on and directing one's life processes at every stage. Everything seems to be done according to plan, as if the most detailed blueprints were being followed. The step-by-step process has been explained as a sequence of reactions, the workers being motivated to each step by the effects of the preceding one. By observing the process in lower experimental animals we can see how first the broad general construction of the body is worked out; then how certain cells are marked off for the organs, certain ones for the respiratory and digestive systems, certain ones for the muscles, others for the skin, features, etc.

The generalized cells now begin to develop into special ones. In those marked off for the circulatory system the rudiments of hearts, veins and arteries begin to be formed (here is where the "plumber" genes step in to construct the great chain of pumps and pipe-lines); from the generalized bone cells the skeleton begins to be shaped; from the skin cells, the rudiments of features, etc. With each stage the specialization is carried further along in the developing embryo. The amazing way in which the development of every human being parallels that of every other proves how infinitely exact and predetermined are the genes in their workings.

Another remarkable feature of the process is this: That despite the growing differences in the various specialized cells, *into every cell, as it is being created and constructed, go exact replicas of all the chromosomes with their genes.* Thus, the same gene which produced eye color in your eye cells will also be found in your big toe cells, and the same gene which directed the fashioning of your big toe will also be found in your eye cells—or in your ear and liver cells, for that matter! Probably, then, in addition to every special task that each gene performs, it also takes part in general activities which make its presence required everywhere.

But we recall now that the individual starts life with two chromosomes of every kind, which means also two genes of every kind. If, in terms of chain-gangs, we designate the chromosomes by letter, there would be two Chain A's, two Chain B's, two Chain C's, and so on up to the last pair—where in the case of a girl, as noted in the preceding chapters, there would be two Chain X's, but in the case of a boy, only one X Chain, the other being a Y Chain. With this latter exception, the corresponding chain-gangs (AA, BB, CC, etc.) would be exactly alike in the number of workers each contained, and in the *type* of worker at each point in the chain.

If the No. 1 gene in Chain A contributed to you by your father was an architect, so would be the No. 1 gene in the Chain A from your mother. The No. 2's in line might be carpenters, the No. 3's decorators, etc. All the way from Chain A to Chain X, the genes at each point in *all human beings* are exactly the same in the *type* of work to which they are assigned. In other words, every individual starts life with *two* workers for each job, one sent by the mother, one by the father.

But the corresponding genes in any two human beings are far from the same. To be sure, they are sufficiently alike in their effects so that the difference between even our pigmy Hottentot friend and our tall blond "Nordic" are insignificant compared to the difference between either one and an ape. Nevertheless, within the range of human beings, the corresponding genes are exceedingly variable in their workings, leading to many peculiar effects and the marked differences that might exist between individuals, even those in the same family.

CHAPTER X

PEAS, FLIES AND PEOPLE

ALTHOUGH there are no statistics on the subject, we dare say that millions of husbands since the world began, and a not inconsiderable number of mothers, noting that some child in no way resembled them, have had the cold suspicion creep up that it actually was not theirs.

Many times, perhaps, in the case of husbands, this suspicion has been justified; and in rare instances, possibly (but much more rarely now) the wrong infant may have been wittingly or unwittingly foisted upon the mother. In the majority of cases, however, the doubts were groundless, and today can often be quickly dissipated as the result of the findings of two men:

One, an obscure Austrian monk of Civil War days, who cultivated garden peas.

The other, a living American scientist, who cultivated, and still cultivates—fruit-flies.

How can ordinary garden peas (the same peas that you get at any Rotary Club luncheon with your chicken and candied sweets) and fruit-flies (the sort that buzz around bunches of bananas—and not the best bananas, either), how can these have any bearing on the parentage of a child? They can because, as we know now, the mechanism of heredity in peas and flies, and in all other living things, is basically the same as it is in man. This is one of the amazing facts that is being made increasingly more evident, and that is one of the hardest for the layman to accept.

When in 1857 the plump Abbot Gregor Mendel, waddling about in the garden of the monastery at Brünn, Austria (now held by Germany), set out to clarify his mind about the heredity of peas, he himself did not dream that he was at the same time about to throw lasting light on the heredity of human beings. Mendel had

49

ONE OF MENDEL'S EXPERIMENTS WITH PEAS

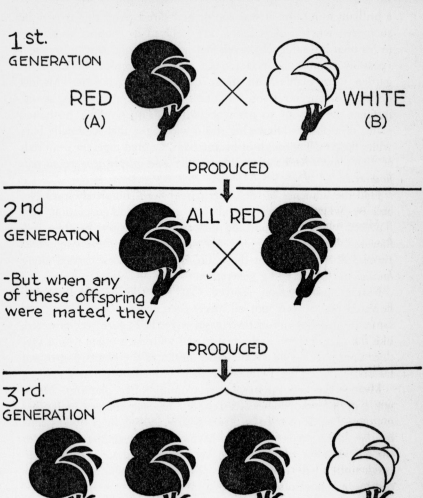

1st.
GENERATION

RED
(A)

×

WHITE
(B)

PRODUCED

2nd
GENERATION

ALL RED

×

-But when any
of these offspring
were mated, they

PRODUCED

3rd.
GENERATION

3 IN **4** RED
(Like Grandparent "A")

1 IN **4** WHITE
(Like Grandpt. "B")

a brilliant mind, but it was simple and direct. And this is why he succeeded where others failed. He resolved to confine his studies to his own little thirty-by-seven-foot patch and not to wander afield (possibly because he was too fat to travel comfortably). In his garden were plants with many different characteristics. Mendel decided to concentrate on just one character at a time. So, as one instance, he set out to see what would happen when he mated plants of a pure red-flowering strain with those that habitually bore white flowers. Thorough in his methods, he bred together hundreds of such plants. And this was the result: *The offspring were all red-flowered.*

Had the influence of the *white* parent been completely lost? No, because when Mendel mated any two second-generation red-flowered plants together, the offspring were three in four *red-flowered, but one out of four was pure white like the white grandparent.* This proved that the white factor had been carried along *hidden* in the preceding generation.

Further investigation showed that the third generation red-flowered plants were not all alike, even though they *looked* the same. In only one out of three cases were they "pure" red-flowered, like the grandparent, and when mated with each other would produce only red flowers. In the other instances the plants had mixed factors, both red and white, like their immediate parents.

Mendel checked the results in planting after planting. Meanwhile, in different patches of his garden, he experimented with other matings—breeds of tall pea plants with breeds of short ones; plants having yellow seeds with those having green; wrinkled seeds with smooth, etc. For everything he kept exact figures, carefully tabulated, until finally the evidence pointed overwhelmingly to these conclusions, now often referred to as

THE "MENDELIAN LAWS"

1. The inherited characteristics are produced by genes (called by Mendel "factors") which are passed along *unchanged* from one generation to another.

2. In each individual these genes are found in pairs, and where the two genes in a pair are different in their effects, one gene

dominates the other so that it might be referred to as a "dominant," the other as a "recessive."

3. When seeds are formed in any individual, the members of each pair of genes *segregate out,* independently of the other pairs, *with just one of every two mated genes* going from each parent to *each offspring.*

These conclusions Mendel embodied in a paper which he read before his local scientific society and which was then printed. But almost no attention was paid to it. The scientific world of the time was in a turmoil over Darwin's theory of evolution. The few who saw Abbot Mendel's paper ignored it. And so Mendel, little aware of the scientific treasure he had unearthed, turned to other things and passed on at the age of sixty-two.

But recognition did come—sixteen years too late. In 1900, three biologists, almost at the same time (although they were working independently) chanced on Mendel's paper and quickly realized its importance. Their reports set the world of biology feverishly experimenting to see whether the Mendelian findings applied to other living things—including man. Yes, in many cases Mendel's "laws" did seem to operate. But in other instances the results were either inconclusive or flatly contradictory. Biologists were floundering about in confusion, and might still have been had not a very large man named Thomas Hunt Morgan happened to become intensely interested in a very little fly named *Drosophila melanogaster.*

The drama which might be called "Man Meets Fly" began in 1907. Professor Morgan, then at Columbia University, found the fruit-fly an ideal subject for his experiments. For one thing, the Drosophilæ, mère and père, do not believe in birth control. At the age of twelve days they are ready to breed and within another twelve days each female produces some 300 offspring. Starting from scratch, within two years one can get sixty generations of flies, as many as there have been generations of mankind from the time of Christ. Moreover, the fly has many easily distinguished variations and the cost of boarding it is trifling. The reward for all this is that the Drosophila has today become the most famous experimental animal in science, and is assured immortality, even though individually it might prefer a speckled banana.

With the Drosophila, then, Morgan was able to prove that while the Mendelian principles held firmly, the mechanism of heredity was not nearly so simple as Mendel had suggested. There were many complicated forms of gene operation, Morgan showed, and many environmental factors that influenced the genes. All this he and a brilliant corps of students and collaborators made indisputably clear. They identified hundreds of special genes in the Drosophila. They showed at which points on the flies' chromosomes these genes were located. And they actually bred flies of almost any kind specified as easily as a pharmacist would compound a prescription.

All this time, everything learned about the gene workings in flies was being applied to the study of other living things, up the scale from the most elemental creatures to man himself. Jennings with the paramecium, Goldschmidt with moths, Castle with rabbits, Wright with guinea-pigs, Stockard with dogs, Davenport with studies of humans—these are but a handful of the hundreds of brilliant investigators who pyramided the facts on which our present knowledge of the genes so firmly rests.

So it is by way of Mendel with his peas and Morgan with his flies that we have finally arrived at an understanding of the complexities of human heredity. If you turn back again now to the figurative drawings of our "chain-gangs" (chromosomes) you will see why we have shown that while genes at corresponding points in the paired chains are the same in the type of work to which they are assigned, they are not necessarily the same in their characters. The two "A-1" architect genes, one coming from your father, the other from your mother, may have been as different in their manner of working as are any two human architects. So, too, just as any two plumbers might differ, or any two masons might differ (even though they belonged to the same union) any two paired genes might differ greatly in what they do and how they do it.

There are strong genes, weak genes, alert genes, and inactive genes; temperamental genes and freak genes; constructive genes and destructive genes; in fact, if we endow them with personalities genes individually have almost as many different characteristics as have the people they create. Ever present, moreover, are the factors of environment, which may make any given gene act one way under some conditions, another way under other conditions, just as the work of a human artisan is affected by food, weather, accident, spats with fellow-workers, etc.

The best way of illustrating all this is to tell what genes do with regard to our own features, organs and characteristics. It will then be clear why in some instances we needn't be at all surprised if we have a child that looks nothing like either parent, whereas in other instances a child of an unexpected type may rightly be regarded with suspicion.

CHAPTER XI

EYE COLOR

AMONG the characteristics of a child which most often are unexpected and baffling to parents are the coloring of its eyes and hair —and sometimes its skin.

Nevertheless, because color is on the surface and is quite definite in its nature, it offers us one of the simplest means of studying and analyzing the action of genes.

Color, to begin with, is not a positive substance but an *effect* produced by the reflection of light on different materials. When we speak, then, of different genes "producing" different colors, what is meant is that given genes take part in the production of different *pigment materials*. The color *effect* of these pigments is not important to Nature. Where pigment is produced in the skin, eyes or hair, it is usually to insure protection from the sunlight. The pigment deposited in the otherwise translucent iris of the eye shades the retina within; the pigment in the skin protects the flesh underneath. Even the pigment in the hair affords protection to the hair cells and the scalp.

In the eye we have our most interesting range of color effects. Geneticists believe that the first human beings all had very dark brown or black eyes, and that by mutations throughout the ages the original eye-pigment genes gave rise to variations which now provide us with all the many known lighter shades.

To produce the color effects, the genes do not mix pigments, nor, in fact, are different pigments produced to correspond with what we know as the eye colors. There are really only one or two basic eye pigments, and a few variations of these. What any given eyes look like is determined by the amount of these pigments and the way in which they are distributed in the iris.

The iris, as you probably know, is the small disk around the pupil.

(Or, rather, one should say that the pupil is the hole in the iris.) Without any pigment the iris would look something like a tiny, transparent doughnut. It has, however, two clearly defined parts as if it had been slit in half and pasted together again. Thus we speak of the part facing out as the "front" of the iris and the other half as the "rear."

While a number of genes participate in the pigmenting process, it is a single "key" gene that usually determines the result.

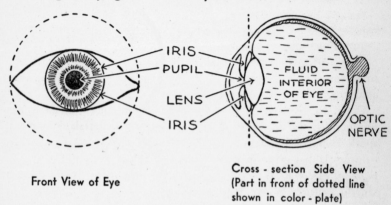

Front View of Eye

Cross - section Side View
(Part in front of dotted line
shown in color - plate)

In BLUE EYES the gene is a weakling which produces no pigment whatsoever in the front of the iris, but manages to produce a certain amount in the rear. But this pigment is a dark substance, not blue. The blue eye color that results is an *optical effect,* just as is the blue of the sky, and is caused by the reflection and diffraction of light by the pigment and other particles in the eye.

In fact, *all eyes are basically just as "blue" as blue eyes.* The other eye colors are due to the *addition of pigment in the front of the iris.*

In GREEN EYES the rear of the iris has the same kind of pigmentation as in blue eyes, but in addition the "key" gene or a special gene lays down a certain number of dilute brown or yellow pigment cells in the front of the iris. Superimposed on the "blue" background, these produce the effect of green.

In GRAY EYES the gene involved distributes lightly a number of *black* (or dark brown) pigment cells in the front, and these against the blue-appearing background produce the gray effect.

WHAT MAKES YOUR EYE COLOR—

—BLUE

An optical illusion
(There is no blue pigment in the eye)

Effect is due to reflection of light from tiny dark pigment granules in **REAR OF IRIS**

(Cross-section)

← Pupil

GENES

If "true" blue-eyed you carry two "blue-eye" genes

(One alone is recessive to all others except Albino)

—GREEN

Effect is due to scattered yellow pigment in **FRONT OF IRIS** acting with the blue reflection (yellow + blue = green)

(Gene action of green and gray eyes not yet clearly established)

—GRAY

Effect is due to scattered dark pigment in **FRONT OF IRIS** screening blue reflection from behind

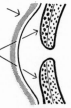

—BROWN
or Black

Effect is due to concentrated dark pigment in **FRONT OF IRIS** masking blue reflection (The heavier the pigmentation, the darker the eye)

Two brown-eye genes

or one

One of any lighter shade

—PINK
(Albino)

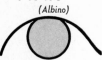

An Illusion
(The eye is really colorless)

Effect is due to reflection from pink blood vessels

An albino carries two albino genes

But persons of any other eye color including blue may be carrying a hidden albino gene

In BROWN EYES the "key" gene is active enough to so fill the front of the iris with pigment that no blue reflection can be seen.

And finally, in BLACK EYES the gene is of the most vigorous type, and lays down an intense deposit of pigment in the front of the iris (and perhaps the rear also).

All the other in-between eye-color effects are produced by the varying degrees of pigmentation, and also by the "pattern" in which the pigment is distributed.

ALBINO EYES should be dealt with separately because they are not due to any eye-color gene but to a defective "general" gene which interferes with all pigmentation processes. Thus, the true albino eyes have *no pigment whatsoever,* in either the front or rear of the iris. The *pink* effect is due partly to tiny blood-vessels in the partition of the otherwise colorless iris, and partly to the reflection from other blood-vessels behind.

Let us see now what happens when an individual receives one kind of eye-color gene from one parent, a different gene from the other parent.

In eye color, as in most other processes, some genes can do the same work singly as well as if there were two. The blackest, or darkest eye-color gene, if only one is transmitted, will produce the same effect as if two were transmitted. That is to say, if a child should receive just one dark-eye-color gene from one parent, no matter what other gene it received from the other parent—green, gray, blue or even albino—that child would have dark brown eyes.

This follows the principle of *dominance* and *recessiveness* which Mendel discovered. Just as the gene for red-flower dominated that for white-flower in his garden peas, in human beings the gene for black (or brown) eyes dominates that for blue eyes (or any other of the lighter shades). But, you might ask, doesn't the blue-eye or other recessive gene do *anything* when coupled with the dominant brown-eye gene?

Possibly you may recall having gone to a party planning to sing, or to play the piano or exhibit some other accomplishment, and just as you were preparing to perform, some one else got up and did the same sort of thing, much more forcefully than you could do it. If you were an ordinarily shy person, the chances are that you kept your performance to yourself for the rest of the evening.

That is what happens when a little Blue-Eye gene arrives and finds a big domineering Brown-Eye gene on the scene. Little Blue-Eye sits back with never a peep out of it through all the long lifetime of the individual in which it finds itself. But there is always "another time." Just as you might go to the next party, and in the absence of a menacing competitor, perform handsomely, so the Blue-Eye gene need not be permanently squelched. To a gene, the "next time" means the next individual to which it is sent—that is, to some future child. Again little Blue-Eye gene goes forth hopefully (and if necessary again and again, generation after generation) until in some child it finds itself coupled, not with a "bully" Brown-Eye gene, but with a kindred Blue-Eye gene. And this time, glory be, the two Blue-Eye genes happily fall to work, and the result is a blue-eyed baby!

In all mixed matings the blue-eye gene has a hard time of it, for it is also dominated by the light-brown, green and gray-eye genes; by all the rest, in fact, except the albino gene, which all normal genes dominate. As for the other contests, the general rule is that the genes for darker colors dominate those for the lighter shades. But present evidence is still not clear as to what happens when a green-eye gene and a gray-eye, both of apparently equal potency, get together.

From all the foregoing, you may make these guesses about the eye-color genes you are carrying:

If you have black or brown eyes:

(1) Where both your parents, all your brothers and sisters and all your near relatives also have dark eyes, in all probability you carry *two* black (or brown-eye) genes.

(2) Where both your parents have dark eyes, but one or more of your brothers and sisters or other near relatives have eyes of a lighter shade (gray, green, blue) you may be carrying, in addition to the dark-eye gene, a "hidden" gene for the lighter shade. The greater the number in your family who have light-colored eyes, the greater the chance that you carry such a gene.

(3) Where one of your parents has black or brown eyes and the

other light-colored eyes you definitely carry one dark-eye gene and one for a lighter shade. If the light-eyed parent has gray or green eyes, your "hidden" gene may be either a gray, green, or blue one. If the parent has blue eyes, then you definitely carry a hidden blue-eye gene.

If you have gray or green eyes:

Regardless of what eye colors your parents have, you carry no dark, but only light-colored genes, which may be gray, green or blue. If *one* parent has blue eyes, however, then you definitely carry at least one "hidden" blue-eye gene.

If you have blue eyes:

Regardless of the eye colors of your parents, you are almost certain to be carrying *two* blue-eye genes.

If you have albino eyes:

You *must* be carrying two albino genes.

To all the foregoing deductions there may be, more or less rarely, some exceptions. As we have learned, environmental factors can swerve a gene from its course and alter its workings. One cannot always be positive that a person whose eyes are, or appear to be, blue, really carries two blue-eye genes. In rare instances a person may receive at conception one, or even both genes, of some darker shade, and at some stage thereafter something may happen to *inhibit* or modify the usual gene workings so that blue or blue-appearing eyes result. Disease and age may be among such modifying influences. Any mother knows that her brown-eyed child was born with slate-blue eyes, and that it may take up to two years or more before the "true" eye color of a child is revealed and that even thereafter the color may never be constant. In old age, brown eyes may again become bluish. Cataracts, or some other eye defect, may also rob brown eyes of their color and make them appear to be a watery-blue. One cannot therefore always tell merely by looking at people's eyes what genes they may be carrying.

Still another modifying influence in human eye color is that of *pattern* in pigment distribution, also determined by genes. There are eye types with the pigment in rings, in clouds, in radial stripes, or spread over the whole iris. The pattern genes have not been too closely studied, but it appears that where parents have a radial, ring or cloud-eye pattern, most of the children will have the same. If, however, a child receives different "pattern" genes than a given parent, even though the color genes are the same, the eyes may look different.

One peculiar phenomenon, which occurs about once in a thousand times, is that of unmatched eyes—the two eyes in the same person being of different colors. Among motion-picture celebrities, Colleen Moore and Lionel Stander have this eye-condition. How it occurs may be explained in several ways: A person may inherit one brown-eye gene and one blue-eye gene, which would normally make both eyes brown. But in the very earliest stages something may happen to the brown-eye gene in the rudimentary eye cell on one side of the face, leaving the field on that side to the blue-eye gene. Or, starting with two blue-eye genes some pathological condition may increase the pigment production in one of the eyes, making it brown.

While most unmatched eyes are believed due to environmental factors, this condition might also be inherited as the result of a one-sided eye-nerve defect which can be transmitted through a certain gene. The condition, by the way, is prevalent among many domestic animals, including dogs, cats and cattle.

Sex also seems to play a part in eye color. Women's eyes as a general rule are slightly darker than those of men. There are more brown-eyed girls than boys, and, generally, more males with blue eyes than females. These conclusions have been reached through studies of several hundred thousand school children, with additional studies made in the adult population. Exceptions have been noted in the cases of Russians, Scots, and Bulgarians, among whom, for some reason, the sex-factor in eye color does not seem to be prevalent.

Although the range of human eye color is normally confined to variations of brown, blue, green and gray eyes, rare cases have been reported of persons with eyes of tortoise-shell color (mottled yellow and black), and also of persons with ruby-colored eyes. But we may eventually see eyes of many other colors. Even so serious a geneticist as Professor Jennings believes that new eye colors in man could conceivably be produced by means of chemicals. We may therefore yet see the time when some women will change the color of their eyes just as they now change that of their hair. When that day comes, and a man says to a girl, "Where did you get those big blue eyes?" she may reply: "At Antoine's, corner of De Peyster Avenue and Thirty-second Street!"

CHAPTER XII

HAIR COLOR

GENTLEMEN (and particularly a certain European dictator) we are told prefer blondes.

There must be some truth in this, for otherwise how account for the great number of women who go to beauty parlors to have their dark hair bleached? Is there any record of *blondes* converting themselves into *brunettes?* (Unless, perhaps, to avoid the police.)

Even more than blond hair, red hair has a certain social significance. Which might lead to this question, assuming that you are a prospective parent:

"What are the chances of a child of yours being a blond or a red-head?"

As you already have gathered, looking at your own hair and that of your mate may not in itself provide the answer. You must try to ascertain what *genes* for hair color you both carry.

Pigmentation of the hair follows the same general principles as does that of the eyes. Often, in fact (but not always), the two are related. In hair we deal with the pigmentation of hair cells, and just as in eyes the basic actions of the color genes may be modified or changed by "meddling" genes and by many environmental factors.

A dark-brown pigment known as *melanin* is chemically the principal element in our hair coloring. If the "key" hair-color gene acts to produce a heavy deposit of melanin in the hair cells, the result is black hair; a little less melanin, very dark brown hair; still less, light brown; and very dilute, blond hair. The shade of hair color is further influenced by the way the hair cells are constructed, by their air content and by their amount of natural oil, or greasiness.

Red hair is due to a supplementary gene which produces a diffuse red pigment. It is often present with the "key" melanin gene.

62

WHAT MAKES YOUR HAIR COLOR—

	DUE TO		GENES YOU CARRY

—WHITE
(Natural)

No
pigment
granules
among
hair cells

(If white hair is
not due to age or
disease)

(But all hair
color types may be
carrying one hidden
White-Hair Gene)

—BLOND

Yellow
effect
produced by
dilute
pigment

—RED

Effect
produced by
dissolved
red pigment
diffused with
the scattered
pigment granules

*(The "Red-Hair" Gene
is a special one
which shows its
effect if not
masked by
very "Dark-Hair"
Genes)*

—BROWN

Effect
produced by
heavy deposit of
pigment granules

(The heavier the
deposit, the darker
the brown)

(Red Gene may make
hair reddish-brown)

—BLACK

Intense
deposit of
pigment
granules

Gene
for
any
lighter
shade

NOTE: ANY GENE SYMBOL USED HERE MAY REFER TO MORE THAN ONE GENE

If the melanin gene is very active, making the hair black or dark brown, the effect of the red gene will be completely obscured. (The claim has been made, however, that a hidden red gene may betray its presence in black-haired persons by a *glossiness* of the hair.) Where the melanin gene is weaker, the red-hair gene can manifest itself, and the result will be a reddish-brown, or chestnut shade. If the brown-hair gene is an utter weakling, or if it is absent, distinctive red hair will be produced.

In relation to a "blond" gene, we are not so sure of the action of the red-hair gene. Theoretically, it should dominate the blond, but we have cases, nevertheless, where blond parents have a red-haired child. With rare exceptions, however, the blond gene is definitely recessive to those for all darker-hair shades.

This leads to these conclusions:

If you have dark hair, you are carrying either two dark-hair genes, or one dark and one for any other shade.

If you have blond hair, you carry two blond genes.

If you have red hair you are carrying either one or two red genes, supplementing blond or brown genes.

The basic hair-color genes are found among all peoples, although not by any means in the same proportions. Red-heads are found even among Negroes and are quite frequent among the usually black-haired Latins. While blonds also are not uncommon among Latins and other black-haired peoples, we have no way of knowing to what extent the blond gene may have arisen among them by mutation, or to what extent it was introduced through interbreeding. The mutation theory seems to be the most plausible one in the case of blond Indians found among certain black-haired tribes, notably in Panama.

White hair can be due to various factors, genetic and otherwise. In its most striking form it is caused by the albino gene, which, as we have already seen, also robs the eye of color. White hair might also be due to an extremely weak blond gene, or to some "inhibiting" gene or condition which would interfere only with the hair-pigmenting process. White-haired persons of this type, quite common among Norwegians, Swedes, etc., differ from albinos in that they are normal in eye and skin pigmentation. And finally, there is the white hair due to age, disease, etc. In fact, in all hair colors there is the constant possibility that other factors may alter the effects of the "key" genes.

Age plays a much more important part in hair color than it does in eye color. The hair-color genes may be slow in expressing themselves. Often mothers have wailed as they have seen the golden locks of their young child turn later into an indefinite murky brown. On the other hand, a child born with black hair may have the second growth of hair much lighter in shade.

Light hair as a rule has a tendency to turn darker from childhood on through maturity. This also applies to red hair. Rarely does hair become lighter in color as a child grows up. Constant exposure to the sun, or bleaching by salt water, drugs, or some other artificial means, can of course easily lighten or change hair color, and climate can also be an influence. But regardless of surface changes, the pigment particles will still be there, so that under a microscope a scientific Sherlock Holmes could easily tell whether a blond was natural or artificial.

The hair-color change that comes with age is one of *decolorization*. Not merely the pigment, but the air content, oil content and structure of the hair are affected. The time at which hair pigmentation begins to slow down often seems to be governed by heredity. Where a parent has grayed prematurely, in many cases a child will begin to gray at about the same time.

Nerves or gland disorders, diseases and other physiological factors may also affect or change the color of hair. The belief has long been prevalent that sudden shock can turn a person's hair white "overnight." Quite possibly some sudden nerve upset might affect the hair-pigmenting process, causing the new hair to *grow out* white; but a little study of the hair structure will show that no shock could be communicated instantly along the whole length of all the hairs already grown out, to destroy the pigment there. For lack of authenticated cases the "turning white overnight" stories will have to be lumped with the myths about children being born with white hair because their mothers were frightened during pregnancy.

In passing, it might be noted that localized environmental conditions in different parts of the body may account for discrepancies in color or shade between the hair on the head and that elsewhere. Gland-action, perspiration, under-exposure to air, etc., may cause such differences. Thus, men with brown head-hair may have fair or reddish pubic hair. Strangely enough, where in men the tendency is for this hair to be lighter than the head-hair, in blond women the pubic hair is usually darker than their head-hair.

We have dealt with environmental influences at some length because it is important for parents to rule out these factors before they can ascertain what hair-color genes they may be carrying and can pass on to their children. Unless changes in parents' hair are caused by genes, they can have no meaning with regard to the hair color of their child.

CHAPTER XIII

SKIN COLOR

Judy O'Grady and the Colonel's lady, both being white, might very well be sisters under the skin. But whether the black man, yellow man and white man are brothers under the skin is a question that has long agitated the world and still causes strife and bitterness.

Scientifically, the matter of skin color is important because it has long been used as a basis for the broad classification of human beings into so-called "White," "Black" and "Yellow" races. Although the "blending" effects in offspring of mixed matings was thought to contradict the Mendelian laws, we are now able to show clearly that the "skin-color" genes act in precisely the same way as do other genes.

One's skin is in some respects like a wrapping. The skin serves many purposes, among them that of protecting the flesh beneath. For one thing, it must shade the delicate blood-vessels from strong sun or light rays. Nature therefore calls on certain genes to fill the skin with pigment particles; and because the human being is a migratory animal, the amount of pigment produced is governed to some extent by the needs of the individual, varying with the seasons and other influences (including disease).

Persons of the so-called "White races" may range all the way from the very light-skinned "Nordics" of the cold climates to the extremely dark-skinned southern Italians and almost-black Arabs. The difference in complexions among Whites in various countries is due in part to gene variations, in part to the degree of exposure to the hot sun. The black skin of the Negro is, however, *not* due to such exposure, although it may be modified by more or less sunlight. Shakespeare was laboring under a familiar misapprehen-

66

sion when he had the Prince of Morocco refer to his complexion as "The shadow'd livery of the burnish'd sun."

It might be noted that the terms "White" or "Black" are often used arbitrarily without regard to skin color, and may have different meanings in different parts of the world. In the south of the United States a person who has any distinguishable fraction of Negro blood is grouped with the "Blacks" and must ride with them in the "Jim Crow" cars. In South Africa, on the other hand, a fraction of white blood makes a person "White." The "Jim Crow" laws there apply only to those who are full-blooded Negroes.

The skin-color genes among the various peoples differ not merely in the amount but in the type of pigment they produce. In Whites the basic pigment is the brown melanin, diffusely distributed in the epidermis so that the blood-vessels below shine through and produce the "flesh color" which artists suffer agonies trying to copy. Among Mongols, Eskimos and American Indians, the brown-color gene is either supplemented with or replaced by one producing yellow or yellowish-red pigment. In Negroes it is believed that several skin-color genes are at work, some producing yellowish and dark-brown pigments in greater intensity than in lighter-skinned peoples.

Examples of how "multiple" genes operate are offered in matings between full-blooded Negroes and Whites. Although at first glance the skin color of their children might seem to evidence a blended action of the black and white parental genes, analysis shows that the color genes are at work independently, and that only in the *effect* they produce is there any blending. The segregation of the genes is revealed if, in the next generation, the mulatto offspring mate with similar mulatto offspring. Had the genes blended, all the offspring would have the mulatto color of their parents. Instead, such offspring are of a variety of shades, ranging from the darkest black of any Negro grandparent, to the light skin of the fairest white grandparent.

How this sorting out and recombination of the genes takes place is shown in our accompanying color-plate. We can see by this why a truly black-skinned child can be produced only if *both* parents carry some Negro-skin-color genes. This should dispose of the old superstition, common in yesterday's fiction, of how a woman with some hidden Negro blood, "passing" as white and married to a White, might give birth to a coal-black baby. Where a black baby does unexpectedly turn up, it can be taken for granted that (a) both parents have Negro ancestry, or (b) that the parentage is doubtful. In reverse, it would be equally impossible for a Negress with hidden white blood to be mated with a full-blooded Negro and give birth to a white child.

Apart from the pigment they produce, the skin-color genes may also influence the manner in which skins react to strong sunlight. Take the familiar examples of stenographers on their vacations. In the case of one, the more she is exposed to glaring sunlight, the more her genes will rally to increase pigmentation. A beautiful tan will result. In another girl (usually true of very fair-skinned people) the pigment genes may be unequal to the task. Unless she properly protects herself, her flesh may actually be *broiled,* sometimes with serious results.

There are white persons who through constant exposure to a hot sun can become almost as dark as some Negroes. However, their coat of tan can never offer them the same protection from the sun's rays as does the natural pigmentation of the Negro. Where normally fair Whites do become dark-skinned, it should be clear that this is only an *acquired* characteristic that can have no effect on their children. White families can live in the tropics for generations, and yet their children will continue to be born as fair-skinned as if their forebears had never strayed out of Hoboken, New Jersey.

Do Negroes become lighter when they are kept out of the sun? Yes, somewhat. While the basic skin color of the full-blooded Negro is always dark, it may vary in intensity under different conditions. Some Negroes, however, are genetically lighter-skinned than others. Increasing intermarriage, with the constant admixture of white-skin genes, has greatly diluted the "mean" (average) color of the Negro population. It is estimated, in fact, that *the Negro population of the United States today does not contain more than 5 percent of "full" Negroes, who have no white blood whatsoever.*

Matings between Whites and Yellow people have also been extensively studied, but are of less importance to us. Of interest, how-

SKIN COLOR

IF A NEGRO MATES WITH A WHITE:

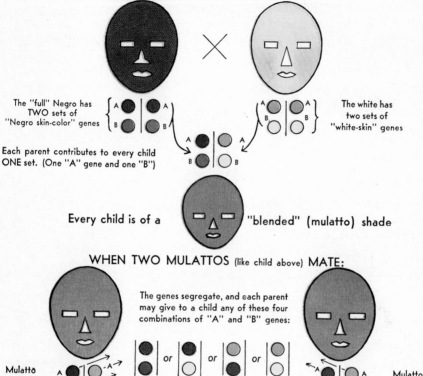

The "full" Negro has TWO sets of "Negro skin-color" genes

The white has two sets of "white-skin" genes

Each parent contributes to every child ONE set. (One "A" gene and one "B")

Every child is of a   "blended" (mulatto) shade

WHEN TWO MULATTOS (like child above) MATE:

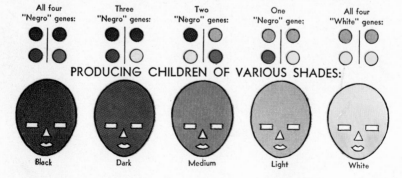

The genes segregate, and each parent may give to a child any of these four combinations of "A" and "B" genes:

or   or   or

Mulatto Skin Genes

Mulatto Skin Genes

From both parents together a child may get any of nine combinations, including these:

| All four "Negro" genes: | Three "Negro" genes: | Two "Negro" genes: | One "Negro" gene: | All four "White" genes: |

PRODUCING CHILDREN OF VARIOUS SHADES:

Black   Dark   Medium   Light   White

(NOTE: Only two types of skin color genes are shown, but there probably are more)

ever, are the instances of where a remote Mongol ancestor may reveal himself in a European or American infant through the "Mongolian spot." This is a patch, or concentration of pigment cells, toward the lower end of the spine occurring as a hereditary effect in many, if not almost all, infants among Eskimos, Indians, Chinese and kindred peoples. It disappears by the end of the first year. Where this spot appears not infrequently among infants of Austrian or Hungarian descent, or sometimes among those of some other nationality, it often reveals the presence of some Mongolian invader in the remote branches of the family tree.

Freckles provide a more familiar example of spotting in humans, which may have a definite hereditary basis. Freckling is often transitory, appearing in childhood and disappearing with maturity. Frequently it is associated with red hair and white skin, indicating the likelihood of some multiple gene action. A rarer form of spotting in humans, just as in lower animals, is the presence from birth of permanent white patches over the body, due to an eccentric dominant gene.

In the general skin-pigmenting process, the genes do not assert themselves in full strength until after infancy. Characteristic pigmentation begins during the embryonic stage. Negro babies at birth have skin of a light sepia color. "White" babies are anything but white at birth (as every one knows!). Their flaming redness is due to the fact that their as yet very thin, and very sparsely pigmented, skin allows the blood-vessels beneath to shine through.

Changes in skin color in later years may be due to various other influences besides those already mentioned. "Addison's disease" gives the sufferer a bronzed skin. Pregnancy also tends to darken the skin in a woman. Jaundice produces a yellowish skin, as does addiction to certain drugs. Tuberculosis may give a person white skin with very red cheeks. Still other diseases produce their characteristic skin effects. But, as we must constantly keep in mind, all such influences can in no way change the skin-color genes which the individuals transmit to their children.

CHAPTER XIV

THE FEATURES

I𝐹 we expect to find in the plastic features of our face (nose, eye-shape, ears, lips, etc.) and in our body form as a whole, such clear-cut examples of gene dominance and recessiveness as occur in our coloring processes, we are due for a measure of disappointment.

This is not because the "sculptor" genes are less definite in their work than the "color" genes. It is because we know less about them. Their effects are much harder to study, our plastic features being not nearly so independent in their development as are our color effects, and being also influenced by many more external factors. Added to all this is the difficulty of classification.

In eye color, for instance, "blue" is blue, applied to any one the world over. We know exactly what is meant by "blue" when we say a child or a man of sixty has blue eyes, a girl or a boy has blue eyes. But in describing features or form we can use such terms as "large," "small," "broad," "narrow," etc., only relatively. A nose that would be large on a child would be small on an adult; a nose that would be broad on an Englishman would be considered narrow among Negroes; a nose that would look handsome on a Leslie Howard would be a monstrosity on a Greta Garbo.

Consider the members of your own family, or your friends. You say that this one of you has a "large" nose, that one a "small" nose. If you measured the noses you would be surprised to find that the difference between them might be no more than three-sixteenths or a quarter of an inch. Similarly, you would find that the difference between what we call "enormous" eyes and average eyes might not be more than an eighth of an inch in width.

For this reason, geneticists and anthropologists who have studied human features have confined themselves largely to crosses between peoples with marked differences—Whites and Negroes, Europeans and Chinese, etc. (This is why, also, in this book so much attention has been and will be given to "mixed" matings.) Nevertheless, the "inter-racial" studies have been checked sufficiently with observations of matings among people of all kinds to lead to certain fairly definite conclusions regarding our specific features.

THE NOSE. The "nose" genes are among those that can be most clearly analyzed. Some studies might indicate that there is one "key" gene producing the general shape of the nose, but most authorities agree that three, and possibly four genes are at work, each on a different part. That is, there would be separate genes for the bridge (its shape, height and length); the nostrils (breadth, shape and size of apertures); the root of the nose and its juncture with the upper lip; and the "bulb," or point of the nose.

Often, it is true, the nose as an entire unit appears to be "inherited" from one parent, as might be almost the entire face. (The present J. Pierpont Morgan, for instance, bears a striking resemblance to his late father.) Where such resemblance occurs in a set of features between a parent and a child, it can be assumed that the different genes involved were passed over in combination and were almost all of them dominant over those of the other parent.

Very often, on the other hand, a child has a nose which seems to be a "cross" between that of both parents. This would bear out the theory that several unit factors are involved. At any rate, it is clear that distinctive genes are at work, and that they sort out independently. If this were not so, the nose of every child would be a "blend" of its parents' noses, and eventually in a fairly homogenous population, the noses of all persons would look alike. But we know, of course, that this is not so; that even in the most inbred peoples noses of every shape and size appear, proving the Mendelian segregation and sorting out of the "nose" genes.

In the bridge, the most important part of the nose, shape and size are dependent on how far out from the skull and at what angle, the "bridge" gene works until it stops.

At the same time other "nose" genes are acting to determine the *breadth* of the nose, ranging from the thin bridge found among "Nordics" to the broad bridge found among Negroes; and these, or still other genes, are at work on the nostrils and the "bulb" or

HOW THE "NOSE-BRIDGE" GENE WORKS

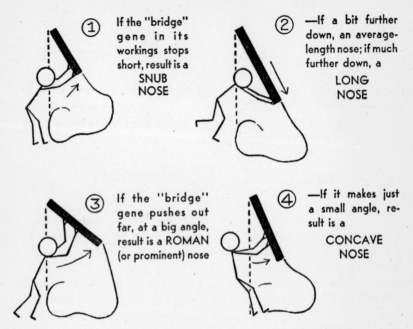

① If the "bridge" gene in its workings stops short, result is a SNUB NOSE

② —If a bit further down, an average-length nose; if much further down, a LONG NOSE

③ If the "bridge" gene pushes out far, at a big angle, result is a ROMAN (or prominent) nose

④ —If it makes just a small angle, result is a CONCAVE NOSE

tip of the nose. What happens when the paired genes from the two parents are radically different is suggested by the illustration.

With the various nose genes sorting out independently, we can see how persons may have a large nose with small nostrils, a small nose with a wide bridge and large nostrils, or any other combination. The full effects of the nose genes do not assert themselves until maturity; in fact, the genes may keep on working throughout life. As many readers have learned to their regret, the pertest, daintiest little noses of childhood may blossom out after adolescence into veritable monstrosities. Moreover, during and after middle age, there may be a final "spurt" in nose development, so that often, in later years, racial or familial characteristics become most apparent.

Being the most prominent of the features, the nose may also be most affected by environmental factors. Nose diseases (such as

"DOMINANCE" AND "RECESSIVENESS" IN NOSE-SHAPES

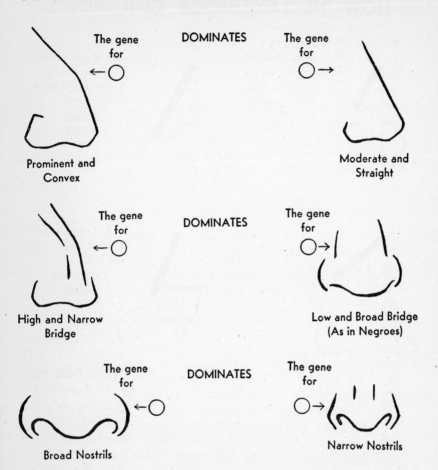

The gene for ←○ DOMINATES The gene for ○→

Prominent and Convex

Moderate and Straight

The gene for ←○ DOMINATES The gene for ○→

High and Narrow Bridge

Low and Broad Bridge (As in Negroes)

The gene for ←○ DOMINATES The gene for ○→

Broad Nostrils

Narrow Nostrils

NOTE: *It should be clear that it is not any type of nose itself that "dominates" another nose, but the gene producing the nose effect that dominates the other gene.*

sinusitis), structural disorders (deviated *septums*), childhood accidents, blows, blood disorders, alcoholism, etc., all can wreak havoc with nose shapes. Despite all this, however, the genes do manage to assert themselves and a knowledge of what "nose" genes the parents carry can lead to a pretty fair prediction of what the noses of their children will look like.

THE EYE. The form and shape of the eye, as we see it, are conditioned by the shape of the individual socket, and by the way the lids grow. A "large" eye may be due either to the fact that the eyeball and the socket are large, or because the eyeball protrudes and pushes back the lids around it (which may happen through some disease, as for instance, goiter). Where normal, the gene for wide eye dominates that for narrow.

The "slant" or "almond" eye is often confused with the Mongolian eye found among Chinese, Japanese, Eskimos, etc. In the slant eye, the inner corner is rounded, the outer pointed, and slightly higher. The Mongolian eye, however, is due to a skin fold overlapping the inner corner of the eye which gives it its oblique appearance. While the gene for "slant" eye is *recessive* to that for "straight," the gene for Mongolian eye is usually *dominant*.

Another dominant (fortunate for the ladies) is the one which produces long eyelashes. Where a mother has long lashes she can count on one of every two daughters "inheriting" them.

THE EAR. In ear-shape the Mendelian inheritance of several characteristics has been noted:

The gene for long ear seems to dominate that for short.

The gene for wide ear dominates that for narrow ear.

The gene for free lobe dominates that for affixed (although not always completely).

(A rare abnormality has also been uncovered recently where small, turned-in *cup-shaped* ears are inherited as a dominant.)

Ears, by the way, like the nose, may continue to grow and develop until late in life.

THE MOUTH AND TEETH. Lips are so delicately shaped and formed that only in crosses between widely divergent races can we find clear instances of how conflicting genes work.

The "broad lip" gene of the Negro appears to dominate the "thin

"EYE-SHAPE" GENES

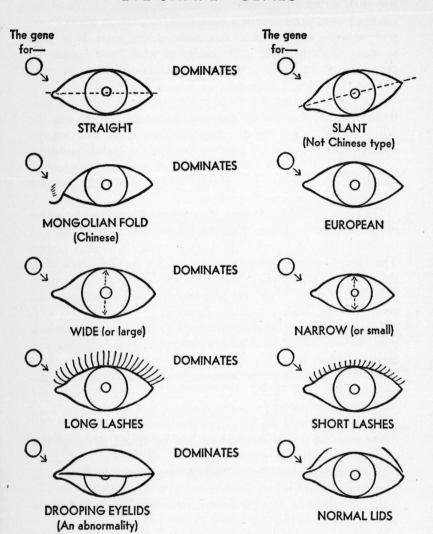

The gene for— DOMINATES The gene for—

STRAIGHT   SLANT (Not Chinese type)

MONGOLIAN FOLD (Chinese)   EUROPEAN

WIDE (or large)   NARROW (or small)

LONG LASHES   SHORT LASHES

DROOPING EYELIDS (An abnormality)   NORMAL LIDS

75

lip" gene of the White. Among Whites themselves, characteristic lip forms have been noted in various families, but geneticists have not yet studied this feature sufficiently to enable us to say what happens when a "cupid's-bow" gene meets a "thin-lip" gene, etc.

An abnormal condition, the Hapsburg lip (named for its prevalence in the Spanish royal family) reveals itself clearly as due to a dominant gene. The Hapsburg jaw also goes with the lip, an example of how the shape of the lips may be conditioned by the underlying teeth and jaw formations.

In teeth, genes are at work to produce the many characteristics noted among individuals, but little attempt has been made as yet to single out the modes of inheritance. (Except in cases of serious teeth defects which will be dealt with later.) Prominence of teeth and jaws, however, has been set down as a nearly *recessive* condition.

HAIR FORM. The hair has been subjected in times past and present, throughout the world, to more artificial changes than probably any other human feature. But of all hairdressers the greatest are the infinitesimal "hairdresser" genes with which a person starts life. They determine whether one's hair is to be straight, wavy, curly, or kinky as in Negroes. Of course, we may artificially alter the surface effects of the genes' work; or environmental influences, such as age, climate, disease, may somewhat modify hair form. But under the microscope we can see that the different forms of hair are actually different in their *construction,* which explains their eccentricities of growth.

In cross-section, straight hair is round; wavy hair is slightly elliptical; curly hair is more elliptical; and kinky hair is almost flat. Kinky hair is also characterized by the "bunching" of the hair in spirally twisted locks. In woolly hair, the extreme form of kinky, these spiral twists are very small and clumped together close to the scalp. (In addition to the gene which produces the form of the individual's hair, there may be another gene that determines its collective growth.) Although common among Negroes and typical of the Bushmen of Australia, woolly hair appears sometimes among Whites in whom there can be no presumption of Negro blood.

The basic differences in hair form are caused by the way the

THE "HAIRDRESSER" GENES

HAIR FORM: STRAIGHT WAVY CURLY KINKY

Produced by
genes shaping
HAIR FOLLICLE

OPENING:	Round	Slightly elliptical,	Oval	Almost flat,
SIDES:	Straight	Curved	Very curved	Bent

genes shape the follicles, or pipelets, up and out of which the hair grows. If you use toothpaste, you know that there are some tubes from which the paste comes out like a flat ribbon, from others perfectly round, from still others almost square. The form is dependent on the shape of the opening in the tube. In the same way, by the manner in which they shape the follicles, the "hairdresser" genes determine the form of the hair. By additional slight differences in construction and through environmental factors, the minor variations in hair form are created.

In the matter of dominance and recessiveness, the workings of the hair-form genes seem fairly distinct. They appear to be graded in potency by the degree of curliness they produce. The "woolly"

Where a different kind of gene is received from each parent, the effect is as follows in order of dominance:

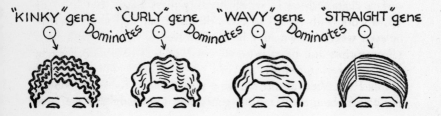

"KINKY" gene Dominates "CURLY" gene Dominates "WAVY" gene Dominates "STRAIGHT" gene

gene is the most potent, and seems to dominate all others. The "kinky" gene, in turn, dominates the "curly," the "curly" dominates the "wavy" and the "wavy" dominates the "straight." Thus, for straight hair there could only be "straight" genes involved. As proof of this two straight-haired parents almost invariably have all straight-haired children. In matings between parents with other hair-forms the results cannot be so easily predicted unless we have a fair idea as to which two genes each one is carrying.

A special gene, which determines the "stiffness" of the hair, may also be at work to complicate matters. The "stiff-hair" gene found among Chinese and Filipinos is a dominant. Apart from this special gene, hair-thickness (i.e., coarse hair vs. fine hair) has not yet been clearly analyzed. Thus, in matings between two Americans of relatively the same descent, where one has thick hair and the other fine hair, we cannot yet predict what type of hair their offspring may inherit.

An interesting hair-characteristic is the *whorl,* the manner in which the hair grows wheel-like around the point at the top of the head. Some people appear to inherit a "clockwise" whorl; others a "counter-clockwise." The "clockwise" gene is reported as dominant, studies made in Germany revealing that the clockwise whorl appears in about 74 percent of the population; that about 20 percent have the counter-clockwise whorl; that among the very small remainder there is a *double whorl.*

The distribution of body hair, the forms of beard and mustache, the shapes of eyebrows (and their growing together, as among Greeks and Turks) are all determined or strongly influenced by genes.

THE SKIN. Complexions, skin-thickness, folds of the skin, ridges on the palms and soles of the feet and fingerprints are among other surface characteristics in which heredity plays a part. But how the genes work with regard to these details is not sufficiently known, or even where known may be too involved to be dealt with here. (Fingerprints and palm patterns, however, will be discussed again in the chapter on twins.)

THE FACE. Viewing the face as a whole, one of the most interesting points about the "feature" genes, and something that we have taken for granted, is the precision and symmetry with which they do their work when they produce *two* features of the same kind— two eyes, two ears, corresponding teeth, and the two sides of the face in general. Here we have evidence of how consistently the genes do their work. If the genes did not construct the features in specified ways, down to the most minute details, one eye would be radically different from the other, one ear from another ear, etc. (The theoretical mechanism by which the features are reproduced *in reverse* is too involved for explanation here.) As it is, minor differences do exist between corresponding features and sides of the face, but except in some abnormal instances these result from the slightly different conditions encountered by the duplicate genes, or from external effects as the body develops.

During the intra-uterine stage something may happen to make one side of the face different from the other; in early infancy there is always the possibility of some slight accident; throughout the formative period and even well into life, sleeping habits, habits of speech and eating, and various eccentricities, may produce changes in the shape of the mouth, jaw and cheekbones which are characteristic of individuals or of entire groups or nations; and age, through a gradual slight increase in the size of mouth, ears, nose, etc., continuing throughout life, may greatly modify appearance. Environmental influences, however, do not produce nearly so great an effect on the individual features as they do on the body as a whole. This we shall see when we turn now to the general body form and stature.

CHAPTER XV

BODY FORM AND STRUCTURE

If you are short or tall, fat or thin, did you "inherit" the tendency for your type of figure?

The marked differences between body form in peoples of diverse races and nations—between Europeans and Hottentots, Chinese and Moors, American Indians and Dutch burghers, etc.—might lead one to suppose that *all* such differences were hereditary; and further, that among individuals of the same race these differences would be inherited in the same way. Which is to say, that because tall Scotchmen kept on breeding tall children, and pigmies kept on breeding pigmies, stature was fixed by heredity, and all tall parents would have tall children and all short parents would have short children.

Anthropologists have tried for years to find some structural or constitutional basis for classifying humans into various groups. But today it becomes increasingly clear that while genetic factors most certainly are at work in laying out the general skeletal and constitutional aspects of the body, so many different kinds of genes are at work—and, what is more important, so many *environmental* factors are involved—that the classification of peoples on this basis is a formidable, if not impossible, task.

Where groups of human beings have been isolated in the same environment for generations, and where there has been considerable inbreeding, we do find that all individuals of one group may possess many distinctive characteristics in contrast with all individuals of some other extreme group—the pigmies, for instance, compared with the tall Galloway Scots. But when we look for similar marked characteristics differentiating larger groups—Whites, Negroes, Mongols, or even Scandinavians, English, Italians, etc.—we meet with confusion. Within a general world population we will find Blacks that are as tall as the tallest Whites and hulking Chinese and Japanese wrestlers that will dwarf many a "Nordic." (The tallest of "peoples," by the way, are the Negroes of the Lake Chad region of Africa, the males averaging 6 feet 1 inch.) With the few exceptions that are the result of selective processes, there are no body forms exclusively typical of any "race."

Comparing one individual with another, however, there are differences in bodily proportions which often have a hereditary basis. But these differences are relatively slight, for we find no such hereditary variability among humans as we do among other animals of the same species—the giant St. Bernard dog, for instance, compared with the pint-sized Mexican Chihuahua. Between the very tallest of humans—the Lake Chad Negroes—and the smallest pigmy Negrillos (who average 4 feet 6 inches in height) there is a difference in height of little more than 25 percent. Even with these, we cannot be quite sure to what extent their differences are due to "stature" genes, and to what extent to other factors.

Two interesting "experiments" are on record where an attempt was made to deliberately breed tall people or short people. The Prussian king, Friedrich Wilhelm I, set out to produce a race of tall soldiers by marrying his giant grenadiers to tall women. His death stopped the experiment. (We may assume that left to their own devices, his grenadiers probably picked out the shortest and most petite Gretchens they could find.)

Catherine de' Medici, who had many cute ideas, took the opposite tack by setting out to breed a race of dwarfs. She did promote quite a number of dwarf matches, but these unfortunately (or perhaps fortunately) proved sterile, as such matches usually do. Misshapen dwarfs (*achondroplastics*), by the way, should not be confused with midgets (*ateleotics*) who are normally proportioned. Where midgets are mated with midgets, and the female succeeds in having a child, it is usually of normal size.

From the moment of conception and through puberty, innumerable factors bear upon the action of the "stature" genes. The mother's health, gland disorders, food habits, climate, living conditions, occupation, exercise, modes of walking and sleeping, all influence the body structure. This is strikingly illustrated when we transplant a group of people to another environment, and watch the effect on their offspring, who grow up under different conditions than their parents. In the United States, the anthropologist Franz Boas found that within one generation children of immigrants (notably Jews and Japanese) grew to an average height of two inches more than their parents. The better conditions for development offered children here in more recent years are undoubtedly responsible.

This applies also to the children of native stock. In various studies it is reported that American college students today are not only taller but heavier than were those of twenty years ago; and even ten years ago evidence was advanced (by Horace Gray) that American boys of native stock averaged two inches taller than those of fifty years before. A similar increase in stature is reported in countries throughout the world where living conditions, hygiene and nurture have been improved. All this is no surprise to livestock breeders, who know that proper or improper feeding and care may produce, from the same strain, huge prize dairy cattle or stunted animals with a "scrub-cow" look.

Granted that their environments were approximately the same (the environment is never *exactly* the same, even in twins), the differences in height between individuals can then be ascribed to the general influence of genes. But how these "stature" genes operate is still not too clear. It does appear, though, that the genes for tallness are usually recessive to those for shortness. This would imply that:

Two "normally" tall parents are probably both carrying "tallness" genes, and will have all tall children. But—

Two "normally" short parents may be carrying hidden "tallness" genes in addition to the dominant "shortness" genes, and can therefore have children who, while for the most part short, may also include some of any height. In other words, *it is much more likely that short parents may have a tall child than that tall parents will have a short child.*

SKULL FORM, or head-shape, has been extensively studied by anthropologists in search of an "index" for classifying "races." While there is unquestioned evidence that in head-shape, as in stature, genes do play an important part, there is also unquestioned proof

HEAD SHAPES

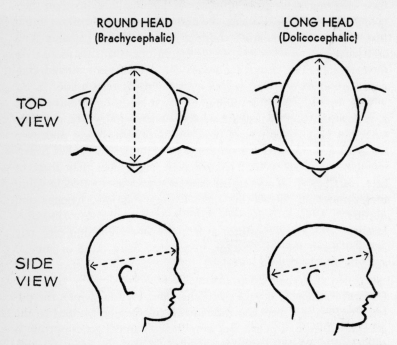

ROUND HEAD
(Brachycephalic)

LONG HEAD
(Dolicocephalic)

TOP
VIEW

SIDE
VIEW

that environmental factors can and do greatly modify head form.

Broadly speaking, people are classified as "round-headed" or "long-headed"; or, as your hat-store man might say, "long oval" or "broad oval." In general terms, the "long oval" is most common among Negroes; the "round oval" is most common among many "Nordic" Whites. Yet one can quite easily find a great many Negroes with round heads, rounder than those of many Whites, and many Whites with long heads, longer than those of the average Negro. The best that can be said at the present stage is that the factor, or factors, for the broad-and-short head appear to dominate those for long-headedness.

Quite possibly some of the genes for head-shape work through the glands, whose peculiar effects may often be hereditary. Dr. Charles R. Stockard, in his studies of dogs, attributes to glandular workings many of the differences which distinguish dogs of the various types—bulldog, dachshund, etc. While no such extreme variability exists in humans, he believes that the "bulldog" type of human head, the "dachshund" type (long and thin), the "Pekinese" type (big eyes, little nose) may similarly be caused by gland differences.

The artificial shaping of heads, as is widely known, is practised among some primitive peoples. Almost in the same way, habits of eating, sleeping, and talking may modify the head-shapes of people in our own civilization. In the United States there seem to be "normalizing" conditions at work; we see that the children of "long-headed" Sicilians and Scots tend to develop shorter heads; that the children of Jews from Eastern or Central Europe, whose parents are often characterized by broad skulls, develop longer and narrower heads. The marked round heads in certain sections of Germany are also held to be in part due to environmental factors peculiar to the locality.

Environment plays its largest rôle in head-shape before and during birth, and in infancy. The shape of the mother's pelvis may exert an important influence in the prenatal period. During infancy, the manner in which the infant sleeps, and in the ensuing early years the type of cap, hat or head covering the child wears (which differs among various peoples) all may be instrumental in modifying the head form.

BODY FORM. If we find difficulties in isolating the genetic factors for stature and head-shape, they are as nothing compared to identifying those for weight and girth. Innumerable environmental influences may produce in people degrees of leanness or stoutness. Moreover, while stature is virtually "set" after puberty, body weight may fluctuate throughout life. In the face of this, nevertheless, attempts have been made to classify human form according to types. Various indices have been used, but the most familiar classification is of three types, common to both sexes:

The *"asthenic"*—tall and slender, somewhat flat-chested, with narrow, drooping shoulders.

The *"pyknic"*—short and fat, thick-neck, protruding abdomen, barrel-shaped thorax.

The *"athletic"*—the intermediate type, with broad, square shoulders, muscular limbs, large hands and feet.

The assumption is that while environmental factors may modify or alter the human form, generally in a given population persons are destined for one body type or another by inheritance. Also, an attempt has been made to show that the "asthenic" type is characteristic of the "Nordics," the "pyknic" type of the Alpine peoples, and the "athletic" type of the Dinaric peoples (southeastern Europeans). The theory involved falls down when we see that all the types are represented in all races, and that while the proportions may vary in the races, environmental factors may explain these differences just as easily as might genetic factors.

Applied only to individuals, however, there does seem to be fair evidence that slenderness or obesity "runs" in certain families, and that under average conditions there are genes which will condition a person's weight. It appears, moreover, that obesity may be caused by dominant factors. Slender parents as a rule have slender children, whereas fat parents will have some children who are fat, and others who may be of varied figures.

Whether through heredity or not, it is clear that certain persons are predisposed to plumpness, whatever they do and whatever they eat, and that others are not.

BODY DETAILS. Almost any detail of the body structure, on examination, indicates that characteristic genes are at work. The types of breasts found among women show the influence of heredity. In some peoples, for instance, they are apt to be placed high and closer to the armpits, with the nipples larger.

An interesting peculiarity among Hottentot and Bushman women is the condition known as *steatopygia,* which may be politely described as a protuberance of the rear anatomy. Whether or not this is due to a special gene confined to these peoples, or due to the overactivity of a gene also found among White females (who might therefore have relative degrees of *steatopygia*) is not known.

OTHER DETAILS. The shapes of the hips and pelvis among women of different nationalities, the length of legs and arms (as in Negroes compared with Whites), the length and shapes of various muscles, the size and weight of bones, and many other bodily details indicate specific inheritance. Occupation and living habits may, however, be responsible for various differences among individuals. If the son of a blacksmith has brawny arms, like his father, should we conclude that his arms were "inherited," or may we not also assume that he developed such arms by working in the smithy, just as his father did? Very often, as we look at families of tailors, or families of policemen, or families of farmers, etc., we are likely to confuse the bodily characteristics that resulted from similar working and living habits with those that might be due to heredity.

In your own case, you may find that many of your bodily characteristics which seem an integral part of you are merely the results of "conditioning." Whether they are, or on the other hand whether they have a hereditary basis, becomes important when you try to guess what your children will look like. And this is now what we're about to help you do.

CHAPTER XVI

WHAT WILL YOUR CHILD LOOK LIKE?

WE have gone far enough in identifying genes linked with various characteristics so that, given certain facts about you and your mate, we could make some fairly accurate predictions as to what your children would look like.

Were we able to breed people as the geneticist breeds flies, we could make many more predictions, with greater accuracy. By constant breeding and inbreeding, geneticists have established strains of Drosophila, ranged in rows of bottles in their laboratories, whose genes they know almost as well as the chemist knows the make-up of his various compounds. In fact, with almost the same precision that the chemist mixes compounds, the geneticist can "mix," by mating, two flies of any strains and predict the types of offspring that will result.

We cannot, of course, ever expect to do anything like that with human beings. Pure strains of humans cannot be produced, like flies, by long inbreeding of parents with children, brothers with sisters, etc. And where flies have 300 offspring at a time and three generations to a month, human couples do not average more than four offspring to a marriage, and only three or four generations to a century.

So, genetically, in most respects we humans are unknown quantities. With regard to your own genes, you can only make guesses, but in this you will be helped considerably not merely by the characteristics which you yourself reveal, but by those which appear in your parents, grandparents, brothers, sisters and other close relatives. As was noted in the "Eye Color" chapter, if you are dark-eyed, the chances of your carrying a "hidden" blue-eye gene increase according to the number of your relatives who have blue eyes, and their closeness to you. Going further, if you marry a blue-eyed person and have a blue-eyed child, then you know definitely that you carry a blue-eye gene. On the other hand, if two, three, four children in a row are all dark-eyed, the presumption grows that you haven't a blue-eye gene.

Likewise, where both parents are dark-eyed, the appearance of a blue-eyed baby is proof conclusive that both carry "hidden" blue-eye genes. But if all the children are dark-eyed, it still might mean only that *one* of the parents has no blue-eye gene.

These qualifications hold for every case where persons have some characteristic due to a *dominant* gene (dark hair, curly or kinky hair, thick lips, etc.) and wish to know what chance they have of carrying a "hidden" gene which might produce a different trait in their child.

But before we try to make any predictions these facts should be clear:

All forecasts as to the types of children people will have are based on *averages determined by the laws* of chance.

Wherever *dominant* and *recessive* genes are involved, it is like tossing up coins with heads and tails. Toss up coins long enough, and the number of heads and tails will come out even. So if you are carrying one dominant and one recessive gene for any characteristic, were it possible for you to have an unlimited number of children, you'd find that *exactly half* would get the dominant, half the recessive gene.

With *two* parents involved, the results will be like those obtained in "matching" coins. This, of course, conforms with Mendel's laws.

When we think in terms of the *characteristic* produced, the result in "mixed" matings will be that the dominant characteristic (dark eyes, dark hair, etc.) will show up *three out of four times,* the recessive only *one in four,* as it requires a *matching* of the recessive genes.

Of course, where one parent carries *two* dominant genes, all the children will show the dominant trait. Where one parent carries a dominant and a recessive, and the other parent *two* recessives, *half* the children will show the dominant trait, half the recessive.

But here is something else to bear in mind:

Wherever it is a question of a child's getting one gene or an-

THE LAWS OF CHANCE

IF YOU TOSS A COIN WITH TWO DIFFERENT SIDES, ONE "HEAD", ONE "TAIL" —

The odds are exactly even that it will land

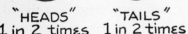

"HEADS"
1 in 2 times

"TAILS"
1 in 2 times

— SIMILARLY, IF YOU CARRY A MIXED PAIR OF ANY GENE, ONE "DOMINANT", ONE "RECESSIVE"

When you mate, the odds are exactly even that any child will receive

THE DOMINANT GENE
1 in 2 times

THE RECESSIVE GENE
1 in 2 times

IF YOU AND ANOTHER PERSON EACH TOSS A COIN

-The odds are exactly

1 in 4 times
BOTH
HEADS

1 in 4 times
BOTH
TAILS

2 in 4 times
ONE "HEADS"
ONE "TAILS"

—SIMILARLY, IF YOU AND YOUR MATE EACH CARRY A MIXED PAIR OF GENES FOR SOME TRAIT

You: Your Mate·

Every time you have a child the odds are exacty

1 in 4 times
Child will
receive   BOTH
                 DOMINANTS

1 in 4 times
Child will
receive   BOTH
                 RECESSIVES

2 in 4 times
child will
receive   ONE
                 DOMINANT
                 ONE
                 RECESSIVE

No matter how many times coins are tossed, the odds will always be exactly the same for the next toss

No matter how many children you have or how many "in a row" are the same type, the odds will be exactly the same for the next other, or having such and such a characteristic, *the odds for every child are exactly the same.*

Some gamblers might dispute this, but if you toss up a coin one time, and it comes up heads, that does not mean that the next time there is any better chance of its coming up tails. *There is the same fifty-fifty chance on each toss-up.* Even, if through an unusual "run," there would be ten heads in succession, on the eleventh toss there would still be an exactly even chance for either "heads" or "tails." (This applies to dice, roulette or any other game of chance. Many a gentleman has lost a fortune trying to disprove it.)

So, let us say, if the odds are even for your having a blue-eyed child, and your first one is brown-eyed, that doesn't mean that the odds are any better that the next will be blue-eyed. Even if four or five children in a row are born with brown eyes, there is still that same fifty-fifty chance, no more and no less, that the next child will have either brown or blue eyes.

But perhaps we need not have gone into all this. In the "boy or girl?" question we say that there is a 106 to 100 chance that the child will be a boy. And yet, authorities like Eddie Cantor will tell you that the fact of their having had two, three or four girls in a row in no way bettered the odds that the next one would *not* be a girl!

In "boy or girl?", however, it is a simple question of one or the other. But in the case of features or form—in fact, of any detail in the body—there are innumerable variations to contend with. If you and your mate conform to the average, you will find the forecasts here presented fairly dependable. Always, however, *allow for exceptions and*—whatever happens, do not blame us (or the geneticists on whose studies these tables are based) if the baby does not turn out the way the forecast indicated.

And now to Sir Oracle!

HOW TO USE THESE "CHILD FORECAST" TABLES

First: If this is to be your first child, find out as much as possible about what genes you and your mate may be carrying by consulting the detailed treatments of each feature in preceding chapters, and by studying other members of your families.* Make allowances for all characteristics influenced by *environment.*

Second: If you have already had one or more children, also study each child for additional clues as to your genes.

Third: Remember that no matter how many children you have had, or what they look like, the *odds* that your next child will receive a given characteristic are exactly the same as if it had been the first.

Fourth: In consulting the tables, look for your own characteristic in *either* of the "parent's" columns. (They each apply equally to father or mother.) If you and your mate are of different types, look first for the type *most pronounced*—the darkest coloring, the most extreme hair form, etc.

Fifth: Remember that these "forecasts" are based on averages in large numbers of matings. With just one child, that child might be the *exception.*

Sixth: Wherever age is a factor, make due allowances for its future effects or changes that may be expected to take place.

* In the following pages, "family" refers not only to parents, brothers, and sisters, but to grandparents and other close relatives.

EYE-COLOR FORECAST

IF EYES OF ONE PARENT ARE:	IF EYES OF OTHER PARENT ARE:	*Child's Eyes Will Be:*
BROWN (or **BLACK**)		
Type 1. If all this parent's family were dark-eyed	× No Matter What Color	Almost certainly *dark*
Type 2. Where some in this parent's family have lighter-colored eyes (gray, green or blue)	× Brown, Type 2	Probably *brown*, but possibly some other color
	× Gray, Green OR Blue	Even chance *brown* or lighter color (most likely like that of lighter-eyed parent)
GRAY or **GREEN**	× Gray, Green OR Blue	Probably *gray* or *green*, but possibly *blue*. (Rarely brown)
BLUE	× Blue	Almost certainly *blue*. (Rarely a darker shade, the possibility being less if parents' eyes are light-blue)
ALBINO (Colorless)	× Normal-eyed parent of any eye-color	*Normal*, leaning to shade of normal parent's eyes, *unless* this parent carries hidden "albino" gene, when 1 in 2 chance of child being albino
	× Albino	Definitely *albino*

EYE-SHAPE FORECAST

Width: Where just one parent has wide eyes, child will quite likely have them.

Slant: If one parent has slant-eyes (but *not of Chinese type*) child will not be likely to have them unless slant-eyes also appear in the family of the other parent. If, however, the parent's eyes are of the Chinese, or Mongolian, type there is great likelihood that child will have them.

Lashes: Where just one parent has long lashes, child may be expected to have them.

HAIR-COLOR FORECAST

IF ONE PARENT'S HAIR-COLOR IS:	OTHER PARENT'S HAIR-COLOR:	Child's Hair-Color Will Be:
DARK (Brown or Black)		
Type 1. Where all in this parent's family had dark hair	× **No Matter What**	Almost certainly *dark*
	× **Dark, Type 2**	Probably *dark*, but possibly some lighter shade
Type 2. Where there are lighter shades among others in this parent's family	× **Red**	About equal chance (a) *dark* or (b) *red-brown* or *red*, with (c) some slight possibility of *blond*
	× **Blond**	Probably *dark*, but possibly *blond*—rarely *red*
RED	× **Red**	Most probably *red*, and occasionally light-brown or blond
	× **Blond**	Even chances, (a) *red* or (b) *light-brown* or *blond*
BLOND		
Type 1. If medium shade	× **Blond**	Fairly certain *blond*, with rarely *brown*. (*Red* possibly if this shade is present in either parent's family)
Type 2. If flaxen or white	× **Blond—Flaxen** or white	Certainly blond, but with shade of darker parent apt to prevail

HAIR-FORM FORECAST

IF ONE PARENT'S HAIR IS:	OTHER PARENT'S HAIR:	*Child's Hair Will Be:*
CURLY		
Type 1. If all in this parent's family are curly-haired	× **Any Form,** except kinky or woolly	Almost certainly *curly* (rarely any other)
Type 2. If some wavy or straight in this parent's family	× **Curly,** Type 2	Probably *curly*, possibly *wavy* or *straight*
	× **Wavy**	Even chance (a) *curly* or (b) possibly *wavy* or occasionally *straight*
	× **Straight**	Probably *curly* or *wavy*, possibly *straight*
WAVY		
Type 1. If no straight-haired persons in this parent's family	× **Wavy** OR **Straight**	Almost certainly *wavy*, rarely *straight*
Type 2. If there are some with straight hair in this parent's family	× **Straight**	Even chance *wavy* or *straight*. (Rarely anything else).
STRAIGHT	× **Straight**	Almost certainly *straight*
KINKY		
Type 1. Where all in this parent's family are kinky-haired	× **No Matter What** Hair Form	Almost certainly *kinky*
Type 2. Where other hair-forms appear in this parent's family	× **Curly** OR **Wavy**	Even chance (a) *kinky* or (b) *curly* or *wavy;* rarely *straight*
	× **Straight**	Almost same as above, but with greater possibility of *straight*

Woolly: While fairly frequent among Negroes, it is rare among Whites. Where, however, it appears in even one parent half the children will have woolly hair.

FORECAST OF FACIAL DETAILS

NOSE

(Nose-shape is not "inherited" as a unit. Different characteristics of the nose may be "inherited" separately, one detail sometimes from one parent, another from the other parent. Environmental factors also have great influence.)

Generally: Where both parents have about the same type of nose, a child *on maturity* will have a similar type.

But: If just one parent has a *broad* nose, a *long* nose, or a *prominent* nose, and the other parent a *moderate* nose, the child's nose will very likely be of the more extreme type (on maturity).

Where any nose peculiarity has appeared in several generations of either parent's family there is an even chance that the child will "inherit" it.

EARS

Large. If just one parent has large ears, the child will very likely have similar ears.

Affixed Lobes. Where only one parent has *affixed* ear-lobes, or absence of lobes, and the condition does not appear in the other parent's family, there is little likelihood that the child will have such ears.

MOUTH

Lips. If just one parent has thick lips, the child will probably have them.

If just one parent has a heavy, or protruding underlip (Hapsburg type) the child has an even chance of "inheriting" it.

STATURE FORECAST

Both parents tall. The child on maturity will almost certainly be tall, or taller than average.

Both parents short. The child will probably be inclined to shortness, but may possibly be taller than the parents, and even very tall.

One parent tall, one short. The child will probably incline toward the *shorter* parent.

BUILD

If both parents are **slender,** the child will be more likely to be like them than if both parents are fleshy. But build is a highly variable characteristic, dependent on so many conditions and genes that it can hardly be predicted.

(**For the inheritance of "abnormal" conditions and characteristics of all kinds, in features, form and appearance, see later chapters.**)

HOW TWO HOMELY PARENTS MAY
HAVE A BEAUTIFUL CHILD

FATHER

Bald

Murky-green eyes

Long-lashes lost through disease

Misshapen mouth due to bad teeth

Bad nose due to accident

MOTHER

Black, straight hair

Dull-brown eyes

Drooping eyelids

Bad skin (local disorder)

Protruding under-lip

BUT they may carry and pass on to their child hidden genes for

—Blond, curly hair
  Blue eyes
  Long lashes
  Pretty nose
  Cupid's-bow mouth
  Lovely complexion

RESULT: A
"BEAUTY CONTEST"
WINNER

HOW TWO HANDSOME PARENTS MAY
HAVE A HOMELY CHILD

FATHER

Curly, black hair

Large, black eyes, long lashes

Well-shaped mouth and chin

MOTHER

Wavy Blond hair

Blue eyes
Long lashes

Regular teeth
Pretty mouth

BUT they may carry and pass on to their child hidden genes for

—Dull-brown, straight hair
  Murky-green, small eyes with short lashes
  Protruding jaw and teeth (and, alas, other irregularities)

RESULT: AN
"UGLY DUCKLING"

CHAPTER XVII

WHAT MAKES US TICK

You have seen what produces your external appearance. But you are much more than a hollow doll with such and such kind of eyes, hair, skin, etc. While your "looks" may be extremely important, your real importance as an individual lies in what is within your shell: your organs—brain, nerves, heart, lungs, glands and other functional parts. These are "what make you tick" and they are what account for the greatest differences between individuals.

In fashioning and constructing every one of our organs we know that genes are involved. We know that differences in the organs of different individuals are often inherited. But the task of identifying these hereditary differences is vastly more complicated than it was in the case of features, for we are here dealing not with easily recognizable characteristics but with functions and effects. In that regard, mere appearances are of very little help to us, for in very few cases have we yet been able to establish by mere surface inspection the nature of the important organs and their hereditary aspects.

We have reason to believe that different types of brains, hearts, livers, lungs, stomachs, etc., are inherited, but we have not yet been able to identify and classify such genetic differences, even between the organs of our by now familiar examples, the "Nordics" and the Hottentots. In the construction of every organ, many genes must be involved. However, only when a specific gene takes a strange and unusual turn, producing some easily recognizable abnormality, do we have any clue to what it does.

The glands form a group of organs which hold special interest because almost every peculiarity in humans is being ascribed to them these days. When people talk of "glands" they do not mean such old standbys as the liver and kidneys, or the gastric and salivary

97

glands, etc. They refer to the "ductless" (endocrine) glands—the pituitary, thyroid, parathyroids, pancreas (one part), suprarenals, pineal, thymus and the testes or ovaries. These introduce into the blood certain all-powerful substances called "hormones," the effects of which are often confused with the direct action of genes. It is quite true that the glands are conditioned by heredity; but glandular differences among individuals may equally be due to environment. All this will be clarified later.

As general or specific effects of the glands and other organs, there are a vast number of characteristics which show distinct hereditary influences. Among these may be cited the age and onset of menstruation, of puberty and of "change of life." All of the functional hereditary effects of the glands and other organs reveal themselves, as we have said, when they deviate from the "normal." Where these differences are so extreme as to be classed as "abnormal," we have our most striking illustrations of gene activity.

"Normal" and "abnormal," by the way, are vague words wholly inadequate to express what we mean. "Abnormal" means "not normal"; but "normal" cannot be defined except in relation to some standard that in itself is usually highly variable. For instance, if a man eats three pounds of meat at a sitting, we'd say he has an "abnormal" appetite; but suppose that man were seven feet tall and weighed three hundred pounds? An abnormal appetite for others would be normal for him. Four feet six inches would be an abnormal height for a man in northern Scotland and five feet eight would be normal; but five feet eight inches would be an abnormal height among pigmies, whereas four feet six would be normal.

In other words, an abnormality is a deviation from some arbitrary standard which may vary according to the point of view. It should not be confused with a "defect," for an abnormality may be favorable or unfavorable. An idiot is abnormal, but so also is a *genius*. All of this again will be dealt with in much greater detail presently.

But first let us consider the primary "abnormality" in humans: where *one individual* immediately after conception becomes two, three, four or even five individuals.

CHAPTER XVIII

DUPLICATED HUMANS

IN any discussion of heredity, one question is sure to pop up, like a heckler at a political meeting. The inevitable question is: *"Which is more important, heredity or environment?"*

We have tried to bring out that both forces go hand in hand in shaping any one's life, and that consideration of one without the other is impossible. You will therefore understand why the geneticist counters with, "Which is more important, the fish or the water in which it swims?"

The first question can have meaning only when it is applied to some specific characteristic or circumstance. Millions of young men have been killed in battle. In their case, which factor was more important in bringing on early death, heredity or environment? Obviously, environment. On the other hand, we know of many conditions which are produced by heredity, and which nothing yet within our power can change. A person is an *achondroplastic* dwarf —with a large, misshapen head and stunted arms and legs—due to defective genes. Which is more important in causing this condition, heredity or environment? This time, obviously heredity.

But when we deal with more general circumstances and characteristics, with the sum total of any individual's life, the question becomes infinitely more complicated. In your own case, you may often have thought, how would you with your given heredity have turned out under different conditions? Or, under the same conditions, to what extent might you have been different with a slightly different heredity?

That is what geneticists, as well as psychologists and sociologists, are trying to answer. And the only way it could be answered—or at best, partly answered—is this:

1. If there were *two* of you to start with and each were exposed to different conditions; or

2. If you started life with somebody else at the same time *within the same mother* and after you were both born developed under approximately the same conditions.

Is either of these situations at all possible?

Yes, for Nature has most thoughtfully provided us with *twins,* who, willy-nilly, are human guinea-pigs for such experiments.

For the first experiment we have "identical" twins; for the second, "fraternal" twins. The two types differ in this way:

Identical twins are the product of a single fertilized egg which, shortly after it begins to grow, splits in half to form two individuals. Each has exactly the same hereditary factors, and they *are therefore always of the same sex.*

Fraternal twins, on the other hand, are the product of *two entirely different* eggs which happen to have been simultaneously matured by the mother and fertilized, approximately at the same time, by *two entirely different sperms.* They may therefore each carry quite different genes, and be as unlike as any other two children in the same family, as often as not, in fact, being of opposite sex.

In other words, *identical* twins are, from the standpoint of heredity, *exactly the same individual in duplicate.*

Fraternal twins are *two entirely different individuals* who merely through chance were born together.

The important distinction between the two types of twins was not known nor fully realized until recently. In earlier years, twins were considered "identical" if they were of the same sex or resembled each other fairly closely. Even when the "one-egg" and "two-egg" distinctions became known and when biological facts of their birth were considered, mistakes in diagnosing them were frequently made. It was believed that the "one-egg" (identical) twins were always encased in a single fetal sac, with one placenta, whereas the two-egg (fraternal) twins invariably had separate fetal sacs and separate placentas. While generally true, it has now been found that this is not an invariable rule. Sometimes the sacs and placentas of fraternal twins are fused; and sometimes in identical twins (or even

HOW TWINS ARE PRODUCED

IDENTICAL TWINS
Are products of

A single sperm   and   A single egg

In an early stage the embryo divides

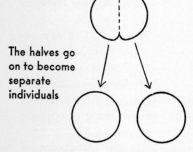

The halves go on to become separate individuals

Usually — but not always — identical twins share the same placenta and fetal sac

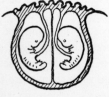

But regardless of how they develop, they carry the same genes and are therefore

Always of the same sex — two boys or two girls

FRATERNAL TWINS
Are products of TWO different eggs fertilized by TWO different sperms

They have different genes and may develop in different ways, usually— but not always — having separate placentas and separate fetal sacs

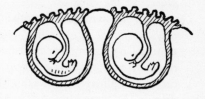

Also, as they are totally different individuals, they may be

Both of the same sex

Two boys

—or two girls

—Or a mixed pair

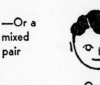

One boy   One girl

triplets, quadruplets, etc.) where their division has taken place at an early stage, each may grow a separate placenta and become encased in a separate sac.

Today, in classifying twins as "identical" or "fraternal" geneticists no longer consider midwives' or even doctors' reports. They have much more certain evidence in the form of "correlation" tests. By comparing the twins with regard to many characteristics known to be definitely inherited or influenced by heredity, they can tell whether or not the degree of resemblance, or "correlation," is high enough to stamp them as "identicals." Among the characteristics used for comparison are sex, blood groups, blood pressure, pulse and respiration; eye color, and vision; skin color; hair color, hair form and hair whorls; palm, sole and finger patterns; height, weight and head-shape, and facial details. The correlation in these characteristics is so much greater between two identical twins than between two fraternal twins that there is almost no possibility of confusing them.

Now why are geneticists so concerned about this distinction? Because on it depends whatever conclusions may be drawn from studying twins.

Inasmuch as identical twins have exactly the same heredity, whatever differences there are between them must be due to *environment*. Or, on the other hand, when identical twins develop in different environments—there being instances where they were separated in infancy—distinctive characteristics which have developed in both of them might be ascribed to heredity. Thus we may get some light on the question of what might have happened had there been *two* of you.

The study of fraternal twins takes a different direction. Inasmuch as fraternal twins have a much more similar environment and developmental experience than individually born persons, the question is how much more alike this similarity in environment makes them.

If *heredity were everything,* then identical twins would be exactly like each other in all respects, even if reared apart. But innumerable studies show that they are far from *exactly* alike.

On the other hand if *environment were everything,* then fraternal twins, reared under the same conditions, would also be alike, regardless of how different were their genes. But here we find that although they show a closer resemblance to each other than do non-twin brothers and sisters, "fraternals" even when of the same sex are less alike than are identicals reared apart.

The various studies of twins have comprised an important source of evidence for geneticists, and some of the conclusions will be presented in succeeding chapters. You will always have to keep in mind, however, that these conclusions can never be *absolute*. No identical twins are really *identical* because they cannot possibly have had identical environments, even before birth. If their environments were always identical there would never be any instances, as there frequently are, of one identical twin being born alive while the other is dead. They would either both be dead, or both born alive.

Differences between identical twins may also be due to the manner in which they were separated in the first stages. If the separation takes place in the earliest embryonic stage, before any body differentiation has begun, twins are as identical as possible. But if the division takes place later, when the potential right and left sides of the embryo are already laid out, the twin that comes from the right half might develop a little in advance of the other, and might be born slightly heavier and with greater vigor. This slight lead may be carried on throughout life, and may be productive of other differences, both physical and psychological.

"Mirror-imaging," or reverse-patterning, in identical twins is an interesting phenomenon that often results when their division takes place after the embryo has begun to differentiate. (See page 104.)

Thus, the one that developed from the half that was marked out for the right side might be right-handed, and the other left-handed. Similarly, in the hair whorls the whorl of one may be clockwise, of the other counter-clockwise. Dental irregularities in twins, birthmarks, freckle patterns and other details also often occur on reverse sides in the paired identical twins.

Freak twins of various kinds occur when there is an incomplete separation of the halves of the original embryo. In *Siamese* twins the separation is sometimes almost complete, but only in rare instances is the link between them so slight that it can be severed by operation without danger. Where the division is only partial such freaks may result as twins with one body and two heads, or one body with four legs and four arms, or duplicated organs, etc. All but a few of such human monsters perish before birth, fortunately, and are of little interest to us here because there is no evidence that they are due to heredity.

HOW "MIRROR-IMAGING" MAY BE PRODUCED IN TWINS

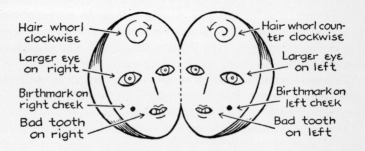

Hair whorl clockwise
Larger eye on right
Birthmark on right cheek
Bad tooth on right

Hair whorl counter clockwise
Larger eye on left
Birthmark on left cheek
Bad tooth on left

Think of the early human embryo as a solid sphere with a design running straight through. Cut in half (like an apple) the halves would show the parts of the design in reverse.

Normal twinning, however, does apparently have some hereditary basis, as the tendency of twinning to run in certain families is well known. In the case of identicals, should a specific gene play any part in causing the initial egg or embryo to split in half, then such a gene could just as easily be carried in the sperm as in the egg, and the twinning could therefore be due to the father as well as the mother. In fraternal twins, it devolves upon the mother to mature two or more eggs simultaneously. The tendency to do this might be inherited, or, in the opinion of some authorities, might be induced by external factors.

In either identical or fraternal twins, conception is one thing, but the bringing forth of the twins is another, and is greatly dependent upon the mother's condition. An interesting fact is that twins occur in the United States (and European countries) about once in every

90 births, whereas in Japan they occur only once in about 160 births. Does that mean that "twinning" genes are only half as common among Japanese women as among American women? A more likely conclusion might be that the smallness of the Japanese women, their narrower pelves, and perhaps some other constitutional or environmental factors do not enable them to *bring forth* twins as often.

The age of mothers seems to be an important influence in producing fraternal twins, but not identicals, indicating that the maturing of two eggs at a time is more a matter of environment. Older mothers have a better chance of producing fraternal twins than do younger ones. The frequency of two-egg twin births increases with the age of the mother up to the years between 35 and 40, and thereafter declines. However, even mothers between 45 and 50 average more twins than do young mothers between 15 and 20.

We have confined ourselves so far, in the matter of multiple births, only to *twins*. But all the basic facts brought out in this chapter also apply to the higher multiples.

Once in about 8,000 births triplets occur, and because there are three of them, it is possible for all three to be identicals—developed from one egg, or for two of them to be identical twins, developed from one egg, and the third a fraternal, developed from a different egg. Interesting examples of this latter kind of triplets are three well-known American scientists—Robert, Wallace and Malcolm Brode, physicist, chemist and zoologist, respectively. Robert and Wallace in relation to each other are identical twins, but each in relation to Malcolm is fraternal.

Quadruplets occur once in about every 700,000 births, with only a few sets surviving. Here various combinations are possible: (1) All four identicals; (2) three identicals and one fraternal; (3) two identicals and two fraternals; (4) or, more rarely perhaps, all four fraternals. The well-known Keys quadruplets, Roberta, Mona, Mary and Leota, of Hollis, Oklahoma, are probably of the No. 3 type, derived from three eggs, two of the girls being identical twins and two fraternal twins.

Among lower animals, it may be noted, the kittens or puppies in a litter are usually "fraternals"—products of different eggs. How-

HOW TRIPLETS MAY BE PRODUCED

Ⓐ Single sperm fertilizes single egg

Ⓑ Two separate sperms fertilize two separate eggs

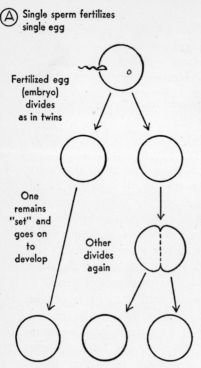

Fertilized egg (embryo) divides as in twins

One remains "set" and goes on to develop

Other divides again

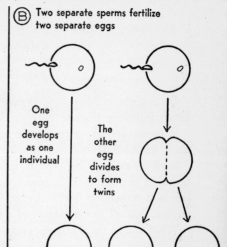

One egg develops as one individual

The other egg divides to form twins

RESULT: Triplets, two of whom are really identical twins, the other a fraternal twin of theirs, of the same or opposite sex.

RESULT: IDENTICAL TRIPLETS
(Always of same sex)

Ⓒ A third type, of "unmatched" triplets, can result from the union of three separate sperms and three separate eggs.

ever, one species of mammal, the armadillo, habitually gives birth to four "identical" offspring at a time, suggesting the possibility that in humans, too, a tendency to give birth to such higher multiples may be inherited.

Finally we come to the rarest and, to date, the most remarkable of all multiple births among humans. But that is sufficiently important to justify a special chapter.

CHAPTER XIX

THE DIONNES

On a night in May, 1934, Nature poured into the lap of science a lavish gift—the Dionne quintuplets.

If twins are of value in the study of heredity, how infinitely more valuable would be five children born at one time!

Such an event is believed to have happened not more than sixty times in the last five hundred years—and in all cases the babies perished soon after birth. *Never before, in the history of medical science, had all five members of a set of quintuplets survived.*

What made the Dionnes even more distinctive, and thus more valuable for study, was the fact that all five were *"identicals,"* the product of a single egg and therefore all carrying *exactly the same hereditary factors*—to the very last of their thousands of genes.

This, by the way, was not established until later. From certain conditions attending their birth, good Dr. Allan Dafoe, who ushered them into the world and miraculously kept them there, came to the conclusion that they were identicals, developed from a single egg. But certain other reputable authorities considered them "fraternals." However, as the quintuplets grew and an intensive study of them was carried on by a group of scientists of the University of Toronto, it became apparent that Dr. Dafoe had been right—that there wasn't a chance in the world of their being anything but identicals.

Some of the many points of similarity in the Dionnes, including such an unusual characteristic as mild "webbing" between their second and third toes, will be listed later. But also there are some important *differences*. And it is these differences which give us a clue as to how the Dionnes were born.

The quintuplets could have been produced, theoretically, in various ways. Starting with the single egg (or embryo) they would first have had to divide into two. But from that point on:

107

THE DIONNE QUINTUPLETS

(A) SIMILARITIES

—And all five have the same "Webbed Toes" (2nd and 3rd)—on each foot.

All have same
- Blood group "O"
- Medium-brown eyes mixed with gray
- Same eye pattern, same eyelashes, same light-brown eyebrows
- Same hair-color (dark, slightly reddish-brown)
- Same hair-form: Wavy
- Same feet pattern
- Same complexion: Light and fair

(B) DIFFERENCES (At age of three)

YVONNE	ANNETTE	CECILE	EMILIE	MARIE
HAIR WHORL				
⟳	⟳	⟳	⟳	⟳ ✔
HANDEDNESS :				
Right	Right	Right	LEFT ✔	Right
VISION :				
+.75	+.75	+.75	+1. ✔ (Slightly far-sighted)	+1.25 ✔ (Most far-sighted)
EYE FOCUS				
Normal	Normal	Normal	Lingering trace of cross-eyes ✔	Still slight cross-eyes ✔
MANNER OF HOLDING OBJECT				
			✔	✔

108

1. One-half might have doubled and then redoubled, forming *four* individuals, while the second half went on to develop by itself, intact.

2. Or the two halves might have each redoubled, forming four individuals, and then one of these could have divided again to make the required five. *This, it is believed, is the way the Dionnes were produced.*

It also would have been theoretically possible for even more divisions to have taken place, with six, seven or eight individuals created, of whom only the five survived. Dr. Dafoe did believe that there were six and that one of these failed to develop.

There is, however, interesting evidence to support our theory that the Dionnes were in the early stage *four* individuals, and that one of these re-divided again to make the added fifth child. Our clue is provided by the *differences* among the children.

We find that *three* of the Dionnes—Cecile, Annette and Yvonne, are similar *in all characteristics noted*. But both *Emilie and Marie differ from the others* in several respects.

Both Marie and Emilie are more far-sighted (Marie the most) than the other three, whose vision (eye refractive error) is uniform.

Both Marie and Emilie were mildly cross-eyed long after this condition (*strabismus*), found in all infants, disappeared in their sisters. In Emilie it had at last reports almost disappeared but was still showing in Marie.

Both Marie and Emilie have slenderer faces and more sloping palates than their sisters.

Both Marie and Emilie, as infants, displayed a peculiar mannerism in grasping things—holding a spoon, for instance, as indicated on the chart—Marie with her right hand and Emilie with her left. The other quintuplets did not have this mannerism.

Both Marie and Emilie, at the age of three, had seventeen teeth, whereas their sisters had only sixteen.

All the foregoing facts would indicate that Marie and Emilie were in some way paired and set apart from the others. As this could not possibly be due to any differences in heredity, we must look for some environmental factor, and the most logical one would be this:

HOW THE DIONNE QUINTUPLETS WERE PRODUCED
(Theoretical probability)

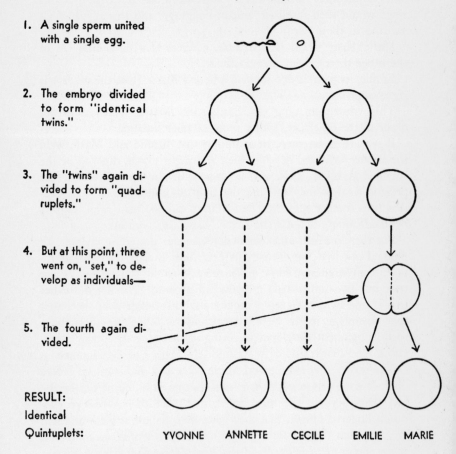

1. A single sperm united with a single egg.

2. The embryo divided to form "identical twins."

3. The "twins" again divided to form "quadruplets."

4. But at this point, three went on, "set," to develop as individuals—

5. The fourth again divided.

RESULT:
Identical
Quintuplets: YVONNE   ANNETTE   CECILE   EMILIE   MARIE

That when the embryo reached the four-division stage, three of the divisions were "set" and went on to form Cecile, Annette and Yvonne, respectively.

But that the *fourth part divided again,* one-half going to form Emilie and the other, Marie.

We can go even further: Granted that Emilie and Marie came

from the same fourth-part embryo, if differentiation had already begun before they divided, then the characteristics of "hair whorl" and "handedness" would already have been set. A division at this stage would then result in "mirror-imaging," and this is just what we find in these two!

Marie's hair whorl is *clockwise,* whereas that of Emilie (as of the other three) is counter-clockwise.

Emilie, in turn, is *left-handed,* whereas Marie (like the others) is *right-handed.*

This "mirror-imaging" in Emilie and Marie, which does not occur in the others, is further proof of their linkage.

If we are right, then, in assuming that Emilie and Marie were the last to form and develop, then we might expect them to be the smallest at birth. This, too, accords with the facts. Even at the present writing they still are the smallest and lightest.[1] The possibility is further suggested that Marie's development came slightly behind Emilie's because she is the "baby" of them all.

But there are still other deductions. In our preceding chapter we pointed out that not even twins ever have exactly the same intra-uterine environment. How much more so would this be true of not two, but five individuals growing all at once! We noted further that if one twin has even a slight initial advantage over the other, that advantage might be increased and carried along throughout their subsequent development, bringing in its wake other differences. And that is just what we find with regard to the Dionnes.

The theory that Emilie and Marie were at a disadvantage before birth in comparison with their sisters seems to be borne out by the fact that they are the most far-sighted, that their cross-eye condition lingered longer, that they were the smallest at birth and still are, and that they continue to be the most *retarded in almost all other phases of their development, with Marie consistently the last.*

The mentality, achievement and behavior of the Dionnes will be discussed in later chapters. For the present we need go no further than their physical make-up to prove for ourselves this significant fact:

[1] A photograph of the quintuplets, with their heights and weights as of August, 1938, is reproduced in Chapter XXXIV.

That with four years of life behind them, and reared under the most scientific and most uniform environment that has ever been provided for any group of children in history, the Dionne quintuplets, despite their exactly identical heredity, are nevertheless not all the same and are *not* developing in an identical way. As with any other individual the minor differences with which the quintuplets started life were sufficient to develop in each a special internal and external environment of her own. The child who had any slight advantage to begin with over another might tend to increase that advantage. Or here and there other factors might enter to create new advantages or nullify old ones. One might eat a bit more than the next, one might learn a little faster than the next, one might exercise a bit more than the next, one might be slightly more exposed, or more susceptible, to a cold than the next. Little by little jigsaw patterns of circumstance are being fitted together to make each of the Dionnes an unmistakably distinct individual. Already their parents and others close to them can, although not too easily, distinguish any one from the others.

If such differences can develop among five children with identical sets of genes, and with as uniform environments as science can create, we can now realize how almost futile it is to answer, in the case of ordinary individuals, "Which is more important, heredity or environment?"

The story and the lesson of the Dionnes are far from being finished. While the entire world prays that they will live a long and happy life, geneticists are even more ardent in their prayers for them. No human experiment holds forth greater promise. Secretly many a scientist wishes that there were another set of identical quintuplets that could be separated at the instant of birth and that each of these could be reared in an *entirely different environment,* as deliberately different as science could make it. One child might be reared in the slums; a second in the wealthiest of homes surrounded by every luxury; a third perhaps among half-starved illiterate mountaineers in Kentucky; a fourth in the home of a professor at Harvard; and perhaps a fifth in just an average middle-class home of an average couple, or on an average mid-western farm.

How would such a set of quintuplets, dispersed among such widely different environments, compare with the Dionnes? Would they still resemble each other? Or would they, despite the similarity for which their genes had destined them, be radically different in their figures, features, manners, health, intellects, behavior, accomplishments, in their adjustments to life, in their failures or successes, in the men they would marry, in the time when the final curtain would be lowered on their lives?

Not until an experiment of this kind is performed to provide a basis of comparison can even the study of the Dionne quintuplets give us the conclusive proof that we seek. Nevertheless, the Dionnes can teach us a great deal, and we shall all continue to watch them anxiously, waiting to see what different paths their lives may take despite their identical heredity. One thing we have already learned is that not even in the case of these five does Nature ever repeat herself in creating the substance and pattern of an individual.

CHAPTER XX

THE "BLACK" GENES

HENRY FORD, Mr. General Motors *or* Mr. Rolls-Royce could hardly be blamed if he disapproved of Mother Nature as a producer of mechanisms.

No reputable automobile manufacturer would think of turning out a car unless it had been rigidly inspected and every part found as free from flaws as he could make it. But Nature exercises no such care with regard to the human machine. For reasons of her own, perhaps, which we little mortals are not privileged to understand, she creates individuals with every conceivable kind of flaw, defect or "abnormality."

No human being is free from hereditary imperfections. But in most of us, fortunately, the defects are so slight that they hamper not at all, or very little, our progress through life. In some persons, however, the defects are serious enough to interfere with important functions, to produce abnormal appearance which may make social adjustment difficult or, in rare cases, to cause premature death. Wherever genes produce such detrimental effects we have given them the name of "black" genes. And *only when these "black" genes are involved* in producing a defect, disease or abnormality can we consider it, in the scientific sense, as *hereditary*.

The greatest error that was made in the past was to assume that because a condition was inborn or congenital, present in an individual at birth, or because it appeared in successive generations, it was, per se, inherited. An example of where this error is still commonly made is in syphilis.

Syphilis is not, never was and never can be inherited.

One of the most dramatic episodes in our experience bears upon this point. Some years ago we were conducting a "baby contest" in a large state, the ostensible purpose of which was to select that state's most "perfect" baby. A more important objective was to have babies, considered "perfect" by their parents, brought in for examination by doctors who might uncover unsuspected diseases or defects.

With a first prize of $1,000 and other attractive prizes as a lure, thousands of babies were entered. At the end of weeks of examinations and reexaminations the field was narrowed down to a half-dozen or so infants brought together in a central place. Every one of them was already in line for a prize. The question now was merely in which order the prizes would be awarded.

Proudly the mothers took their infants into the final examining room where a jury of leading pediatricians waited to make the selections. Only the doctors and the writer were left in the room with the babies. Never were babies more carefully scrutinized. Suddenly one of the specialists who was examining a two-year-old baby, whispered excitedly to his colleagues, "Look at this!"

The others crowded around. And then came the gruesome pronouncement, *"Congenital syphilis!"*

No one else, of the various doctors that had examined the child, had detected the almost imperceptible symptoms. The child had already been publicly proclaimed as among the prize-winning finalists. All that could be done would be to award it the last prize.

A shudder still runs through us as we recall how the mother was officially presented with the handsome token for her baby as one of the most perfect in the state, and then taken aside and informed that the child had syphilis. But that was not all. As she returned with her baby to her home town, where proud townspeople and relatives were waiting to welcome them as conquering heroines, the mother carried with her the knowledge that the child had *acquired* the disease from her.

For the only way that a child can be born with syphilis *is through the infection by its mother while she is carrying it.* The mother herself may have had the disease to begin with; she may have been infected by her husband when the child was conceived or at any subsequent time up to its birth. But the germs had to be in her to be transmitted to the child. All this is also true of gonorrhea.

A father, no matter how diseased, could not transmit syphilis or gonorrhea directly to his child through his sperms. No sperm cell can carry a venereal disease germ (or any other germ known today) and function. The germs can, however, be carried in the *seminal fluid* together with the sperms. Where germs enter the embryo after development is well under way, the child as a result of the disease acquired may be born blind, deaf or with any of various abnormalities. If, however, the germs are not transmitted until the moment of birth, or just before, the disease may not manifest itself outwardly until later.

We have dealt at such length with syphilis because ever since Ibsen's "Ghosts" startled the world, the belief has prevailed that the disease can be inherited, and that a "syphilitic" taint may persist in a family for generations. Attending this was the theory, called *"blastophthoria,"* that syphilis, as well as drunkenness, drug addiction, prostitution, etc., might in some way permanently affect the germ cells in a family strain, leading to increasing degeneracy and *progressive* weakening from generation to generation. The cases of the poor Jukes and Kallikaks, the classic "horrible examples" of the eugenists, have been cited as evidence. But as we have seen in previous chapters, no disease, drug or habit can alter the *genes* in the germ cells, and there can therefore be no such thing as an "acquired" hereditary taint.

When a child is born into the world with syphilis, or some terrible affliction resulting from it, the question as to whether the condition should be termed "congenital" or "inherited" may seem to be mere quibbling. But this is emphatically not so. For if a *congenital* condition is cured (as syphilis can now be cured) the child—no matter how diseased its parents were—can grow to a healthy maturity and marry and have children without the slightest fear that they will *inherit* that defect. But where a condition is inherited, *no matter whether it is cured or not,* and no matter how healthy the individual himself may be when he marries, there is always the possibility that he may pass on the "black" genes that may reproduce that condition in his children. Syphilis may be wiped from the face of the earth in a few generations merely by treatment and prevention. Inherited conditions may persist forever, for they could be eliminated only by preventing all carriers of the "black" genes from breeding.

Hence the importance of distinguishing between diseases or abnormalities *acquired* before or after birth and those *truly inherited*.

Mere familial inheritance—the occurrence of a condition in the mother and in several of her children—may be misleading. Rickets was long considered as being hereditary because it clearly "ran" in families. And yet now we know that it is a disease due to dietary deficiency, the result mostly of poverty, and that it is the *poverty running in families* that causes it.

In cases where the inheritance seems always to stem from the mother—and affects children of both sexes—there may be every presumption that not heredity, but a faulty *intra-uterine environment* is to blame. Cretinism and "Mongolian" idiocy are two such conditions which are directly due to the unfavorable condition of the mother. Innumerable other defects, diseases, and abnormalities are traceable either directly or indirectly to the mother's influence, but for the most part these must be ruled out here as having no bearing on the mechanism of heredity.

Before a condition is stamped as hereditary the geneticist subjects it to the most searching study and analysis. The chance of error in considering human pedigrees is great because methods of diagnoses are variable, the identity of the male parent is not always certain, facts about other relatives or ancestors not living may be mere hearsay, etc. Where, therefore, in the following pages, a condition is unqualifiedly cited as inherited, it may be taken for granted that it is so considered by leading authorities; but where the statement is qualified, the implication is that while many, even a majority of the authorities consider it hereditary, there are others who may not be convinced.

So we come to specific cases. The list of "black" genes already definitely identified, or whose existence is clearly suspected, is a long and formidable one. Coming suddenly on the rather gruesome array, you may have a sinking feeling. Let us assure you, then, that the great majority of known "black" genes are of minor importance to society at large because the conditions they produce are rare. In only a few of the major diseases or defects that afflict mankind are "black" genes known to play an important rôle—*and in many of these cases the way already has been pointed to prevention or cure.*

Many "black" genes, however, produce what we call *direct* inheritance. Certain malformations of the features (deformed ears, teeth, etc.), skeletal defects (curved spine, extra fingers and toes, etc.) and other easily recognizable defects are passed on from parents to children, always in the same form, generation after generation, with no way yet known of preventing their appearance. But in diseases due to hereditary defects in the *functioning* of organs or parts of the body, there is generally no such *direct* inheritance. The "black" genes involved usually have a *tendency* to produce undesirable effects, but under some conditions they will, and under other conditions they won't. All this will be brought out when we deal with specific cases.

It is our plan to present here in more or less detail all human defects, diseases, disorders or "abnormalities" in which heredity is known, believed or assumed to play any part—and which may be of interest to any considerable number of our readers. We do not intend to bore the many for the sake of the few. Even as it is, you may be inclined to skip lightly through the next several chapters, stopping only at those items that touch you personally. To make this easier, we have arranged the "black" genes in sections and under easily found headings.

Finally, all the "black" genes" dealt with, and additional ones of minor interest, will be summarized in a later chapter, in which you will also find "inheritance" predictions.

CHAPTER XXI

OUR PRINCIPAL ENEMIES

THE twelve diseases which take the largest toll of deaths in the United States yearly are:

	Deaths per 100,000 (*Approx.*)
Heart diseases	266
Cancer (malignant tumor)	111
Pneumonia	93
Nephritis (kidney disease—acute and chronic)	83
Cerebral hemorrhage (brain softening)	81
Tuberculosis	56
Influenza	26
Diabetes mellitus	24
Appendicitis	13
Infantile diarrhea, enteritis	12
Hernia, intestinal obstructions	10.5
Syphilis	10
Liver cirrhosis	8

Of all these, heredity has so far been clearly indicated as a dominating influence only in diabetes and in one form of heart disease, namely, rheumatic heart disease.

In tuberculosis, there is no possibility of *direct* inheritance, but some believe that heredity may be a contributory cause in the form of constitutional defects (such as a weak respiratory system) which may make certain individuals an easier prey to the tuberculosis germ.

In cancer, some authorities believe that there may be a hereditary influence, but proof of direct inheritance exists so far only with regard to certain rare cancers.

Appendicitis has been linked with heredity by only a few authorities and is very much in the doubtful class.

In nephritis (kidney disease), cirrhosis of the liver, and infantile diarrhea, no inheritance has been shown.

Syphilis, pneumonia, influenza—all "germ" diseases—have already been ruled out.

So, as we turn to the detailed consideration of the most serious diseases, we are immediately limited to only four: Heart disease, diabetes, cancer and tuberculosis.

HEART DISEASE. The "common" forms are rheumatic heart disease, the severe form of children's rheumatism which strikes down mostly children and persons under forty; high blood pressure (including hardening of the arteries), which generally does not occur until late in life; and syphilitic heart disease.

As previously stated, only childhood rheumatism shows any clear evidence of hereditary influence. In some of the various high-blood-pressure diseases, recent evidence has indicated a *presumption* of heredity, but no adequate proof. Of the remaining important types of heart ailment, *congenital* heart disease shows little evidence of heredity, and *syphilitic* heart disease is obviously not inherited.

Childhood rheumatism, which is characterized by joint pains, fever and inflammation of the heart, is one of the most puzzling of diseases. It affects 2 percent of the childhood population, and accounts for 80 percent or more of all deaths from heart disease of persons under forty (or 25 percent of all "heart" deaths). In addition to its fatal consequences, childhood rheumatism every year makes many thousands of children invalids for life in greater or less degree, the heart condition often becoming worse with each repeated attack. (St. Vitus' dance, a nervous condition, is believed by most authorities to be one of its manifestations.)

Childhood rheumatism had long been known to run in families, but only recently, after long research, has the rôle of heredity been proved. Evidence points to the conclusion that a single pair of *recessive* genes is involved. Where a child receives such a gene from each parent, the two genes together should be expected to produce the disease. *But that does not always happen,* because what is inherited is not the disease itself, but a susceptibility to its development under certain conditions.

One of the peculiarities of childhood rheumatism is that certain environments may partially or completely suppress its appearance. Most striking is the fact that *the disease is very widespread among the poor and relatively rare among the rich*. In New York City, for instance, in the squalid tenements of Third Avenue, there is an extremely high proportion of children with childhood rheumatism. Yet a stone's-throw away, on fashionable Park Avenue, the incidence of the disease among the children of the wealthy is far below average expectancy! (The same contrast prevails in London.)

Another peculiarity of childhood rheumatism is its prevalence in certain climates. The disease has very seldom been observed in the tropics, but as we go farther away in either direction within the temperate zones we find it more and more prevalent. In the northern cities of the United States—New York, Chicago—the disease is common. In southern cities, particularly New Orleans and Tucson, Arizona, or semi-tropical Florida and Puerto Rico it has rarely been reported. Yet among Puerto Ricans who have settled in New York, among adults as well as children, the disease takes a heavy toll. Once again, why? We may know, perhaps, in the near future. But as yet, childhood rheumatism continues to be one of the most baffling afflictions of mankind.

Also baffling in its nature, but not nearly so clear as to its inheritance, is *"high blood pressure"* (which includes several ailments). It directly causes half the heart-disease deaths, carrying off one in every 1,000 persons yearly. Many others are incapacitated by it.

One fortunate aspect is that high blood pressure does not generally occur until late in life. However, this greatly hampers the study of its possible inheritance, for in families where research is being carried on, many individuals have already died as the result of other ailments, and there is as yet no way of knowing if they had not also carried genes for high blood pressure. Some recent evidence indicates that susceptibility to this condition may be inherited, but there is considerable doubt.

CANCER. While proof of the inheritance of common cancer has as yet not been brought forward, the question is still undecided. Why this should be so, with almost 150,000 persons dying annually of the disease in the United States alone, with millions of dollars being spent and thousands of experts engaged in its study, becomes clear only when we consider what cancer *is*.

Cancer is not the name of a specific disease, as is diabetes or childhood rheumatism. Cancer is a general term for malignant growths which attack organs or tissues of the body. There are hundreds of different kinds of cancers, unlike each other in many ways, having only this in common: They are abnormal and destructive growths which begin by attacking some specific part or type of tissue.

These cancer growths are not introduced into the body from the outside, like some malignant seed, germ or parasite. How then, do cancers originate? Through some irritation, or perhaps spontaneously, a few cells at a given location undergo some malignant change and begin to multiply, forming a mass. Often some of these now cancerous cells become detached and migrate through the blood-stream to other locations, thus hastening their destructive action. Breast cancer cells may become implanted in the stomach, lungs, or other parts. A lung cancer therefore might be due either to cancerous cells that had originated in the lungs, or to breast cancer cells that had migrated. In fact, a cancer in one part of the body might have originated at one of many other points. *There are more different kinds of cancer than there are of all other known human diseases.* All this has vastly complicated the problem of diagnosing specific cancers.

You hear it said "cancer runs in that family." A grandmother, a mother and a daughter all have cancer of the breast, one of the most common forms of cancer in women. Should you not conclude that this condition is clearly hereditary? Let us see.

We find that there are more than a score of known varieties of breast cancer. Some of these cancers grow to large size, others may be no larger than a pinhead. Some grow rapidly, causing death in a few weeks, others may develop slowly, over a period of thirty years. Some remain localized, others fragment and are carried in the blood-stream to different parts of the body, to the bones, lungs, etc., where they take root. Some cancers are very susceptible to

X-ray and radium and may be easily destroyed or cured by surgery. Others are highly resistant.

Thus, in grandmother, mother and daughter, where all have breast cancers, each of their cancers may be entirely unrelated to the others. The grandmother's cancer might be a slow, small growth that originated in old age and did not interfere with her normal life; the mother's cancer might have appeared at the age of 40, and have been successfully eradicated by X-ray treatment. The daughter's cancer, however, might have appeared when she was just sixteen years old, and might have been so malignant as to cause her death a few months later. The breast cancers in the three generations of women might therefore be no more related than three cases of stomach trouble, one resulting from overeating, another from drinking bad liquor and a third due to stomach ulcers. But, while this might well be so, on the other hand it does not rule out the possibility that the cancers might equally be influenced by *hereditary* factors.

The suspicion that some of the common cancers might be inherited may be an important aid in combating the condition. Where a patient has obscure symptoms the knowledge that other relatives have had cancer in the same region of the body has sometimes permitted earlier diagnosis and treatment. This is particularly true of stomach cancer, which has in the past frequently escaped recognition until the sufferer was incurably ill or had already been claimed by death. This has been reported as running in families.

Many cases are known in which non-hereditary factors are directly responsible for producing certain types of cancer. As an example, cancer of the mouth shows a definite correlation with poor mouth hygiene—broken and neglected teeth, badly fitted artificial teeth or diseased gums. These may result in abrasions, irritations or sores, whose end result may be cancer (although certainly not in every case). The worse the condition of the mouth, the greater the danger of developing a cancer growth.

In certain cancers of the intestines and in the skin cancer known as *neurofibromatosis* and in a few other less common types, we know of no external agent which may play a part, leading to the conclusion that in these hereditary factors are primarily responsible.

Other types are known in which both hereditary and external factors seem to be necessary for the cancers to develop. And finally, there are a few rare types—malignant freckles and certain tumors of the eye and skin, to be discussed later—which have been definitely proved to have a hereditary basis. But again the reader is cautioned not to confuse *these rare types* with the common types, nor the proved cases of the inheritance of specific types of cancer in other animals, such as mice, with those in humans.

The human species is generally susceptible to cancer. Given a prolonged exposure to cancer-producing factors it is believed that most persons will eventually succumb. The reader may recall the case of the girls who worked in the watch factory in New Jersey painting luminous dials with radium paint. Almost every one of those girls died of malignant cancer. Nevertheless, present evidence indicates that *under ordinary conditions* of exposure to cancer-producing factors, *there seems to be a definitely greater susceptibility of persons of certain families to the disease than others.* Figures in the United States have led some authorities to conclude that the presence of cancer in a near relative increases tenfold the possibility that a person may die of the disease. However, the relative difference between susceptible and immune strains for cancer is much less than for many other *proved* hereditary diseases, such as diabetes.

The mechanism of transmission of human cancer factors, for all except the few rare types noted, can only be guessed at. Almost certainly, authorities believe, no genes working singly produce the common forms of cancer, and the interaction of a number of genes is probably required. One interesting theory as to the way cancer-producing agencies work is that they start all the trouble in just a single cell, by precipitating a malignant "mutation" or upset in one or more of its genes or chromosomes, which would make the cell lose its property of orderly growth and harmony with other parts. It may thus become an "outlaw," growing and multiplying without restraint, preying on the rest of the body without contributing to its orderly processes.

The theories are plentiful. But in many of its major aspects cancer still remains a stubborn and inscrutable foe.

DIABETES. Diabetes (the "sugar-sickness") which afflicts about one percent of the population, *is produced in most cases through the inheritance of genes* which make one vulnerable to its attack.

The disease results from a failure of the pancreas to secrete sufficient *insulin*—vitally necessary for the conversion of sugar in the body processes. This is why large amounts of sugar accumulate in the blood, causing degeneration in the kidneys and also producing poisons that may cause death. Recent genetic studies indicate that a pair of recessive genes are responsible.

Inheritance of two "diabetic" genes need not, however, portend the certain development of the disease. The disease does not usually manifest itself until the age of fifty, and may even then develop in some individuals only if they become very fat, if they overeat, worry excessively or overstrain themselves. There are almost twice as many cases of diabetes in women as in men. Consequences of childbirth are held responsible for this, as in unmarried women the diabetic rate is no higher than in men.

During the World War the number of diabetic deaths fell in all countries where there was a shortage of food, and rose again immediately as normal food rations were restored. In accordance with the principle involved, diabetic sufferers were formerly subjected to mild starvation, a treatment particularly dangerous to afflicted children who, through malnutrition, rarely were able to survive. Today, however, with the momentous discovery that insulin derived from other animals can be artificially supplied to the body, diabetics may be enabled to lead almost normal lives.

Several unrelated hereditary conditions, some of whose symptoms approximate those of diabetes, are often confused with it and cause unnecessary fear.

Diabetes insipidus is related to true diabetes only in name, and in the fact that, as in diabetes, there may be abnormal thirst and frequent urination. Aside from the possible inconvenience, it has no harmful effects. There is no abnormal production of sugar in the blood or urine, and there is no danger that the condition will develop into diabetes or produce its other harmful effects. This condition, which is believed to be a pituitary gland disorder, differs from true diabetes further in that it is inherited through a *simple dominant gene.*

Sugar urine (*renal glycosuria*) is the condition in which there is an excessive amount of sugar in the urine, but with none of the harmful effects which attend a similar symptom in diabetes. It is inherited, probably, as a dominant. (When you are told by an insurance company that there is sugar in your urine it might be the result of this harmless condition.)

TUBERCULOSIS. The prevailing opinion among tuberculosis experts is that heredity is no ally of this Public Enemy No. 1 of our youth. As every one now knows, tuberculosis is caused by a germ—the *tubercle bacillus.* Intimate contact with a tubercular person is necessary to acquire the disease. Inasmuch as tuberculosis germs breed most easily in sunless and poorly ventilated quarters, and find their readiest victims among those who are poorly nourished, the disease is usually correlated with slum conditions and poverty.

Tuberculosis germs are found in countless billions almost everywhere we turn in civilized countries. At one time or another undoubtedly they have invaded all individuals; it is quite likely that *almost every one of us has had tuberculosis in a mild, usually imperceptible degree.* In most of us, fortunately, the condition is soon suppressed or never develops to the stage where it can be called a disease. Only when the germs get out of hand, multiply enormously and begin to destroy the tissues of the lung do we call a person tuberculous.

Once tuberculosis gets a foothold in one member of a family, undisputed evidence shows that it spreads to others in the household. But not every one will acquire the disease under the same exposure. The reason that some do not succumb, authorities believe, is that they may have been rendered immune as the result of a previous mild attack (explained in the preceding paragraph).

The "acquired immunity" theory, however, has been disputed in some quarters, where it is maintained that some persons develop tuberculosis more easily than others because they have "inherited" weaker respiratory systems. This belief was widely held in previous days, but has failed to stand up under searching investigation. The spectacular decrease in tuberculosis mortality, during the last gener-

TUBERCULOSIS AND ENVIRONMENT

ECONOMIC STATUS IN VARIOUS NEIGHBORHOODS

(As indicated by average monthly rentals)

DEATHS FROM TUBERCULOSIS

(Approximate averages per 1,000 pop.)

(Based on figures compiled in Cleveland, O., for 1928-32, by Howard Whipple Green)

ation, which has attended the improvement in living conditions gives evidence that this disease is chiefly a social problem.

GOITER. The question of whether this disease is inherited is open to doubt. We refer here to the common form of goiter, attended by a swelling of the thyroid gland in the throat. It has long been considered hereditary, and still is so considered by many authorities. One thing is now clear: That the disease is the direct result of iodine deficiency in the body processes, either because of lack of iodine in the diet, or because of the failure of the thyroid gland to convert it properly.

While it is theoretically possible for defective thyroid glands to be inherited, one may now seriously question the earlier conclusions that the high incidence of goiter in certain localities and regions (such as the vicinity of the Great Lakes) was proof of such inheritance. In one experiment made among schoolgirls at Akron, Ohio, in the so-called "goiter belt," it was shown that of 2,100 who were fed minute amounts of iodine for three years, only five developed goiter, as compared with 495 cases of goiter that developed among 2,305 of their schoolmates with an iodine insufficiency.

Another fact which might indicate that goiter is primarily an environmental, rather than a hereditary disease, is this: As is well known, it occurs much more frequently among women than among men, and also, where it "runs" in the family, it usually appears to have come through the *mother*. Thus, we have the strong likelihood that not defective genes, but a failure of the mother to supply her children with sufficient iodine in their intra-uterine stage led to their acquiring the disease. One of the most unfortunate consequences of thyroid deficiency in a mother may be the birth of a *cretin*—a type of defective child that formerly always grew up to be a deformed imbecile. Today, however, by glandular treatments, medicine has made it possible for such children to develop normally.

On the basis of present evidence we may conclude that common goiter, where apparently transmitted through the mother, is *acquired* or *congenital,* and not hereditary.

DIGESTIVE DISEASES. Of all the many diseases associated with the digestive processes, few have been definitely linked with heredity.

Except for diabetes, there is not a single one of these conditions of any importance which can be conclusively blamed on "black" genes.

In *ulcers* of the stomach and intestines, heredity has been claimed, but has not been established. Polycystic disease of the kidneys, a rare disorder, serious in pregnant women, is generally considered hereditary, but the manner of transmission is uncertain. *Acholuric family jaundice,* characterized by fragile blood cells, with occasionally anemia, jaundice and enlarged spleen, has been established as due to a dominant gene.

ALLERGIC DISEASES. Asthma, hay fever, eczema and allergies to various foods and substances, have been extensively studied. Many investigators claim that allergies are definitely inherited through dominant genes, but the evidence is somewhat clouded by the fact that in almost every family there is some one who is allergic to something—ranging from colds and cats to—actually—the ink on colored comics in the Sunday papers!

Migraine (sick headache) which some consider as also allergic in origin, has likewise been reported as a hereditary condition, but the evidence for this is inadequate.

CHAPTER XXII

FOR MEN ONLY

A SINGLE "black" gene in one little boy may well have been a motivating factor in bringing on the Russian Revolution and in changing the course of the world's history.

The gene was that for the dread "bleeding" disease, *hemophilia,* which found its way, by one of Queen Victoria's grand-daughters, to the last little Czarevitch. As the world knows, it was because of his affliction that his credulous parents, the Czar and Czarina, became victims of the designing Rasputin, who held out hopes of a cure through supernatural powers. From Rasputin, as from a spider, spread a web of intrigue, cruelty, debauchery, demor-alization and mass indignation which may have brought on the collapse of the empire. *If* the Czarevitch hadn't had hemophilia, *if* his parents hadn't become the prey of Rasputin, *if* Rasputin hadn't demoralized the court . . . Thus a momentous structure of "ifs" can be built up, like an inverted pyramid, resting on that infinitesi-mal bit of substance constituting a single gene.

What interests us here, however, is the long-standing mystery of *why* hemophilia, and scores of other diseases and defects, are always transmitted *only by way of mothers to their sons.*

Poor males! In the chapter on "Boy or Girl?" we pointed out that the chance of survival among males is considerably less than among females. Now science pours further salt on their wounds by showing *why* men are an easier prey to many ills than their supposedly weaker opposites.

We saw that the only initial difference (in the primary cell stage) between a male and a female is that the female has two X chromo-somes and the male just one X paired with a bit of a chromosome designated as a Y. Very clearly the Y contains many fewer genes than the X; in fact, it may be considered as only a fragment of some original X. Thus, while a daughter inherits the same amount of genes from each parent, a son *inherits more genes from his mother than from his father*. And that means that he can also receive *more defective genes* from her.

So here's the answer to our mystery:

If a female gets one "black" gene in one of her X chromosomes, the chances are that there will be a normal gene for the job in the other chromosome. (Like a motorist with a spare tire when there's a blow-out.)

If, however, a male gets just one "black" gene in his single X chromosome, he is headed for trouble, because usually there is *no* corresponding gene in his Y chromosome to do the job. (So he's like a motorist who hasn't any spare tire when there's a blow-out.) Thus, the defective "blood coagulating" gene being in the X chromosome, if just one of these is received by a male, he will have hemophilia. The disease is usually fatal in early life. While comparatively rare, it has achieved prominence chiefly because of its occurrence among some of the progeny of Queen Victoria of England, who was a carrier. Her son, King Edward, and his descendants, escaped, but two of her granddaughters, the Czarina and the Queen of Spain received the gene, the latter transmitting it to Alfonso's son, the hemophiliac Count of Covadonga. This tragic young man, after battling the disease all his life, was finally claimed when he bled to death in September, 1938, from wounds sustained in an automobile accident at Miami, Fla.

For a female to be victimized by hereditary hemophilia, she would have to receive a hemophilic gene in *both* "X" chromosomes. Theoretically, this could happen, but no case is known of a woman with true hemophilia. The explanation, it is believed, is that two hemophilic genes together prove *lethal,* killing the individual before birth. A number of women have shown symptoms of mild hemophilia, but this may have been another blood disease or perhaps their one normal gene was not sufficiently strong to counteract the "black" one.

COLOR-BLINDNESS: A much more common condition than hemophilia (if not so dramatic) that victimizes males is hereditary color-blindness, the inability to distinguish between red and green.

"SEX-LINKED" INHERITANCE

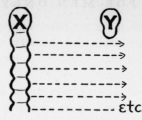

The "X" chromosome is many times larger than the "Y."

The "Y" chromosome lacks duplicates of almost all the "X" genes.

εtc.

If a recessive "black-X" gene is circulating in a family,
(A) for COLOR-BLINDNESS

DAUGHTER	SON
Receiving one "color-blindness" gene usually has in her second "X" a normal gene to block it.	Receiving a "color-blindness" gene in his single "X" has no normal gene to block it.

Result: Perfectly NORMAL (but a carrier)   Result: COLOR-BLIND

(B) "CRISS-CROSS" TRANSMISSION
As in Hemophilia

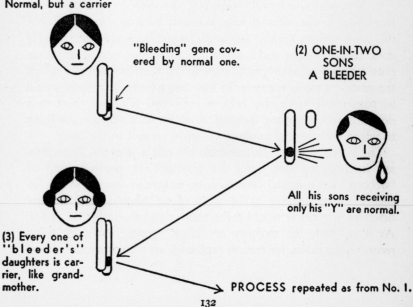

(I) WOMAN
Normal, but a carrier

"Bleeding" gene covered by normal one.

(2) ONE-IN-TWO SONS A BLEEDER

All his sons receiving only his "Y" are normal.

(3) Every one of "bleeder's" daughters is carrier, like grandmother.

PROCESS repeated as from No. I.

About 4 percent of all males are color-blind. (An immediate question is, how can they distinguish between red and green traffic signals? They can, because the red light appears to them different in intensity than the green.)

The gene for color-blindness is also carried in the X chromosome, and if the one X that a male gets has that gene, he will be color-blind. In a woman color-blindness results only when she receives *two* such genes—one in each X. This happens to about ½ of 1 percent of women, who are color-blind. These women then pass on a defective X to each son, so that *every one of their sons* is almost certain to be color-blind. Their daughters, however, will be color-blind *only if the father also* is color-blind; otherwise they will get a "normal" X from him which will counteract the one from the mother.

A number of additional eye defects and various other conditions which strike particularly at males have been tracked down to "sex-linked" genes. As the X chromosomes must contain a great many genes still not identified, there is every indication that as investigation proceeds, the list of conditions "for men only" will be increased.

In a few cases, however, sex-linked genes may strike *particularly at women.* Here's why:

In hemophilia, color-blindness, etc., the defective gene involved is recessive to the "normal" one. It is only because a male gets only this gene, and *no normal one* to counteract it, as a woman usually does, that it asserts itself. But some conditions now known are caused by a dominant "black" gene in the X chromosome to which the normal gene is recessive. In this case women, therefore, would be particularly vulnerable because their two X's open them to a double chance of getting the gene. An example is a certain condition in which such a gene produces defective enamel in the teeth.

The genes in the Y chromosome are still a mystery. Geneticists are investigating one queer toe condition (a peculiar kind of "webbed" toes), passed on only from fathers to sons, in the belief that this may involve a "black" Y gene. Should there be any defective Y genes it would make matters still worse for the males. As it is, with the majority of "black" genes in the X being *recessive,* the males, for reasons explained, are already special objects of attack. But, alas, their disadvantage as compared with females doesn't stop there. In addition to the "sex-linked" genes they may be victimized by what the geneticist calls a "sex-limited" gene, one effect of which, if you are a man, you may know only too well. We refer to the following:

BALDNESS: Comes a time when the hair on the head of the rugged male begins to loose its hold like the seeds of an autumn dandelion, presently to be gone with the wind.

Dejectedly, fearfully, he watches the teeth of his comb, as if they were some devouring monster, gobbling up more and more of his precious locks. What to do?

INHERITED PATTERN BALDNESS

| Starting at center of crown | Starting at temples | Over whole top of head |

(Baldness patterns tend to be alike in men of the same family)

In some cases, it is true, falling hair is the result of some disease or scalp disorder. In many other cases, perhaps the majority, the hair of a man, healthy in every way, falls out for no apparent reason. What adds to the mystery is that women, even if they have the same scalp condition or disease that a man has, rarely lose their hair to the same extent. When we speak of "baldness" in a woman we usually mean only partial baldness (*complete baldness* in women is almost never seen), and if it is, may be attributed to certain diseases.

The why of all this has long been a mystery. Some "specialists," and many "baldness-cure" advertisements, continue to repeat the old theories that men become bald, while women do not, because through the ages men have cut their hair short, have worn tight hats, have not taken such good care of their hair and scalps as women have, etc. All of these statements have as much evidence to support them as the theory that if you cut off the tails of puppy dogs for a number of generations, the offspring will be born with stub tails.

What, then, is the explanation?

Geneticists find it in a special type of "black" gene, called a "sex-limited" gene. Unlike that for hemophilia or color-blindness, it is not carried in the "sex" chromosome but in one of the "general" chromosomes which both sexes have in common, and which they therefore inherit equally. However, it does not *act* in the same way in both sexes. The "baldness" gene—an example of the "sex-limited" gene, is a *dominant* in men—*one only* being required to produce baldness. But in women the gene acts as a *recessive,* with *two* necessary to produce even partial baldness. Again, why?

Apparently the glandular make-up of the two sexes has a lot to do with the way the gene manifests itself. One theory is that the female hormones suppress the action of a single "baldness" gene, but cannot fully cope with two. Another theory is that the male hormones stimulate the action of the gene. In this connection it is claimed that eunuchs do not become bald, perhaps because they do not produce in themselves the hormones which would make them as susceptible to baldness as are other men.

Whatever the explanation, it appears that ordinary "pattern" baldness can be inherited through a single gene in men and through two genes in women. If a man has this inherited condition, therefore, he may be carrying either one or two "baldness" genes, for the effect is the same in either case. Carrying one gene, however, he will transmit baldness to an average of *half* his sons; but with two genes, to *all* his sons.

A woman, as we have noted, can carry one "baldness" gene without any effect on her. But the gene will, as likely as not, reveal itself in her sons; for even if she is married to a normal-haired man, one in two of her sons may be expected to get her hidden "baldness" gene and to become bald. Where a woman carries two baldness genes, the theory is that on maturity she will have sparse

HOW BALDNESS IS INHERITED

○ ... "BALDNESS" GENE (Symbol).

In *Men*—Dominant. One produces baldness.

In *Women*—Recessive or completely suppressed. Two genes required to produce any degree of baldness in a woman.

◉ ... "NORMAL HAIR" GENE (Symbol).

MEN

Type A

TWO "BALDNESS" GENES

(All of this man's sons will be bald, and if wife is Type A, daughters also)

Type B

SINGLE "BALDNESS" GENE

(Same effect as two genes, but only one-in-two sons of this man will be bald)

Type C

TWO "NORMAL" GENES

No baldness in this man's sons unless his wife is Type A or Type B

WOMEN

Type A

TWO "BALDNESS" GENES

Produces thin hair or partial baldness in women. (All sons will be bald)

Type B

SINGLE "BALDNESS" GENE

No effect on woman herself, but one-in-two sons will be bald

Type C

TWO "NORMAL" GENES

No baldness in this woman's sons unless her husband is bald

hair and in later life partial baldness. With such a condition, she may be expected to transmit baldness to all her sons.

The Samson episode in the Bible has given rise to the belief that a large amount of hair is correlated with virility. But many sturdy men from Julius Caesar down through Bob Fitzsimmons (the prize-fighter) and on to Postmaster-General James Farley—all with heads like billiard balls—belie this theory. Also, the saying goes, "Grass doesn't grow on busy streets." The implication is that intellectual men are inclined to baldness because of their brain activity. But this theory can be refuted by a glance at our Supreme Court judges —Judge Brandeis and the late Judge Cardozo, for instance, with their thick shocks of white hair (and both of them of a people with whom nervousness and high tension are commonly associated)— and also by a study of the faculty roster of any university.

In addition to "pattern" baldness, there are a number of less-common types of baldness, whole or partial, which have a hereditary basis. These, however, are not due to "sex-limited" genes, and affect women as well as men. (They will be found listed in the "Black" Gene Tables in Chapter XXVII.)

Also to be noted as *non-hereditary* causes of baldness are many diseases and constitutional disorders. Among these are syphilis, typhoid fever, pneumonia, tuberculosis, diabetes, rheumatism and certain glandular, nervous and local scalp disorders. Some of the diseases produce only temporary hair-fall; in others the resulting thin hair or baldness may be permanent. To what extent these acquired cases of baldness can be cured we are not prepared to say. But where "baldness institutes" claim today that they can also cure the common hereditary "pattern" baldness, we might venture the opinion that they are being, to put it mildly, optimistic.

We come then to this question: If, for no apparent reason your hair begins to fall out, and from the fact that baldness preceded you in your family you have reason to believe that the condition is hereditary, what should you, or what can you do about it?

We can answer feelingly, for the position is one in which we, who write this, also found ourselves a few years ago. We happened to be living in Paris at the time and when our undue fall of hair became disquietingly evident, a friend sent us post-haste to the outstanding hair specialist of all France.

Monsieur le Professeur occupied an elaborate apartment, betokening his eminence and inspiring great hope for our thinning locks. An assistant took down the case-history of the *"chute des cheveux."* As is the French custom, he tested us for many irrelevant symptoms, filled out a long blank and took it away. At last we were ushered into the inner sanctum of *Le Professeur* himself. The great man sat at his desk, our case-history before him. He looked at the report, he looked at us, and then smilingly bent over. *In the center of his head was a most decided bald spot!*

"Voilà," he said. There was an eloquent silence. Finally the writer sadly asked, *"Il n'y a rien à faire?"* (Is there nothing one can do?)

"Oui," answered the great specialist. *"Il faut choisir vos parents!"*

Which means, as you have probably surmised, "Yes. The one thing you can do is to pick your parents."

And even at this writing, despite anything the barbers or advertisements might tell you, we still don't know of any other way to prevent or cure hereditary baldness.

CHAPTER XXIII

STRUCTURAL DEFECTS

Most apparent of the human "abnormalities," by their very nature, are those which affect external appearance or sensory functions.

At circus sideshows you can see some of the more startling examples of "black" gene caprice—midgets, dwarfs with misshapen heads and bodies, Negro albinos, "India-rubber" men, etc. But for each one of these there are dozens of other surface or structural defects found in the everyday walks of life. In fact, it may be said that most persons have some inherited structural abnormality—if we include as "abnormal," conditions that are unusual, but not necessarily harmful or defective. Going further, and taking into consideration "hidden" recessive genes which singly produce no effect, it is pretty certain that *every one of us is carrying some one or another of these genes.*

Any detailed recital of defects or ailments, as we already have said, cannot help but be a dreary one. So, having little faith in the readability of this chapter, we can only suggest again that you scan the pages for those items which interest you personally. To make this easier we have grouped the various conditions under general headings. (Further, we have omitted some of the minor conditions or variations, or have left out, among many conditions discussed, details about modes of inheritance. These all will be found included in the later Summary Tables.)

GROWTH. The familiar stage or circus midgets (*ateleotic* dwarfs) have normal proportions, but usually do not grow beyond 42 inches in height. Of a different type is the misshapen *achondroplastic* dwarf, with a large head and normal torso, but stubby arms and legs. Both types are hereditary, with multiple genes probably being involved. This explains why it is not uncommon for a pair of circus midgets to produce normal children, and why, in turn,

139

THE DUCTLESS GLANDS

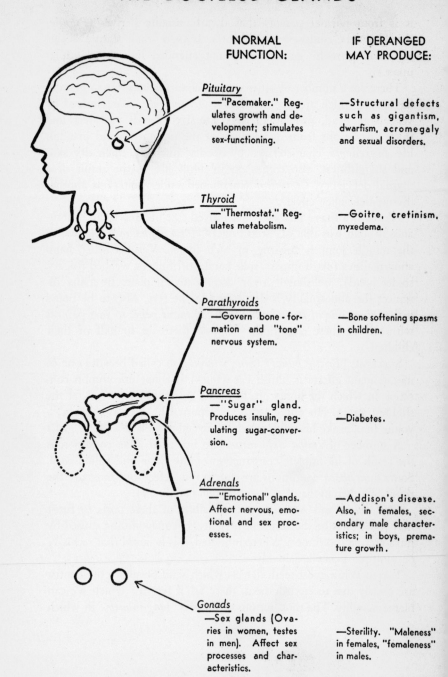

NORMAL FUNCTION:

IF DERANGED MAY PRODUCE:

Pituitary
—"Pacemaker." Regulates growth and development; stimulates sex-functioning.

—Structural defects such as gigantism, dwarfism, acromegaly and sexual disorders.

Thyroid
—"Thermostat." Regulates metabolism.

—Goitre, cretinism, myxedema.

Parathyroids
—Govern bone - formation and "tone" nervous system.

—Bone softening spasms in children.

Pancreas
—"Sugar" gland. Produces insulin, regulating sugar-conversion.

—Diabetes.

Adrenals
—"Emotional" glands. Affect nervous, emotional and sex processes.

—Addison's disease. Also, in females, secondary male characteristics; in boys, premature growth.

Gonads
—Sex glands (Ovaries in women, testes in men). Affect sex processes and characteristics.

—Sterility. "Maleness" in females, "femaleness" in males.

140

it is from normal parents that dwarfs usually derive. (*Pigmies* should not be confused with dwarfs, as their small stature is due to "small growth" genes and is not attended by any glandular upset.) .

There are a number of other growth abnormalities due to glandular upsets, which are not hereditary. *Acromegaly,* characterized by very large head, protruding jaw, oversized hands and feet and thick lips, results from overactivity of the pituitary gland in adult life. *Myxedema,* characterized by obesity, puffiness, thick dry skin and sluggishness, also comes on in adult life as the result of a thyroid deficiency. *Cretinism* (mentioned under goiter) is another thyroid-deficiency effect.

HANDS AND FEET. The very first proved case of Mendelian inheritance in man was that of "stub fingers" (*brachyphalangy*) in which the middle joint is missing in each finger. Various other hand abnormalities (extra fingers, split hand, stiff fingers, webbed fingers, spider hand), are shown in an accompanying plate. In many instances the abnormality is duplicated in the feet. Also to be noted is that *every one of these is due to a dominant gene,* so that parents with any of these conditions will pass them on to half of their children.

SKELETAL. *"Brittle bones"* (*blue sclerotic,* so called because one of its attendant effects is bluish eye-whites) is a not uncommon condition in which the bones are so brittle that they may break at the slightest strain. (In one classic case reported by Professor Mohr, a young man broke his ankle when he turned to look at a pretty girl.)

A number of *spinal deformities* are inherited. One condition is the result of incomplete construction of the spine and spinal cord. Some *hunchback* conditions are due to this defect, but most are the result of tuberculosis of the spine (non-hereditary).

Cleft palate and *hare-lip* (due to failure of these parts to fuse) may sometimes be the result of heredity, but may also be caused by intra-uterine conditions. Where inherited, it is believed that recessive or multiple genes are involved.

TEETH. While most teeth defects which send people to the dentist are clearly due to environment, there are a few for which we can blame heredity. The most serious of those is *"fang-mouth,"* in which

HAND ABNORMALITIES
(All inherited through dominant genes)

STUB FINGERS   EXTRA FINGERS

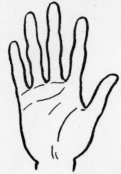

← NO MIDDLE JOINTS

"SPIDER" FINGERS   SPLIT HAND

(All conditions above may be repeated in the feet and toes of the same individual)

none of the teeth, except the four canines, ever grow out. In another condition the *two upper incisors* are the only ones which do not appear. On the other hand, we find the hereditary quirk which produces *teeth at birth*.

Several defective enamel conditions are hereditary. In some the enamel is soon lost or pitted, in others it is discolored, usually bluish. One condition producing brown teeth—a dominant sex-linked one, carried in the X—has already been noted in the preceding chapter. It should be borne in mind, however, that many cases of defective enamel, especially where they are prevalent in a community, are due to such extraneous causes as fluorine or other harmful chemicals in the water or foods.

Some teeth defects occur in combination with such conditions as "cranial soft-spot," brittle bones and cleft-palate, where the mouth and jaws are affected, and with other conditions to be mentioned later.

EYE DEFECTS. The human eye, because of its importance and accessibility, has been so extensively studied that hundreds of hereditary defects or *anomalies* (unusual conditions) already have been brought to light. Some of these are of slight importance, but others produce defective vision ranging up to total blindness.

Out of the blind population in the United States about *10 percent of the cases are attributed to heredity*. The blindness may be present from birth through the failure of "black" genes to construct an iris, retina or some other vital part of the eye; or the blindness may develop later as an aftermath of other hereditary defects, which may at first produce only partial blindness, such as cataracts, glaucoma, optic atrophy, *retinitis pigmentosa,* and "small eyes." Some of these conditions may also be caused by environment. In most cases where children are born blind, or become blind during childhood, not heredity, but a disease of the mother—often syphilis or gonorrhea—is responsible.

Cataract, or opacity of the lens, appears in different forms in different families. It is considered hereditary in all cases except those which come on in old age (these still being doubtful) or which are due to environmental causes (such as infection or industrial hazards). The time of onset—birth, childhood, puberty or middle-age—varies in different families and also appears to be determined by heredity. The genes which cause hereditary cataracts of every type are usually dominant.

Glaucoma is a serious, and rather common condition, in which heredity has been definitely established only in the case of the infantile type, which is usually associated with small eyes. Recessive genes are responsible. In the adult type, however (which may lead to blindness), while there is a possibility that dominant or "sex-linked" genes may be involved, this has not yet been proved.

(The less common hereditary conditions which lead to blindness are listed in the Summary Tables.)

Errors of refraction (near-sightedness, far-sightedness, etc.) may be inherited through variability in the way in which the genes construct the eye. But in these as in all eye defects it should be kept constantly in mind that the gene effects may be greatly modified or influenced by the treatment accorded the eyes, by diseases, by conditions encountered, etc. In one rare congenital condition, *miosis,* or "pin-point" pupil, which formerly doomed a child to blindness, it has now been found that a permanent cure can be rapidly effected by artificially dilating the pupil in the infant.

Cross-eyes are sometimes inherited.

Color-blindness (dealt with in the preceding chapter) is one of various "sex-linked" eye conditions which include *Leber's disease, paralysis of the ocular muscles* (the hereditary type) and several others. Also "sex-linked" is one type of *nystagmus,* which produces a tremor of the eye. (Sometimes, though, this condition may result from such work as mining.)

"Night blindness" (inability to see in dim light), of which several types have been cited as hereditary, has recently been reported as due to Vitamin A deficiency, throwing some doubt on its hereditary derivation. (*"Day blindness," "Mirror-reading,"* Double *eyelashes* and other eye conditions not discussed here will all be found in the Summary Tables, page 188.)

EAR. At least 10 percent of the cases of deafness (and perhaps as high as 25 percent) are considered hereditary. In some instances "black" genes produce deafness at birth but usually their effects are gradual, beginning with partial deafness in childhood and reaching a more serious state in maturity, especially among women after they have been pregnant.

As in blindness, most of the cases of total deafness are due not to heredity but to other causes, chiefly syphilis, contracted from the mother in the intra-uterine state; and also childhood illnesses such as meningitis, scarlet fever, and mumps. (Then, of course, there are later illnesses and accidents.) In tracing deafness back through

ODDITIES IN HUMANS WHICH ARE COMMON
TO OR BRED IN OTHER ANIMALS

IN HUMANS		IN OTHER ANIMALS
Piebald Spotting	Pattern patches of white skin against darker skin	Cows, dogs, etc.
Absence of Sweat Glands	Necessity to pant when overheated	Dogs, wolves
Woolly Hair	Found among Whites as well as Negroes	Sheep
Albinism	Lack of pigment in eyes, skin and hair	Almost every animal from mice to elephants
White Blaze	Patch of white hair over forehead	Horses ("Star" forehead)
Hairlessness	No hair on head or any other part of body	Mexican hairless dog
"Pin-Head" (As in Microcephalic idiots)	Tiny, undeveloped head	Russian wolfhounds
Dwarfism (Ateleotic)	Very small size but normal proportions	"Toy" dogs
Extra Fingers	Occurring on one or more hands and feet	Cats, guinea-pigs
Achondroplasia	Shortened limbs	Dachshunds

several generations these primary causes are often unknown or ignored. The mere fact that a parent and grandparent were deaf is not sufficient ground for fear that a child will inherit deafness. However, if it can be ascertained that the deafness was not due to extraneous influences, there is a fair presumption of inheritance.

Mutism is a natural concomitant of deafness, where a person is born deaf, or stricken with deafness in early infancy and therefore cannot learn to imitate sounds. Only when deafness has come after one has learned to speak is it not accompanied by mutism.

The usual form of hereditary childhood deafness is believed due to a recessive gene or genes, these frequently coming together in a child when the parents are closely related. That more than one set of genes is involved seems evidenced by the fact that children with normal hearing can be born to two parents both of whom are apparently hereditary deaf-mutes.

A common form of hearing impairment is *middle-ear deafness* (*otosclerosis*), coming on in maturity and believed due to multiple genes. The fact, however, that it more frequently affects women after childbirth suggests that environment may play a part in its causation.

"Word deafness" is perhaps more a defect of the brain than of the ear, as the hearing is normal but the individual is unable to understand the meaning of sounds. It affects many more males than females, and appears in infancy.

In the outer ear there are several hereditary abnormalities, including complete absence of the ear, usually on one side. (Other abnormalities are noted in the Summary Tables.)

SKIN. Because, like eyes, skin disorders or abnormalities are quickly recognized, they have been intensively studied, and a great many of them have been established as hereditary. Most of these are not functionally serious, but derive their importance from their effect on the social and economic life of the individual. Such conditions as "scaly skin," "shedding skin," "elephant skin" or "blotched face" (large birthmarks) may greatly interfere with the victim's chance of employment, social adjustment and marriage. Some skin conditions, however, may have serious constitutional effects, and a few may even prove fatal.

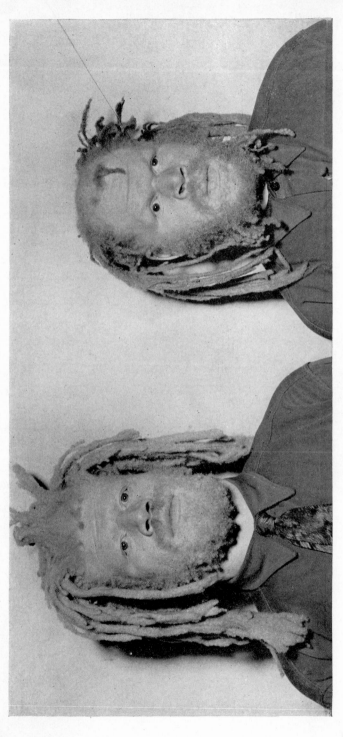

NEGRO ALBINOS

Born of black parents in Roanoke, Va., and otherwise Negroid, these brothers are typical Albinos. They have white skins (note their throats) pale blue eyes and flaxen hair (the odd effect produced by combing out the woolly strands and letting them grow for exhibition purposes). They also have *nystagmus* (oscillating eyeballs) and teeth defects, characteristic of many Albinos.

(Appearing with Ringling Brothers' Circus)

"Rubber-skin" is one of the skin "oddities." The familiar "India-rubber" men may have skin so elastic that it can be pulled out five or six inches on the chest. This is possible because the connective tissues which hold the skin in place are absent. The defect is produced by a rare gene.

Another "oddity" is *thick nails,* which are sometimes so thick that a hammer and chisel are needed to trim them.

Large *hereditary birthmarks (naevi)* are of various types, some due to blood-vessel swellings, some raised, some merely pigmented patches of the skin. The blood type (vascular) when it appears on the cheek is due to a dominant gene. A familiar type of hereditary birthmark is the "Nevus of Unna" appearing on the nape of the neck.

"Dog-men" are those who have a rare condition, *absence of sweat glands,* due to a "sex-linked" gene, and therefore affecting chiefly men. The victim cannot perspire and as in the case of dogs, who also have no sweat glands, must pant when the body is overheated. An added effect may be an incomplete set of teeth, sharp-pointed.

Albinism, already mentioned, is primarily a skin defect. The gene for this (a recessive, two being required to produce the condition, as will be recalled) is found among all peoples, light or dark. The highest incidence of albinism is among the San Blas Indians of Central Panama (7 in 1,000). *Albinoidism* is a mild form of albinism, due to a different and dominant gene. The skin and hair are lightly pigmented, the hair is not as fine as in true albinos, and the eyes are normal. *Partial albinism* has several manifestations. One of these is the condition that produces a "blaze," or patch of white hair above the center of the forehead. The common type is present from birth.

Among the serious hereditary skin conditions are these:

Coffee-colored spots (neurofibromatosis) which appear at birth over various parts of the body, spreading later, and possibly developing into local cancer. Less common is another cancer-producing condition, *malignant freckles.* This is a peculiar type of freckles appearing shortly after birth, and bringing death before puberty in most cases.

In *"scaly skin"* the skin is dry and scaly, easily inflames and continually sheds. In *"horny skin"* the skin is hard at birth, becomes cracked at the joints and may prove fatal. The milder cases may disappear in later life. One peculiarity of this condition is that it is frequently accompanied by small, deformed ears.

Blistering takes two main forms: (a) (*simplex*), where blisters are readily produced on hands and feet, but heal without scarring. This begins in childhood. In the serious form (b) (*dystrophica*), scars are left after healing. Of several types, the most severe is accompanied by nail deformities and may be fatal in infancy.

Light sensitivity (*Porphyrinuria congenita*), also produces blisters, but on exposed parts in spring and summer, with skin easily bruising. In the worst forms the hair falls out and blindness may result. Another peculiar effect may be redness of the urine.

In *"shedding skin"* the skin thickens and falls off, in some cases the complete cast of the palms and soles being shed in the autumn. There is a milder form, where the skin over the entire body flakes continually.

Fatty skin growths, due to a hereditary defect in the fat metabolism of the body, are serious only when they appear in the internal organs, where they may form tumors and cause death. Usually, however, they are confined to the face and scalp, and produce no ill effects.

HAIR. The most common hereditary hair defect, *baldness,* already has been discussed. Some other hair conditions, all due to dominant genes, are:

Complete hairlessness (*hypotrichosis*), absence of hair over the entire body, associated with loss of teeth and deformed nails.

Juvenile hairlessness (*alopecia*) in which the infantile soft down is retained and no real hair develops.

"Beaded" hair (*monilithrix*) in which the scalp hair is scanty and "beaded."

MUSCLES AND NERVES. Inherited muscular defects are not very common. The most serious ones are those in which muscles "shrivel" (atrophy) and become incapable of functioning. Since muscle activity is controlled by nerves, often a nerve defect may lead to inactivity and shriveling of the muscle, so that it is not always easy to tell in a given case whether a defective "muscle" gene or a defective "nerve" gene is responsible.

Ataxia (hereditary), of which *Friedreich's ataxia* is the most common, comes on in childhood and is symptomized by wobbly gait, defective speech and curvature of the spine. *Spastic paralysis,* which also appears in childhood, attacking the lower limbs and spreading upward, is dominant in some families, in others recessive.

(Various other types of muscular and nerve defects are listed in the Summary Tables, page 188.)

CHAPTER XXIV

SICK MINDS

In the seventeenth century three brothers came to the United States bringing with them one of the most terrible of all known "black" genes.

Through these three who settled in New England hundreds of persons in the United States have come to as horrible an end as any one could imagine—death from *Huntington's chorea.*

A single dominant gene causes this condition.

A man (or woman) to all appearances normal, perhaps even brilliant or outstanding, goes on into maturity with no sign of any waiting doom. Then, quite suddenly, perhaps at the age of thirty-five or forty, he begins literally to disintegrate. His speech becomes thick, his brain and nervous system go to pieces, his body collapses. In a few years the individual is a helpless wreck, shortly to be carried off by merciful death. *And no cure for this condition is yet known.*

But this is not all. An individual with a gene for Huntington's chorea may marry and raise a family before the disease strikes. Because the gene is a dominant, all the children of the victim are thus suddenly confronted with the one-in-two possibility that they likewise may be doomed—and there is no way of finding out beforehand. To make matters worse, those with the gene may not always develop the disease, so that they can never be certain that they are not carriers.

The drama in this horrible situation, which confronts scores of persons in the United States today, was recognized by Eugene O'Neill when he used it in his play "Strange Interlude." [1] Lest the

[1] Mr. O'Neill has written to us: ". . . No, I cannot say that I had the hereditary mental defect in 'Strange Interlude' identified as Huntington's chorea. On the other hand, I knew what I wrote was valid because it was based on an actual history. Evidently, from what you say, this must have been a case of Huntington's chorea,

reader be unduly alarmed, we might say that the disease is an extremely rare one, and that *no other type of insanity* is known to be inherited in this way. Society has little to fear from Huntington's chorea. Now that the mechanism of its transmission is known, there is every reason to believe that, either through the voluntary action of the individuals concerned, or through outside pressure, the spread of the disease will be greatly curtailed.

Of far greater importance to society are the much more prevalent types of mental defects—*feeble-mindedness, epilepsy, idiocy, schizophrenia* (dementia praecox) and *manic-depressive insanity.* Are these inherited? And if so, how?

First, let us remember that the human mind is not an organ, but is the end result of a group of functions embracing instincts, emotions, intellect, operations of will, etc., stemming primarily from the activity of the brain. Because of this, when we speak of "hereditary" defects in mentality we cannot be quite so explicit as we were when we dealt with purely physical defects; nor can we generally track down a mental defect to a single gene as we can with Huntington's chorea.

Think of your automobile. What makes it go? The motor? No, the motor without the gasoline, spark-plugs, gears, transmission, wheels, etc., would be useless. Every functional part of the automobile must be in working order, for a defect in just one part may stop the whole process or seriously disturb it. Suppose that an intelligent savage who had never seen an automobile watched you fumbling under the hood. You take out a spark-plug; the car comes to a dead stop. You put back the spark-plug; the car runs. The savage might conclude that it was the *spark-plug* which makes the car go.

This actually expresses the "unit" conception of mentality which prevailed not so many years ago. Because insanity, feeble-mindedness or brilliance seemed to "run" in given families, it was concluded that the different types of minds were inherited as units, with one or two genes determining whether a person was to be

although I never heard it described except by the general term of hereditary insanity. So I think your mention of the disease in 'Strange Interlude' is justified by the fact, even though it gives me more credit as a diagnostician than I deserve."

brilliant, mediocre or feeble-minded. On such a premise rested the detailed studies of our pet horrible examples, the Jukes and the Kallikaks. The factor of environment in governing mentality was almost completely overlooked.

Today we are aware that *everything* that happens to a person, inside his body and out, from the moment he is conceived, affects his mentality. We no longer venture to say, when an individual is mentally "abnormal," to what extent we can blame heredity unless we are quite clear regarding the various circumstances to which that person, his parents and ancestors were exposed. The fact that a feeble-minded child had a reputedly feeble-minded grandfather, or that two persons in the same family are insane, is no longer *prima facie* evidence of heredity. Only when a mental defect manifests itself in the same way in successive generations under different conditions, and with some clear evidence of genetic *ratios,* can we conclude that it is inherited.

We find, therefore, that most of our evidence regarding the inheritance of any of the more general types of insanity and mental deficiency is still presumptive. While authorities are convinced that insanity and mental deficiency can be, and more or less frequently are, inherited, the gene mechanism by which most mental defects can be transmitted is by no means conclusively established.

SCHIZOPHRENIA (or dementia praecox) is a collective term for various mental derangements that manifest themselves after puberty, the first symptoms usually being "inversion" or a lack of interest in outside things. These types of insanity, geneticists have come to believe, can be (but not always are) inherited through *multiple* recessive genes (more than one pair).

An unusual feature of schizophrenia may be its effect on the individual sexually. That is to say, it commonly leads to a loss of interest in the opposite sex so that the individuals do not fall in love, or, if they are already married, frequently leave their wives or husbands, as the case may be. Thus the disease has a self-sterilizing effect, which, coupled with the fact that the individuals are usually short-lived, often acts as a bar to their reproduction. Granted that the condition is hereditary, this latter effect can be considered fortunate by society as it prevents schizophrenics from reproducing.

MANIC-DEPRESSIVE INSANITY, which usually comes on about maturity (although it sometimes appears earlier or in late life) manifests itself by a depressed condition alternating with maniacal tendencies. Unlike the schizophrenics, the manic-depressive insane may be cured after a short stay in an institution, perhaps not more than ten to twenty-five weeks. A dangerous aspect of this condition, however, is that an individual once cured may as a result of undue stress have a sudden relapse. Manic-depressive insanity *can be inherited,* not directly but as a "susceptibility" which, under shock or adverse circumstances will lead to a breakdown. For example, following the stock market crash in 1929 and in the years following, there was a "wave" of manic-depressive cases among some who had lost their fortunes.

The incidence of mental disorders in the general population is much greater than is usually realized. In New York State, it is estimated that *one out of every twenty adults* at some time or another spends a period in a mental institution. Schizophrenia and manic-depressive insanity are responsible for about half of the admissions. Represented among the other half are such conditions as alcoholic insanity, paresis (syphilis) and senile dementia, which have not been discussed here for lack of any link with heredity.

FEEBLE-MINDEDNESS. As high as 5 percent of the population in the United States (according to some authorities) is estimated to be feeble-minded. But what do we mean by "feeble-minded"? Like "insanity," it is a general term. In insanity, a person is mentally normal up to a certain age, and then, more or less suddenly, begins to act queerly. He may even be brilliant at one time and then be a blubbering maniac at another time. A feeble-minded person, however, is not one with a normal mind gone wrong, but with an *arrested or incomplete mental development,* i.e., a subnormal mind. In every other way he may be perfectly normal.

"Subnormal" intelligence, however, is not so easily defined. In the lowest types of human intelligence, those of the idiot or imbecile, we can be fairly clear as to the meaning of "subnormal," or "feeble-minded." But as we go up the scale, we are forced more and more to accept rather arbitrary definitions based on existing intelligence tests. If you score between 90 and 110, you are considered as having a normal "IQ" (intelligence quotient). But if a person scores below 90, he is rated according to the accompanying scale:

90–80: Dull
80–70: On the borderline between dulness and subnormalcy
Below 70: Feeble-minded (mentally defective):
    70–62: High-grade moron
    62–55: Mid-grade moron
    55–50: Low-grade moron
    50–25: Imbecile
    25– 0: Idiot

We can see from the gradings that even if we accept the tests as being conclusive, any variability in the way a person responds under different conditions, or a slight error on the part of the examiner, could lead to faulty classification.

With all this in mind, we can therefore be clear only about the most pronounced types of mental defectives, especially those at the bottom of the scale.

IDIOTS. These have the mentality of an infant and are almost as helpless. A familiar type is the *Mongolian idiot* (misnamed through some resemblance of the features to those of Mongols). Such unfortunates remain underdeveloped, mentally and sexually. Although this form of idiocy was once believed to be clearly hereditary, many authorities now dispute this conclusion and attribute the condition to some nutritive deficiency on the part of the mother while the child is being carried. As evidence is cited the fact that the mother's age plays an important part in the possibility of having such a child.

About 75 percent of Mongolian idiots are born to either young mothers under twenty or to those over thirty-five. The percentage is considerably higher among the latter, especially when it is the mother's first child. Mongoloids are rarely born twice to the same mother. This leads to the belief that the intra-uterine defect or deficiency which might produce a Mongolian idiot can be corrected through the process of giving it birth. If this form of idiocy is inherited—which, as was noted, seems doubtful—it would have to be due to a defect in the mother or to genes in the child which express themselves only if the mother's condition is unfavorable.

The *microcephalic* idiot is an unfortunate with a "pinhead," sometimes exhibited as a "what's-it" in circus side-shows, whose mental age never goes beyond that of an imbecile. It is fairly clear that in some cases microcephaly is due to recessive genes, but it may sometimes be due to other causes.

The *cretin,* another form of idiot, is dwarfed in body and mind by the failure of the thyroid gland to function properly. At the age of twenty-five a cretin may look and act like a very dull small boy. Cretinism may run in families and is believed to be the result of a thyroid deficiency in the mother which communicates itself to the embryonic child, but whether this deficiency is hereditary or not is in dispute.

The idiots as a class, tragic as may be their condition to themselves and their families, are not the mental defectives who present the most serious problem to society. They are proportionately few in number; there is no clear evidence that their condition is inherited; they are rarely allowed at large; and they seldom can propagate.

It is the very large class of the higher type of feeble-minded, the morons, which concerns us most.

MORONS. Those classed as morons reach a mental development at maturity no further than that of a hypothetical "normal" child of twelve. Only by an intelligence test can they be distinguished from persons of normal mentality. (One must be careful not to confuse lack of education with lack of intelligence.) While environment is believed to be a dominant causative factor in many cases of subnormal mentality, there is also reason to believe that some cases are due to *heredity*. However, the uncertainty as to the rôle of inheritance in producing morons—especially those whose intelligence shades into the almost "normal" brackets—is still so great that no agreement has been reached among geneticists as to the genes involved.

EPILEPSY. The brain being part of the nervous system, there is a popular tendency to confuse or link with defective mentality any derangement of a person's nervous system that affects behavior. This is why epilepsy (falling sickness) has so often in the past been associated erroneously with insanity; why, in fact, in so many institutions epileptics were, and still are, housed together with the insane. While the two conditions sometimes do go together the fact that they are far from synonymous is shown by the number of great men and geniuses throughout history who were epileptics.

Epilepsy is a general term referring to various convulsive disorders. In fact, it is regarded as a symptom, and not a disease itself. Usually epilepsy takes the form of convulsive fits, falling, foaming at the mouth, etc., an unhappy spectacle which perhaps every reader has seen. In some cases the epileptic does not fall but becomes pale and stares blankly, being wholly or partly unconscious meanwhile. During such states a person may commit strange acts, even crimes, and not be aware later of what he has done. History, from its earliest recorded pages, contains strange stories of epileptics.

The belief that epilepsy is inherited has long been held. Nevertheless, in some cases diseases and brain injuries or infections have been proved responsible. (In fact, many authorities now believe that all epilepsy is so caused.) But where no such external motivating causes are known, some authorities still hold to the belief that the condition is hereditary.

The process, however, whereby epilepsy may be inherited is apparently much more complicated than earlier analysts thought when they ascribed it to simple recessive genes. Now it would appear that multiple factors, probably several pairs of genes, are involved. All that can be said with assurance is that where a parent has epilepsy, the chance is much greater than average that a child will be epileptic. (One rare form of epilepsy, *myoclonus,* which comes on in childhood and differs from the ordinary type in that there is no loss of consciousness, is definitely hereditary and appears due to a single pair of recessive genes.)

In all the foregoing conditions we must never lose sight of the fact that while heredity may be responsible, similar effects might be produced by external causes. There are many prenatal and postnatal influences, comprising a host of diseases, internal disorders, and accidents, which individually or in combination might turn what otherwise would have been a normal person into one with an unbalanced mind or defective nervous system. Before, then, you begin worrying about insanity in your family background, rule out by careful study and with the aid of your doctor, every possibility that the cases may have been caused by other and non-hereditary factors.

CHAPTER XXV

HOW LONG WILL YOU LIVE?

ONE often hears, "So-and-so is of long-lived stock," or, "So-and-so is of short-lived stock."

Genetically, there may be some basis for such assertions—but not always!

Within certain limits, the life-span of human beings, as of all living things, seems to be set by inherited factors.

The oldest living things are trees. Different varieties are characterized by different limits of longevity, the most venerable of all being the macrozamia trees of Australia which have reached the age of 15,000 years. Soil, climate and other conditions are, of course, vitally important factors, but there is also something in the *nature* of trees that determines their *potential* age and that makes a tree of one variety live longer than another growing by its side.

Animals, whose mechanism is much more complex, and whose lives are far more hazardous, are rigidly limited in their life-spans, but these limits likewise vary with different species. Under the best of conditions elephants die at the age of between 90 and 100, horses at 45, dogs and cats at about 20, oxen at 30.

How long can a man live?

Cold-eyed scientists and insurance actuaries are now skeptical about ancient records of human longevity. Figures in the Bible are believed to be based on a different method of computing years—in fact, on two different methods than were later employed. For instance, the age of Adam is given as 930, of Methuselah as 969, of Cainan as 970, Jared, 962, etc. But all these were pre-flood personages. After the flood we find the ages cut to one-fourth—Abraham, 175, Isaac, 180, Jacob, 147, Moses, 120—leading to the belief that a "year" had a different meaning before and after the deluge.

As we come down to comparatively recent times we find that *only obscure persons,* usually in obscure localities, have been credited with phenomenal ages. England's champion oldster is listed as Thomas Parr ("Old Parr") a Shropshire farmer who died in 1635 at the age (according to tradition) of 152. From less conservative countries come reports of ages ranging up to 185.

To all such figures scientists now raise skeptical eyebrows, attributing them to errors, hearsay testimony, etc. Insurance actuaries believe that human beings have not lived, and do not live, much beyond 106 years. Only three persons in 100,000 in the United States attain the age of 100. The "all time" record for this country, which has any claim to authenticity, is that of a woman who lived to be 110 years and 321 days.

Let us say, then, that 110 years represents the known maximum span of human life. The average life is a little more than half of this (namely, 60 years for males and 64 years for females). Nevertheless, studies show that there are apparently short-lived and long-lived families. This has led to the belief that the degree of longevity is to a large extent inherited through genes, which by acting on specific parts or on the body as a whole, set potential limits to one's life-span.

Perhaps, as in automobiles, every human being starts life with a qualified "guarantee" as to how many years he can be kept going. We might call this "conditioned longevity." That word "conditioned" is extremely important, for nowhere does environment play so significant a part as it does in relation to longevity.

Quite true, Mr. So-and-so may boast that he comes of "long-lived stock," and may produce figures to show that his parents and all his ancestors lived to the age of ninety. But let Mr. So-and-so, driving home from the club some winter night with one-too-many under his belt, try to round an icy horseshoe curve on high, and all the statistics as to his potential longevity may be of no avail.

In the matter of longevity we can think only in terms of broad general averages. You read everywhere that the life-span has been steadily increasing, how in George Washington's time the average expectation of life was about thirty-five years, how in 1901 it was about fifty years and that today it is more than sixty. But applied to yourself, that does not mean that because your parents lived to an

THE HUMAN LIFE SPAN

TWENTY-FIVE YEARS AGO

AVERAGE LENGTH OF LIFE { MALES, 48 YRS. ▮
FEMALES, 51 YRS. ▮

PRINCIPAL
CAUSES
OF DEATH:

Infancy
(up to 1 yr.)

Childhood and Youth
(1 to 19 yrs.)

Maturity
(20 to 59 yrs.)

Old age
(over 60)

PREMATURE CONGENITAL AND ENTERITIS PNEUMONIA TYPHOID CEREBRAL
BIRTH DEBILITY AND DIPHTHERIA CHILDBIRTH HEMORRHAGE
INJURIES MALFORMATIONS WHOOPING MEASLES TYPHOID OTHER (IN WOMEN) OTHER CAUSES
AT BIRTH DISEASES COUGH SCARLET FEVER OTHER
OTHER CAUSES AILMENTS

DIARRHEA PNEUMONIAS ACCIDENTS TUBERCULOSIS ACCIDENTS HEART AILMENTS NEPHRITIS CANCER CEREBRAL HEART AILMENTS
TUBERCULOSIS HEMORRHAGE CANCER
DISEASES OF ARTERIES NEPHRITIS
SENILITY INFLUENZA
DISEASES
CEREBRAL
HEMORRHAGE

TODAY

AVERAGE LENGTH OF LIFE { MALES, 60.7 YRS. ▮
FEMALES, 64 YRS. ▮

—The individual has become no stronger
or longer-lived: Only the obstacles in
his path have been reduced!
(Level 25 years ago
shown by dotted line.)

PREMATURE DIARRHEA AND ENTERITIS ACCIDENTS PNEUMONIA TUBERCULOSIS CANCER HEART AILMENTS HEART
BIRTH CONGENITAL APPENDICITIS HEART DISEASES ACCIDENTS NEPHRITIS HEMORRHAGE
BIRTH INJURIES MALFORMATIONS INFLUENZA INFECTIOUS DISEASES PNEUMONIA (CHILDBIRTH IN WOMEN) ACCIDENTS CEREBRAL DISEASES DIABETES CANCER OTHER
OTHER CAUSES INFLUENZA CAUSES OTHER
PNEUMONIA TUBERCULOSIS OF ARTERIES

Prepared with aid of Statistical Department, Metropolitan Life Insurance Co.

average age of seventy, you will live to be eighty. What has been increased, through hygiene, improved medical knowledge and better living conditions, is not the *potential longevity* of human beings, but *the chances of survival.*

The very young are the ones who have had their expectation of life most sharply increased. The death rate from measles, diphtheria, scarlet fever, whooping-cough—the most fatal enemies of childhood —has dropped more than 80 percent. Many plagues and epidemics that formerly carried off vast numbers of children as well as older persons have been stamped out. All this has projected into later life many individuals who formerly would never have passed into maturity.

Thus, the disconcerting fact is that *for people in middle age today the expectation of life is no greater than it formerly was.*

But granted that each individual has his *potential* limits of life, by what genetic mechanism could these limits be set?

There are various theories as to the direct causes of the body's "natural" breakdown which lead to death. Some lay the blame on fermentation (Metchnikoff); some on changes in the arteries (Osler, Brown-Séquard); some on breakdown of the ductless glands (Lorand), etc. But there is also the belief that in whichever parts of the body the "crack-up" might originate, specific genes are concerned in fixing the "natural" span, or time-limit, for each part. Death might come through a single gene which sets a time-limit for the heart, or through many genes which set limits for the workings of various parts in cooperation with each other.

Have we *identified any of such "killer" genes?*

Yes. Geneticists have discovered that "killer" genes are found in great numbers among all living things, both plants and animals. Most drastic are the "lethals" which may kill off an individual in the very earliest stages or soon after birth. While many of these have already been identified in experimental animals, it has not yet been possible to uncover more than a few lethal genes among humans. All authorities, however, are agreed that there must be many. In fact, there is reason to believe that in numerous instances of "false" pregnancy *the woman actually was pregnant,* but the embryo was killed off by lethal genes; and that many cases of miscarriage can also be attributed to them.

Obviously, no lethal gene could bring death working always singly. If it did, it could never be passed on, for no individual who carried it would live to propagate. Lethal genes, therefore, must work in *twos,* one contributed by each parent. Those genes which singly produce serious effects and which, with two together, have their effects greatly intensified are among the principal lethals. Examples of this are believed to be the genes for *brachyphalangy* (stub fingers) and for hemophilia. There is no case on record of any individual definitely known to carry a pair of either of these genes, leading to the belief that a "double dose" of them proves fatal.

Three other human genes which have been established as lethal if inherited in pairs are those for *"elephant skin," multiple bone fractures* in the embryo, and *familial jaundice* of the newly born. Familial jaundice, however, is a condition which no longer can be considered truly lethal, as it can be cured permanently by giving the infant born with it an immediate blood transfusion. This raises the question as to whether the term "killer" can continue to be applied to this, or to other genes now termed "lethal," when and if cures for their effects are discovered.

In addition to these lethals there are "killer" genes (some mentioned in preceding chapters) which may bring death prematurely. One of such genes is that for *glioma retina* (eye tumor) usually fatal in infancy. This is the condition which recently figured in the news with regard to a Chicago infant, when an "ethical" jury was called on to decide whether to try and save her life by operation or to let nature take its course.

Amaurotic family idiocy, malignant freckles and *progressive spinal muscular atrophy* of infants are also fatal in early life, while hemophilia in a male is generally deadly by maturity. (A few other prematurely fatal conditions will be found listed in the Summary Tables.)

It is conceivable that if there are genes which produce a fatal breakdown at early stages of life, there might also be genes "timed" to bring death at later periods. On this theory (which, let us emphasize, still lacks scientific corroboration) rests the belief that there may be sets of genes, collectively inherited in given families, which in a general way make some of them potentially "long-lived" and others "short-lived."

At first glance the evidence on this score would seem to be conclusive. Extensive studies have been made of hundreds of thousands of individual records by leading insurance companies of the United States, in which the ages at death of parents and sons were compared. The findings were these:

Men with the best parental longevity show unmistakably lower mortality at every age.

At the age of twenty, persons whose parents had a good longevity record have a *minimum* of two and a half years' greater expectation of life than those with a poor ancestral history.

In men aged thirty, the probability of living to the age of eighty was 26.6 percent for those whose parents had both lived to be seventy-five, compared with only 20.3 percent for those whose parents had died under sixty. The chance of reaching the four-score mark was therefore almost one-third greater for those with long-lived parents than for the others.

Further, in another study by Dr. Raymond Pearl it was found that among those who lived to a very old age (ninety to one hundred) almost 87 percent had had one or more long-lived parents and a large proportion had had two or more long-lived grandparents. In comment Dr. Pearl said, "Taking all the evidence in this study as a whole it would seem to leave no doubt as to the importance of heredity in determination of the longevity of the individual human being." [1]

All the foregoing findings, however, demand certain qualifications. The comparative "longevity" records may be weighted in favor of the long-lived families by the fact (as we shall see presently) that the rates vary in different social and occupational levels and are influenced by various other factors. To quote from "Length of Life," by Drs. Louis I. Dublin and Alfred J. Lotka:

"The superior longevity of persons with a good family record may be the result, in part, of more favorable environment as well as a

[1] Dr. Pearl has stressed the fact that, in his opinion, it is the *total genetic constitution* or make-up of the individual, rather than any particular genes (lethal or other), that is most important as a factor in determining length of life. As he points out, the significant rôle of lethal genes is in the fairly early (prenatal) developmental stages.

AS INCOMES DROP, DEATHS OF BABIES RISE

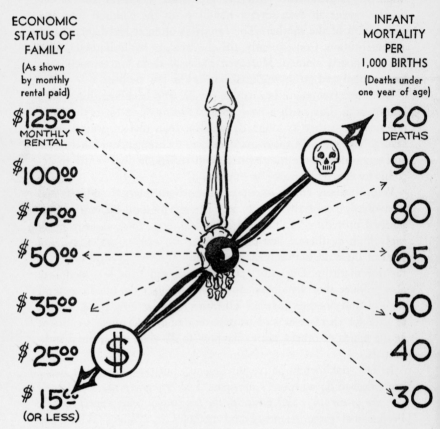

ECONOMIC STATUS OF FAMILY (As shown by monthly rental paid)	INFANT MORTALITY PER 1,000 BIRTHS (Deaths under one year of age)
$125⁰⁰ MONTHLY RENTAL	120 DEATHS
$100⁰⁰	90
$75⁰⁰	80
$50⁰⁰	65
$35⁰⁰	50
$25⁰⁰	40
$15⁰⁰ (OR LESS)	30

(Based on a survey made in Cleveland, O. by Howard Whipple Green — 1932)

better physical inheritance. We know that those with a good family history have the benefit of more favorable environment than those with a poor family history. To have parents survive to old age means in most cases to enjoy a more protected and a more favorable infancy and childhood.

"The premature death of either parent often results in the breaking up of the home, with all its consequent evils to the children. If it is the mother who dies, the children often receive poor care and improper nourishment; and the premature death of the father usually means an even severer handicap for the children than the early death of the mother. The family is often reduced to poverty and destitution. Consequently, the children are badly housed, badly fed and poorly clothed. Moreover, many of them are compelled to leave school and go to work as soon as the law permits.

"All these factors are hazards to the life and health of this group, [comprising those with a poor ancestral history] and it is therefore not surprising that its longevity is lower than that of groups more favorably situated. In these circumstances the influence of inheritance and environment are intertwined. Both undoubtedly operate to account for the differences [in longevity]."

With so many environmental factors—both internal and external —involved, tracing the inheritance of longevity is an extremely complicated procedure. Taking up other instances, there is an exceedingly high death rate among insane persons, idiots and imbeciles. Half of these die between the ages of ten and twenty, and few pass far into maturity. Does this mean that the genes for low mentality also produce short-livedness? In some cases they do, but in general we can find another answer: That mental defectives, being unable to care for themselves and usually receiving inadequate treatment at the hands of others, are easier prey to ills than are normal individuals.

In fact, not merely native intelligence, but position in life has a great deal to do with one's life-span. *The higher up the social scale you are in earnings and position, the longer you may expect to live.* Professional men, scientists and notables in "Who's Who" live longer than do average men. In current mortality tables we find that deaths among men in middle age range about as follows:

For Men Between Ages of 55–64

Class	Annual deaths per 100,000 (*Approx.*)
Upper and professional classes	2,247
Partly skilled or skilled workers and craftsmen	2,490
Unskilled workers and casual laborers	3,060

COLLEGE GRADUATES have mortality rates definitely below the average.

 CLERGYMEN live considerably longer than the general average man.

 DOCTORS have a somewhat higher death rate than other professional men, no doubt because of their special occupational hazards.

 LAWYERS have among the lowest death rates in the professional group.

 TEACHERS have among the lowest death rates for women in any occupation.

 FARMERS are particularly long-lived.

 UNSKILLED LABORERS have the highest mortality rate.

Farmers are in a special class, with a death rate almost the same as that of the "upper" classes, either because their conditions tend to develop health and strength, or because they have to be healthier and stronger to continue as farmers.

The facts regarding mortality are even more striking in the case of babies. *Deaths among infants in the so-called "lowest" classes are several times as high as those in the "upper" classes.* In other words (speaking always in terms of general averages) studies in the large cities of the United States have shown that infant mortality goes higher and higher, step by step, as the incomes of the fathers drop lower and lower. Would this prove that the babies of the poor have "poorer" genes? Hardly. With lower income, of course, is correlated lower educational status, poorer hygiene and living conditions, shorter intervals between births and many other adverse factors. All these are responsible for the higher mortality not only among the infants but among the adults as well. Nevertheless, in the same social and economic levels and within the same environments, there are other factors that produce differences in degrees of longevity among individuals.

First we have the pronounced difference as between males and females. The fact that there is a far higher mortality among male embryos than female was brought out in the "Boy or Girl?" chapter. This discrepancy in death rates continues throughout life, but to a lesser degree. Of babies dying during the first year, there are at least 20 percent more boys than girls. In childhood and youth the males continue to fall in greater numbers, so that before maturity is reached the females have overcome the 6 percent lead that males had at birth, and have caught up with them numerically. Then the females begin to draw ahead. In middle life there are about 15 percent more females than males, and finally, in the very old-age group, there are *about twice as many females as males surviving*.

There is but one logical conclusion: That it is not the male, but *the female who constitutes the stronger sex*. Here science gives the laugh to the deep-rooted idea, perpetuated through the ages no doubt by men themselves, of masculine superiority. For even granting that men have stronger surface development, yet if "fitness" and "strength" are to be judged by the power of survival, then unquestionably women are by considerable odds the strongest and most fit.

Why males are less able to survive cannot yet be told with authority. But inasmuch as the only initial difference between the sexes is the lack of an extra "X" in the male (its place, remember,

FEMALES LIVE LONGER!

AT BIRTH

FEMALES   MALES

PROPORTIONATE
BIRTH RATE

6% MORE <u>BOYS</u> THAN GIRLS

YOUTH

EQUAL
PROPORTION
OF BOTH SEXES

MATURITY

PROPORTION

15%
MORE FEMALES
THAN MALES

**EXTREME
OLD AGE**

**ALMOST
TWICE AS MANY**
FEMALES
AS MALES
SURVIVING

being taken by the abbreviated "Y") the answer may lie here, *in the fact that females get more genes than do males.* As we have seen in preceding chapters, the X chromosome contains many genes which, when defective, produce the "sex-linked" conditions that especially victimize males (because they have no alternative normal X to protect them). There may be more genes in the X, still unknown, which affect other vital processes. It is not unlikely, therefore, that the two X's which a female receives, compared to the single X of the male, may make her more resistant to early adverse conditions and give her a better start that carries through life. (Perhaps Nature has intended this, as Dr. Alfred Lotka suggests, to better prepare women for childbearing.)

Hormonal or constitutional differences (in which, of course, the genes also play a part), and perhaps environmental differences later, may help to explain the differential death rate between men and women. But the fact remains that at every stage the expectation of life for a woman is higher than it is for a man. (See the accompanying table.)

EXPECTATION OF LIFE
(For Whites)

At the age of	A *man* may expect to live:	A *woman* may expect to live:
30	38 more years	41 more years
40	29 more years	32 more years
50	22 more years	24 more years
60	15 more years	16 more years
70	9 more years	10 more years
80	5 more years	5½ more years

(Computed by Statistical Bureau, Metropolitan Life Insurance Co., according to U. S. mortality statistics for 1935.)

Among both men and women, insurance actuaries report that mortality is greater for the young ones below average height and weight and for those over forty who are overweight. No clear deductions can be drawn, however, as to any correlation between body-build and longevity. A better-appearing body may be the result of the same favorable environmental factors that generally are conducive to longer life; an undersized, underweight, or misshapen body may result from the same adverse factors which are prejudicial to longer life.

One hears various theories: Brunettes live longer than blondes; short people live longer than tall (or vice versa); premature gray hairs mean early death; bald-headed men die before those not bald; men with more hair on their chest live longer than those with little hair, etc. *Not one of these theories has yet been found to have any scientific basis.*

Another variable field of speculation has been that regarding the effect of alcoholic drinking on one's age. The best existing evidence is that moderate drinkers live as long as do abstainers but that those who drink to excess have their lives shortened.

We may pause now to ask, first, this question:

Does anything brought out here throw any light on how long you may expect to live?

Well, perhaps not too much. The fact, of course, is that at present we know so little about what lies ahead of any "normal" individual (excluding the relatively few who are afflicted with serious hereditary defects) that it would be folly to attempt any specific estimates of longevity on the basis of family records alone.

Or, in other words, as matters stand today, you must look to your own physical condition and to the way that you live your life for the best forecast of how long you can expect to live. At best, none of us can expect to live (even if we wished) any longer than the *potential* limit that has prevailed apparently from the dawn of civilization.

What of future life-expectations for our children and grandchildren and later descendants? Do we imply that the "conditioned longevity" of humans is forever "set"?

No, for in the opinion of most authorities, the human life-span very likely will be increased. However, even the most optimistic of the scientists believe that so long as the human animal is a functioning mechanism, with life being a continual process of building up and tearing down cells, the potential longevity limits will never be far from where they are today. Estimates for the "maximum" theoretical life-span range from 120 years, in the opinion of Voronoff, to 185 according to the most optimistic Russian, Metchnikoff.

The idea of extreme longevity has been given no little impetus by the feat of Dr. Alexis Carrel in showing how living tissue can be kept alive indefinitely. Doing this with an isolated piece of tissue is far from the same thing as keeping *all* the vital parts and organs of a complete human body growing and functioning *uniformly* through all the varied experiences which come to one in a lifetime. But who knows what science may accomplish?

There is one other interesting possibility: Russian scientists, working in the Arctic, found that plants which had been frozen into the ice for a thousand years or more could be revived and made to grow again. Said Professor P. N. Kapterev: "As a result of our experiments, it can be stated that there is really a possibility of resuscitating organisms long after they have been frozen."

Again, who knows? Perhaps, some day, one of us, fresh out of college, will be frozen by the method described in the frozen-food advertisements: "WHAM! A blast of Arctic cold strikes suddenly and seals in all the freshness. . . ." We could then be kept in *status quo* indefinitely under perfect refrigeration; and a hundred or two hundred years hence we could be "defrosted" and enabled to begin living and moving again in another world, as characters in drama and fiction have already done.

The only immediate method in sight, therefore, of prolonging our days seems to be by spending a stretch of years in an icebox.

CHAPTER XXVI

THE TWILIGHT SEXES

"Male and female created he them. . . ."
—Gen. 1: 27.

FROM a corridor in the office of our psychiatrist friend came the voices of a woman and child. The child's voice was that of a little girl. It broke into a tinkle of bell-like laughter, and then, with a hippety-hop, into our view came, not a little girl, but a boy of about five.

We say "boy." But only the clothes would identify him as such. His head was covered with golden ringlets; from his pink-and-white face shone the bluest of blue eyes, fringed with long dark lashes; his every gesture was that of a little girl. Behind followed his mother, her expression reflecting the tragedy of the situation. For through some strange circumstance or quirk of birth, this child of hers, although healthy in every way, was of a type considered by the world as "abnormal."

"Sad case, that," remarked our psychiatrist friend, when the mother and child had left. The little boy, he explained, had shown these feminine traits almost from infancy. His parents at first had been overjoyed by his unusual beauty. Now they were desperately worried. Both highly educated persons, they knew all about psychoanalysis, "fixations," complexes, etc. But this child did not merely act like a little girl; he *looked* like a little girl. Whatever early environmental upsets might have been involved in "conditioning" the child's behavior, how could they account for his appearance, for the so-called *sexual characteristics* which were so much more like those of a young female than of a male? Was the child born that way? Or, going further, could he have *inherited* such a condition?

172

The answer, as given by many geneticists today, might very well be, "Yes." There are frequent cases of "abnormal" sexuality in humans, as in all other animals, which may be caused directly by "abnormal" sex-genes, by derangements of the chromosome workings or by upsets in the sex glands, due either to primary genetic causes or to later environmental influences.

The Bible says, "Male and female created he them. . . ." There is no need to dispute that. But however distinctly the first man and woman might have been differentiated the one from the other, in the billions that are assumed to have sprung from them one can find every gradation of sexuality. In short, sex is a highly variable characteristic, and there is not quite the clear-cut distinction between "male" and "female" which we've always assumed that there was.

Think back to the chapter on "Boy or Girl?" We learned that the matter of sex determination depends upon which combination of "sex chromosomes" an individual receives at conception.

An X and a Y produce a male.

Two X's produce a female.

This is fundamentally correct. But as in all other human characteristics, the best laid plans of the chromosomes gang aft agley. In the earlier chapter there was no need to bring up the exceptions to the rule or to go into the involved details which explain these exceptions. In fact, it was not until recently that geneticists themselves came to understand the intricacies of sex-determination and to be able to explain how various sex abnormalities are produced.

First: *The X and Y chromosomes are not the sole arbiters of sex.* If there are a great many "sex" genes, as we believe, they are not confined to the X and Y, but may be distributed among the other chromosomes, just as many other genes that have nothing to do with sex are found in the X and Y. Which is to say, in the matter of sex development it is believed that various, and perhaps *all,* the chromosomes, are involved.

The X and Y most probably carry the "directing" genes, which start sex development off in one direction or another. But we know now that *all individuals carry in them the potentialities for either sex,* and that sex determination is merely a process of *modify-*

ing the rudimentary sex glands so that they produce hormones of one kind or another. These in turn lead to the development of male or female reproductive organs and secondary sex characteristics.

Thus, the combination of "sex" genes in two X's starts the individual off in the direction of femaleness.

In the XY combination, either the *absence* of the extra set of X genes, or perhaps the presence of certain other genes in the Y, steers the individual toward maleness. But—between the initial steps taken by the "sex directing" genes and the final result many things can happen. In fact, *the type of sexuality of any individual can be changed in degree or varied at every stage of life.*

If we turn to the lower animals, we can see some rather amazing instances of deviation from what we think of as sex "normalcy." There are creatures that are normally double-sexed, performing both sex functions either simultaneously or alternately. These are known as "hermaphrodites." But they are not freaks. It is normal for the snail, earthworm or oyster—and many other creatures—to be double-sexed, just as are most plants and flowers. For them to be single-sexed would be abnormal.

But how do such queer manifestations apply to human beings? Can a human being also be "double-sexed," or be born as a male and turn into a female, or vice versa?

Let us see first how this can happen in the lower animals. Strangely enough, in even the snail or the earthworm, the sex-chromosome mechanism is basically the same as it is in humans. They, too, start out with the potentialities for either sex. But instead of their genes sending them off in either one sex direction or another, they allow *both potentialities* to assert themselves, so that the organs of both sexes develop. In the oyster, the sex genes are so gaged that they allow first the male organs to develop, and later have these give way to the development of the female organs.

But there are "freak" types, occurring in animals normally single-sexed in which commonly *half* the body is of one sex, and another half of the other sex. These are known as "gynandromorphs." They are fairly common in many species, including butterflies, moths, wasps, bees, flies, ants and spiders. If you were a "child natu-

ODDITIES IN SEX

THE TAPEWORM

is hermaphroditic (double-sexed), each section complete with both male and female organs, and able to fertilize itself.

THE SNAIL AND THE EARTHWORM

while also double-sexed, have their sex organs so placed that each individual must mate with another of its kind, but playing both male and female roles.

AN OYSTER

alternates from one sex to another. It starts life as a male, becomes a female, may turn into a male again, etc.

IN BEES

the same egg, if fertilized, will produce a female; if not fertilized, will develop into a male.

BEFORE

AFTER

IN POULTRY

a female may turn outwardly into a "male," or a male into a "female," as a result of some upset in the sex organs or hormonal balance.

ralist" you may have caught one of these freaks, in which the creature had one kind of pattern or form on one side, and a different appearance on the other side. Or, as frequently happens, the gynandromorph is male in the front half of its body and female in the rear half, or vice versa.

One way in which a gynandromorph might be produced is shown in the accompanying diagram. At conception a certain individual receives two X's, normally destining it to be a female. But at the very first stages of cell division something happens so that one of the X's is left out of a primary cell, this cell giving rise to others with only one X in each. Here, then, is an individual starting life with part of its body containing XX cells, the other part single X cells. The XX part proceeds to develop *femaleness*. The part with the single X goes on to develop maleness, for as we have seen, the Y chromosome is not essential.

In some cases gynandromorphs have the genitalia of both sexes, but whether with one set of sex organs or both, as a rule they cannot reproduce. In contrast to these freaks, hermaphrodites have the reproductive organs of both sexes, either simultaneously or alternately, and are *normally* capable of functioning as both sexes, either at the same time, or first as one sex, later as another.

Now in what way do such queer conditions apply to humans?

We find, first, that true gynandromorphs in which one half of the body is completely male, the other half female can occur only among the more elementary creatures, such as insects, which have no sex hormones as humans have. In human beings or in other mammals, even where a derangement of the sex chromosomes might occur, the sex hormones circulating in the body would produce a "blending" effect throughout. Circus freaks, claiming to be "half man and half woman," are sometimes seen, but these may be set down as spurious. (In these cases the freak is probably a male in whom one breast is overdeveloped, giving him a female contour on one side, a male contour on the other.)

True hermaphroditism in human beings, where an individual may have organs and characteristics of both sexes, is, however, not at all impossible. Every sort of sexual intergradation has been

HOW A GYNANDROMORPH
(Half-in-half creature)
MAY BE FORMED

1. Individual starts out as a potential female with two "X's."

2. In early stage, when chromosomes and cells double, an "X" may get left out of one of the halves.

3. As the cells multiply, those on one side have only one "X," all those on the other side two "X's."

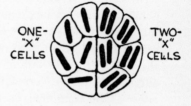

ONE-"X" CELLS   TWO-"X" CELLS

4. The result is a creature male on one side, female on the other. (The one here shown is a fruit-fly, [Drosophila,] gynandromorph.)

    (After Morgan)

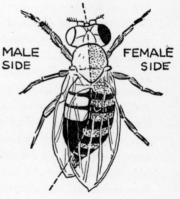

MALE SIDE   FEMALE SIDE

found, from males with undeveloped masculine genitalia to males with all degrees of female genital development, grading into females with undeveloped or incomplete female organs and ranging up to those with rudimentary male organs.

Recently Professor Hugh Hampton Young, of Johns Hopkins University, published an exhaustive treatise on the condition. Dr. Young reports knowledge of twenty indisputable cases of true hermaphroditism, in which the same individuals had within themselves both ovaries and testes.

A much more common condition, estimated to occur as often as once in every 1,000 persons, is that of "pseudo-hermaphroditism." In this, the individual has either ovaries or testes, but *not both,* yet nevertheless may have external organs of both sexes (with one type usually predominant). Thus, while genetically either a male or female, the pseudo-hermaphrodite may be mistakenly classified in infancy or childhood as of the wrong sex. A number of such cases have lately come to the fore where individuals reared as females have achieved prominence as champion "women" athletes. One of these later underwent an operation which "transformed" her into a male by suppressing the rudimentary female organs.

If we seem to be stressing sex abnormalities it is with a purpose. We can imagine no aspect of heredity more important than the fundamental one of sex. By clarifying what are considered as abnormalities we may come to a better understanding of what is considered "normal." For what do we mean by "normal" sexuality in human beings? Dictionaries define "male" as a person having organs for "procreating young or producing sperm for the impregnation of an ovum," and "female" as a "person with organs for conceiving and bringing forth young or producing ova." And yet as we have just seen, there are individuals characterized by society as "male" or "female" who do not correspond with either definition, who may have both kinds of sex organs, or who may have one kind so defective that it cannot be used for reproduction. It is to these persons that we apply the term of "twilight sexes."

The difficulty in defining "male" and "female" is as nothing compared to the task confronting us when we try to define "masculine" and "feminine." These terms geneticists now recognize as being capable of highly variable interpretation. Most authorities believe that *biologically, no person is completely "masculine" or completely "feminine";* that we all begin life with *potentialities* for either sex; and that only because Nature has found it expedient

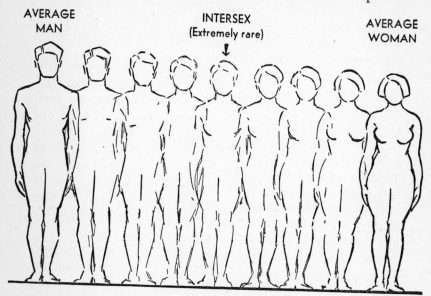

AVERAGE   INTERSEX   AVERAGE
MAN   (Extremely rare)   WOMAN

Between "normal" male and "normal" female there is every type shading from "maleness" to "femaleness" and "femaleness" to "maleness"

for our reproduction does she usually, but *not always,* provide a mechanism to tip the balance of sexuality in either one direction or the other.

Nevertheless, as we have seen, only with respect to a single chromosome of the 48 are males and females genetically different. With "sex" genes scattered through all the other chromosomes, so-called "female" characteristics may just as well be transmitted by a father to his daughter as by a mother, and "male" characteristics just as well by a mother to her son. This is no news to animal breeders. They have long known that the milking qualities of a prize cow can be carried by a bull offspring and passed on by him to his daughter; that the fighting qualities of a bull sire can be passed on through a daughter to her son.

In human beings there is reason to believe that a gene or genes for fertility or twinning can be passed along by a mother through her son just as well as through her daughter. The gene for a father's beard pattern could be passed on to his daughter, and while not manifesting itself in her, could be passed on by her in turn to her son, where it would assert itself. The list could be extended greatly to include a host of "secondary" sex characteristics, the genes for which both sexes carry equally.

As further evidence of all this, when there is some upset in the sex glands of either male or female, the latent secondary sex characteristics of the opposite sex may crop out. Startled farmers have sometimes reported that one of their hens became transformed into a rooster. This can actually happen. In a classic case (reported by Crew) the transformation was due to the destruction of the ovary in a hen, allowing the male glands and organs, always present in a rudimentary form, to develop. The claim was made that this "hen-rooster" actually functioned as both "mother" and "father," first laying eggs and then, in the rooster stage, producing sperm and "fathering" chicks. While the evidence regarding the double functioning is not considered conclusive, experiments have repeatedly shown that when the ovaries of hens are removed they do develop the secondary male characteristics of a rooster—comb, plumage, etc.

In the human female, removal of the ovaries *after puberty* is not known to have any such corresponding effect. However, if removed *before puberty,* when the secondary sexual characteristics of the body are not yet developed, they might seriously alter the physical characteristics of a girl. Even if the ovaries are not affected, some upset in the sex balance or some glandular disturbance, especially if happening in early life, may well produce in a human female secondary male characteristics, such as male body proportions and, later, deep voice, hairiness of body and face, etc.

Among human males the results of castration *before puberty* are well known. But (as in females) even without an operation it is possible that early derangement of the sex glands or sex balance might cause a boy to grow up with "eunochoid" characteristics— secondary sexual characteristics resembling those of a female— large hips, narrow sloping shoulders, absence of beard and body hair, high-pitched feminine voice, etc. In maturity, also, especially in old age, changes in the glandular make-up may often cause men to develop high-pitched voices and perhaps some other secondary female sex characteristics.

To upset a popular fallacy, it might also be made clear that *in neither sex, male nor female, does removal of the "gonads" (testes or ovaries) after puberty, necessarily interfere with sex functioning. Eunuchs may have sex relations as other men. The "sex impulse" in men—in its physical aspects—is engendered and sex functioning governed not by the testes alone but also by hormonal, nervous and psychic stimuli.*

It might also be said that popular impressions as to what constitute "masculine" or "feminine" secondary physical characteristics are also not too well grounded. Hairiness of body and strong muscular development are considered characteristic of males, and yet there are many "normal" women with more body hair or with bigger muscles than the average man. Delicate features, smooth skin and rounded contours are considered "feminine" characteristics, and yet there are many "normal" men who have these characteristics in greater degree than many women. In short, there are biologically normal women who look more "masculine" than a good many males, and biologically normal males who look more "feminine" than do a good many women.

It is not hard to see, therefore, how difficult it is to try to identify genes that produce abnormal sexual characteristics. Only in the case of obvious genital defects or abnormalities has it so far been possible to do this. Among such hereditary abnormalities, some of which are known to "run" in families, are these:

Supernumerary nipples—extra nipples, occurring in males and females. Some individuals have as many as six nipples, the pairs ranged one below the other. (A condition, by the way, abnormal for humans but normal in lower animals.)

Hypospadias—a misplaced opening of the urethra. This occurs in males only, is present from birth and is believed due to a dominant gene.

Sterility may also be inherited, unbelievable as that may seem at first thought. It can be produced quite simply by two recessive genes coming together, just as in the case of lethals. There are several such types of genes which produce incomplete development of the reproductive organs, and with it, sterility. *Sterility in a male* might be produced by a gene transmitted only through mothers. But in the majority of cases of sterility in either males or females it is questionable whether hereditary factors play any great part.

Fertility is also believed by many authorities to be influenced by certain genes. The prolific child-bearing which seems to characterize certain human strains is thought to have some hereditary basis, just as the number of offspring in a litter or the frequency of reproduction among various species of other animals is apparently genetically controlled. No "excess fertility" genes, however, have yet been identified.

The "timing" of sex development is also, quite clearly, influenced by genes. It is no accident that puberty, adolescence, maturity, the climacteric in women, etc., come to most human beings at about the same time, and that in various strains or families there is a frequent deviation from the average "timing." Where the cycles appear to arrive consistently in families either earlier or later, and where no environmental factors seem to be involved, genes are apparently responsible. In rare cases (but not believed due to hereditary factors) the workings of the sex glands are so abnormally speeded up that they can produce *fully developed sex organs in children of the age of two or three*.

Only a beginning has been made in the study of the genetic aspects of sex and of the rôle of heredity with regard to sex abnormalities. As has been said previously, no characteristics could be considered of greater importance. If we think back to the little boy at the beginning of this chapter, and with him include others who deviate sexually from what is considered "normal," we might ask ourselves to what extent such deviations may affect or alter their actions and behavior, and influence the attitude of others toward them. This will be dealt with in later chapters, when we take up the possible *inheritance of abnormal instincts and behavior* —characteristics as yet too vague to be identified or classified here with the "black" genes.

CHAPTER XXVII

"BLACK" GENE ROLL-CALL

This is not a happy chapter.

It summarizes and brings together all the "black" genes previously discussed and some additional ones of lesser import. Also —which is its most ominous aspect—it forecasts the chances of transmitting any given defect, disease or abnormality to a child.

At first glance the array of "black" genes may appear to be Tables of Doom. But really, there are some brighter sides to the picture. As we have pointed out, the list of known hereditary defects is as nothing compared to the interminable array of non-hereditary ills that fill volume after volume in the medical treatises. Moreover, few of the known hereditary conditions are sufficiently common to present grave problems to society, and many of them are serious to the individual only when he considers them as such.

For instance, most of the eye conditions: Near-sightedness or far-sightedness, in their usual form, can hardly be thought of as spelling doom—not, certainly, when there is an optician around the corner. In certain professions and trades (such as soldiering) weak eyes may be a bar or a serious handicap. But we prefer to think of one of the most near-sighted of men, Arturo Toscanini, and of how the very fact of his weak eyes tended to develop in him the miraculous memory which has contributed to his achievements.

If a deviation from the standard for any characteristic is a defect, then we are all, each and every one of us, defectives. Looking through the list of "black" genes (and remember, not all the minor ones are here included), it is more than likely that you will find at least one condition that strikes home to you personally, or that is present in your immediate family. Most cases justify no further comment than, "My, my—so that's inherited. How interesting!"

But, unfortunately, many conditions cannot be dismissed so lightly. For example, blindness, or conditions that lead to blindness; deafness; diseases such as diabetes, hemophilia and other blood disorders; certain tumors; serious and unpleasant skin conditions; deformities of the features and of the body; grave mental disorders; etc. If any of such conditions are present in you or in your immediate family (bearing in mind always that we are speaking of the *hereditary* types) then they may well give you pause. This is when you should study seriously the "forecast" tables.

Even where a condition has already been transmitted, or may be transmitted, an optimistic view may be that a cure or treatment exists or will be made available. Many hereditary conditions or defects once considered extremely grave have had their importance much diminished by the discovery of cures, and there is every prospect that medicine and surgery will provide cures for others. But this, of course, may have no bearing on the immediate present, and will not affect the transmission of the genes involved.

Another fact which may hearten the individual is that no recessive condition, even if present in one parent, will crop out in a child unless a gene for that condition is also carried by the other parent. *No one individual parent* can transmit to a child rheumatic fever, diabetes, albinism, feeble-mindedness or any other condition where *two* recessive genes are required. But this does not console society, for actually, as will be more clearly explained in a later chapter, it is the recessive "hidden" conditions that constitute our greatest problem.

The *time of onset* of any condition is also of great importance. To the lay mind a condition which is present from birth, or that manifests itself in childhood, with perhaps fatal consequences, is considered more ominous than one which does not appear until late in life. Although late-appearing conditions may be more favorable to the individual, from the standpoint of society quite the reverse is true, in many respects. Where conditions do not come on until after puberty they may permit the afflicted individual to reproduce and pass on the genes. Thus, if you are still young, and a condition which has its onset in maturity is known to run in your family, there is always the possibility that it may yet appear in you and that you may transmit it.

As we said, we are not here listing every single one of the known "black" genes, down to the rarest and the most minor ones which are often merely variations of others that are listed. To have attempted such thoroughness would have been to give this book the character of a medical treatise, which we heartily wished to avoid. However, a conscientious effort has been made to present every condition that could be of interest to any considerable number of readers. Further, to permit any "skipping over" desired, the relative importance of the various conditions has been indicated by the use of different type.

A final word of caution: In reading the brief description of each condition, be careful not to confuse it with something else which might have similar symptoms, or which is *not hereditary*. Also be sure to make allowances for the rôle of environment—disease, accident, etc.—and for time of onset. Wherever in doubt—and certainly for every serious condition—it would be well to consult your physician.

We now turn to the tables, presenting first, the lists of the "black" genes, and following them with the "forecasts."

KEEP THESE SYMBOLS IN MIND
KEY TO "BLACK" GENE TABLES

●	**D**	DOMINANT Gene. Only One required to produce effect. A parent with a dominant condition will pass it on to one in two children.
● ●	**R**	RECESSIVE Gene (Simple). Two required to produce effect. For a child to have a recessive condition each parent must contribute the same gene.
MALES ● ──────── FEMALES ● ●	**S-L**	SEX-LINKED RECESSIVE Gene. Carried by "X" Chromosome. Only one needed to produce effect in male, but two required in female (as with any other recessive).
●	**S-L D**	"D" after "S-L" means that the Sex-Linked gene is Dominant (rare), producing effect singly in females as well as males.
● ● +	**R+**	RECESSIVE PLUS. Condition is caused by two or more different pairs of recessive genes acting together.
● +	**D +**	DOMINANT PLUS. Condition is caused by two or more different dominant genes acting together.
D (q) or R (q)		DOMINANT QUALIFIED or RECESSIVE QUALIFIED. Genes may not always produce their effects, or may not always work in same way, or environment is a factor.
?		QUESTION MARK after name of condition indicates "heredity doubtful or uncertain." After gene symbols it means "gene mechanism not established."
✠		BLACK CROSS after gene symbols means the condition is fatal in early life.

SUMMARY TABLES—"BLACK" GENES

Herewith are listed all leading or unusual defects, diseases or "abnormal" conditions, in which heredity has been proved or the possibility of inheritance presumed. (*Note to physicians:* Some of the conditions listed as hereditary may be clinically similar to conditions caused by acquired diseases, for example, eye-muscle paralysis, where the hereditary type is present from birth while the non-hereditary type is a sequel to meningitis.)

The relative importance of the conditions is broadly indicated by the type in which their names are set:

Black Type—Prevalent or common.

Medium Type—Fairly common.

Small Type—Rare.

Condition	Description	Genes Required
INTERNAL AND GENERAL		
Diabetes	"Sugar Sickness". Due to pancreas defect. Middle-age; sometimes childhood.	●● R
False Diabetes	Some symptoms of true Diabetes, but none of serious effects:	
	a. Sugar urine.	● D(q)
	b. Diabetes insipidus. Thirst, excessive urine.	● D
Childhood Rheumatism	Joint pains, chorea, heart effects. Childhood.	●● R(q)
High Blood Pressure ?	Due to hardening of arteries. Late life. *Heredity uncertain.*	?
Kidney Troubles	*a.* Multiple cysts, serious in pregnant women.	?
	b. Urinary disorders. (Black, reddish, etc.)	●● R
Cancer (Common) ?	(Stomach, breast, etc.) *Inheritance doubtful.*	?
Rare Cancers and Tumors	*a.* Malignant freckles. Dark, freckle-like inflammations from sun, leading to cancer. Infancy or childhood, usually fatal.	●● R ✠

Condition	Description	Genes Required

INTERNAL AND GENERAL (*Continued*)

Condition	Description	Genes Required
Rare Cancers and Tumors (*Continued*)	*b.* Sebaceous adenoma. Tumors of skin, brain, etc. Childhood. Frequently fatal.	● D(q) ✚
	c. Retinal angioma. Blood tumor of eye.	?
	d. Ear-nerve tumor, causing deafness, blindness, frequently death.	● D ✚
	e. Glioma retina. Tumor of eye, fatal unless eye removed. Birth or infancy.	●● R ?
	f. Polyposis of the colon. May lead to cancer. Maturity.	?
	g. See also under SKIN: Birthmarks—*a;* Coffee-colored spots (*Neurofibromatosis*); Fatty Skin Growth—*b;* and Scalp Cysts.	
Bleeding Diseases	*a.* Hemophilia. Defective blood-clotting. Birth, usually fatal before maturity.	● S-L (Men only)
	b. Pseudo-hemophilia. Unrelated to above, far less severe. In both sexes.	● D(q)
	c. Nose-bleed—Thrombasthenia. Childhood. More common and serious in females. Other effects. Childhood.	● S-L D
	d. Nose-bleed—Telangiectasis. Similar to above, but purple areas on skin. Usually childhood. Increasing with age.	● D
Anemia	Heredity claimed in some cases; but not established:	
	a. Achlorhydric. Common.	?
	b. Mediterranean. Also bone effects. Fatal.	? ✚
Blood-Cell Abnormalities	*a.* Red corpuscles sickle-shaped. Mainly Negroes. Birth. Occasionally severe anemia, sometimes fatal.	● D
	b. Oval-shaped. Not harmful. Birth.	● D

Condition	Description	Genes Required
INTERNAL AND GENERAL *(Continued)*		
Jaundice	*a.* In new-born, with anemia. Transfusion required, otherwise usually fatal.	●● R(q)
	b. Acholuric. Fragile blood cells sometimes with anemia. Childhood or adult. Sometimes fatal.	● D(q)
Stomach Ulcers ?	Heredity doubtful.	?
Reproductive (Sexual)	*a.* In males: Abnormal opening in ureter. Birth.	● D
	b. In both sexes: Extra nipples or breasts.	?
Allergy	*a.* Sensitivity to certain substances, causing asthma, hay fever, rash, etc. Onset early. Some authorities doubt heredity.	● D
	b. Angioneurotic oedema. Sudden skin or membrane swelling. If in larynx or vital organs may cause death. Puberty or later.	● D
Migraine Headaches	Considered a form of allergy. Heredity in dispute.	● D
BRAIN AND NERVE		
Amaurotic Idiocy	*a.* Brain degeneration with blindness, paralysis, idiocy. Infancy or childhood. Fatal.	●● R ✠
	b. Juvenile and adult forms. Frequently fatal.	● D ✠ or S-L
	c. Eye effect only. Brain normal. Puberty. May be fatal.	?
Epilepsy ? (**Common Type**)	Various spontaneous convulsive disorders. Cause unknown. Heredity claimed but not established.	?
Epilepsy (Myoclonus)	(Rare.) Consciousness not lost during seizures. Childhood.	●● R

Condition	Description	Genes Required
BRAIN AND NERVE (*Continued*)		
Mongolian Idiocy ?	Congenital idiocy due to some intra-uterine effect on embryo. Heredity doubtful.	?
Microcephaly	Extreme or "Pinhead".	●●+R+ ?
Chorea	*a.* Sydenham's, *St. Vitus Dance* (see Childhood Rheumatism under INTERNAL).	
	b. Huntington's. Progressive mental deterioration (see text). Usually middle-age.	● D
	c. Wilson's Disease. With liver cirrhosis, muscular rigidity. Youth.	●● R
Insanity	*a.* Schizophrenia. Various forms of adolescent insanity. (See text.)	●●+ R+ ?
	b. Manic Depressive. Mental depression, sometimes maniacal tendencies. Usually in maturity following undue strain.	●●+ R+ ?
Feeblemindedness	*a.* Sub-normal mentality, with no physical symptoms. Not always hereditary.	●●+R+
	b. With paralysis on both sides. (One-sided generally due to birth injury.)	●● R
	c. Phenylpyruvic amentia, with metabolic disorder and swellings on nerves.	●● R
Cerebral Sclerosis	Gradual failure of intelligence, vision, muscular power. Childhood or youth.	●● R
Mirror Reading and Writing	Seeing in reverse and upside-down. Sometimes with stuttering. Birth.	● D(q)
EYES		
Cataract	Opaque lens; common cause of blindness. Onset, type, varying in different families. Old-age cataracts may not be hereditary.	● D(q)
Glaucoma (Hereditary Type)	*a.* Adult: Pressure in eye-ball, leading to blindness. Usually middle-age. Several types.	● D(q)

Condition	Description	Genes Required
EYES (*Continued*)		
Glaucoma (*Continued*)	*b.* Juvenile type (rare). Onset in puberty.	m.● S-L f. ●●
	c. Infantile type.	●● R
Retinitis Pigmentosa	Gradual filling of retina with pigment in youth, leading to blindness by middle-age. Sometimes with deafness.	●● D ●● R or S-L
Optic Atrophy	Withering optic nerve, leading to blindness:	
	a. Birth type. Occasionally associated with deafness.	● D
	b. Childhood type.	●● R ?
	c. Adult type (Leber's disease). Blindness only in center of eye.	m.● S-L (q) f. ●●
	d. Associated with ataxia.	● D ?
Small Eyes	*a.* Entire eye undersized, frequently with other eye defects. Birth.	● D or S-L
	b. Same, with teeth defects also.	●● R
	c. Extreme form, eye completely absent, thus blindness from birth.	●●+ R+ ?
Glioma Retinae	Tumor of eye. (See under Rare Cancers—*e.*)	
Pin-Hole Pupil	Iris almost closed; may cause blindness. Birth.	● D
Astigmatism	Defective focusing. Birth. Heredity uncertain.	● D ?
Far-Sightedness (Extreme)	Inability to see clearly close-hand. Birth, decreasing with age:	● D(q)
	a. Slight. Not pathological.	
	b. Extreme, with other eye effects.	●● R
Near-Sightedness (Extreme)	*a.* Distant vision blurred. Birth, increasing with age.	●● R (or S-L)
	b. Associated with oscillating eyes and poor vision. (*Nystagmus*)	● D or S-L

Condition	Description	Genes Required
EYES (*Continued*)		
Color Blindness (Partial)	Confusion of red and green. Birth. Several types.	m.● S-L f.●●
Day Blindness	Blurred vision in strong light; also *complete color blindness*. Birth.	●● R
Night Blindness (Complete)	Vision failing in dim light, otherwise normal. Birth. (Most cases due to Vitamin A deficiency.)	
	a. With no other eye defect.	● D
	b. With near-sightedness. 99% of cases males.	m.● S-L f.●●
	c. With extreme near-sightedness.	●● R
	d. Japanese type, like type *a.*	●● R
Cross-Eyes (*Strabismus*)	Eyes not focusing together. Childhood, may disappear later. *Not always hereditary.*	●● R or ● D
Oscillating Eyes (*Nystagmus*)	Eye tremor, usually weak vision. Birth. *a.* Common type, occurring by itself.	m.● S-L f.●●
	b. With head-twitching.	● D
Eye-Muscle Paralysis	Inability to move eye. Birth or later, increasing in severity. (May be result of meningitis.)	● D or m.● S-L f.●●
Drooping Eyelids	(Ptosis) Inability to raise lids. Birth.	● D
Defective Cornea	*a.* Cloudiness over lens, impairing vision. Onset variable.	● D(q)
	b. Opaque ring over iris, giving "spectacled" appearance. Childhood.	● D
	c. Cone-shaped cornea, causing extreme astigmatism. Childhood, progressing.	●● R
	d. Enlarged cornea. Vision usually normal.	m.● S-L f. ●● or ● D

Condition	Description	Genes Required

EYES *(Continued)*

Condition	Description	Genes Required
Displaced Lens	*a.* Due to atrophied suspensory ligament. Sometimes at birth, sometimes adult.	● D(q)
	b. Same, with displaced pupil.	●● R ?
Defective Iris	*a.* Segment of iris missing. Birth.	{ ● D(q) Also R or S-L
	b. Complete absence of iris. Birth.	● D
Inner Lid Fold (Epicanthus)	Fold across inner-eye angle. (Somewhat like Mongolian fold.)	● D(q)
Pink Eye Color	Only eyes unpigmented, with no other albino effects. Birth. Confined to males.	● S-L (Men only)
Mirror Reading	(See under BRAIN.)	
Unmatched Eyes	Each eye of different color or shade. Infancy. Heredity uncertain.	?
Double (Multiple) Eyelashes	Double row of lashes on each lid.	● D ?

EARS AND HEARING

Condition	Description	Genes Required
Deafness	About 30% of cases of deafness hereditary: *a.* Deaf-mutism: Deafness at birth, preventing speech learning.	●● R ?
	b. Middle-ear deafness (Otosclerosis): Noises in ear. More common in women. Maturity. Slowly progressive.	●●+ R+ ?
	c. Inner-ear deafness (Labyrinthine). Middle-age. Slowly progressive.	● D
	d. Ear-nerve tumor. (See Rare Cancers, p. 189.)	
Outer Ear Deformities	All of the following present at birth: *a.* Absence of ear, usually one side only.	● D
	b. Cup-shaped ear (ear turned in).	● D(q)

SUMMARY TABLES—"BLACK" GENES—*(Continued)*

Condition	Description	Genes Required
EARS AND HEARING *(Continued)*		
Outer Ear Deformities *(Continued)*	*c.* Affixed ear-lobe (in varying degrees).	●● R(q)
	d. Imperfect *double* ear (one or both).	● D ?
Ear Fistula	*a.* Tube-like passage, occasionally soreness or ear discharge. Birth.	● D(q)
	b. Internal opening near tonsil. Birth.	● D(q)
Word Deafness	Hearing normal but inability to interpret sound. More common in males.	● D(q)
MOUTH AND TEETH		
Cleft Palate and Harelip	Failure of palate to fuse, sometimes with teeth defects. Birth.	●●+ R+ ?
Defective Enamel	*a.* Teeth discolored, usually brown; childhood.	● D
	b. "Honeycombed" teeth. May have fits at puberty.	● D
	c. Rare forms, affecting mostly females.	● S-L D
Teeth at Birth	Incisors present at birth.	● D(q)
Missing Teeth	*a.* Upper lateral incisors absent or small.	● D(q)
	b. All teeth missing except canines.	● D ?
Extra Teeth	Frequently associated with cleft palate.	● D ?
Auxiliary Teeth Defects	Concomitants of various conditions. (See Brittle Bones, p. 196, Small eyes, *b*, p. 192.)	
SKELETAL		
Dwarfism	*a.* "Lilliputian"—adults less than 4 feet, but proportions normal.	●+ D+(q)
	b. Achondroplastic—Abnormally stunted limbs, head and body average.	●+ D+(q)

Condition	Description	Genes Required

SKELETAL (Continued)

Hand and Foot Abnormalities	Many different types, single genes producing variable effects within same family. Most common: *Stub-fingers*—middle finger joints missing; *extra fingers and toes; stiff fingers*—joints fused; *webbed fingers or toes; split foot or hand.* (See illustration, p. 142.)	● D(q)
Cranial Opening	Infant "soft spot" in skull persisting to maturity, with other bone defects.	● D(q)
Brittle Bones	Fragile bones with bad teeth, deafness, bluish eye-whites. Birth.	● D(q)
Deformed Spine	(Spina bifida.) With various other effects. Birth.	● D(q)

MUSCLE AND NERVES

Muscular Atrophy	Shriveling or degeneration of muscles:	
	a. Peroneal. Only hands and feet. Childhood.	● D or R or S-L
	b. Spinal. Infancy. *Fatal.*	●● R ✠
	c. Progressive, associated with cataract, sterility, etc. Maturity.	● D(q)
Muscle Disorders	Various types, affecting special muscles, with different onsets and genes.	
Muscle Cramp (Tonic)	Thomsen's Disease. Muscle stiffness, delaying movements. Childhood.	● D
Paralysis	*a.* Spastic. Rigidity lower limbs, spreading upward. Childhood.	●● R or ● D
	b. Agitans. Tremor, rigidity, slowness. Maturity.	?
	c. Soft-muscle. More common in males. Youth.	● D(q)

Condition	Description	Genes Required
MUSCLE AND NERVES *(Continued)*		
Friedreich's Ataxia	Wobbly gait, speech defects. Childhood.	● D(q)
Tremor (Hereditary)	*a.* Slight involuntary movements, beginning in childhood.	● D
Hypertrophic Neuritis	Nerve inflammation. Childhood, progressing.	● D
Leg Swelling	(Trophoedema.) Chronic inflammation of vasomotor nerves. Birth or later, spreading.	● D(q)
SKIN		
Birthmarks	*a.* Several types: Red, brown or raised. May be start for cancer-growths. Heredity uncertain.	?
	b. Slight depression over eyebrows, extending to temple.	● D
	c. Numerous pigmented marks of variable size.	● D
	d. Mongolian Spot—Slate-blue patch over base of spine, characterizing Mongoloid peoples. Disappears in childhood.	●●+R+?
Coffee-colored Spots	*Neurofibromatosis.* Dangerous, may lead to cancer, blindness, paralysis or internal effects. Birth or childhood, increasing.	● D(q)
Malignant Freckles	Dark, freckle-like inflammations. Infancy or childhood. (See Rare Cancers, p. 188.)	
Albinism	Lack of pigmentation in skin and hair.	
	a. Complete—Skin and hair "dead" white, with also *pink eyes*.	●● R
	b. Partial—White patches on skin.	● D(q)
	c. White forelock or "blaze". Unpigmented patch of skin on scalp, growing white hair. From birth, both sexes; or puberty, males only.	● D

Condition	Description	Genes Required
SKIN (*Continued*)		
Albinism (*Continued*)	*d. Piebald*—Stripe on back, sometimes with patches of white elsewhere. (In *vitiligo*, somewhat similar "patch" effect, heredity doubtful.)	● D
	e. Albinoidism—Nearly "albino" skin and hair, at birth, some pigment developing later. Eyes normal.	● D(q)
Fatty Skin Growth	*a.* On eyelids (Xanthoma) often with discoloration. May also be elsewhere. Puberty.	● D
	b. Lipoidosis—Numerous small growths on face, scalp. Sometimes in larynx, requiring operation. Birth.	●● R
Blistering	*a.* Blisters easily raised. Childhood.	● D(q)
	b. Same, leaving scars. Birth. Sometimes with defective nails, or baldness.	●● R(q)
	c. Sunlight blistering; scarring. Especially males.	●● R ?
	d. Extreme (*Bullosa connata*). Often causes bleeding, death in infancy.	●● R ✠
	e. Sensitivity to light. Urine frequently red. Birth. Sometimes leads to baldness, blindness, later.	●● R
Scaly or Horny Skin	*a.* Common type, with shedding. Infancy.	● D (or S-L R)
	b. Cracked skin, ears often defective. Birth, may disappear later. Sometimes fatal.	●● R
	c. "*Elephant skin*"—Extreme form of above. Causes premature birth, *death*.	●● R ✠
	d. Psoriasis—Mottled scaly patches decreasing with age. If hereditary, only as tendency.	?

Condition	Description	Genes Required
SKIN (*Continued*)		
Thick, or Shedding Skin	*a.* Skin flaking off over entire body. Birth.	●● R
	b. Same, but skin thicker. Several types, one with casts of palms and soles shedding. Birth or puberty.	● D
	c. Thick or discolored skin on limbs, but not shedding. Childhood, more among males.	● D(q)
Sweat-Gland Defects	*a.* Complete inability to sweat—panting in hot weather, as by dogs. May also be hair, teeth, growth defects. Birth.	m. ● S-L f. ●●
	b. Mild type of above, more among males.	● D(q)
	c. Excessive sweating.	● D
Rubber Skin	Absence of connective tissue, making possible freak stretching of skin. Childhood.	● D(q)
Scalp Cysts	Sometimes on face also. Several types. Puberty or later.	● D(q)

HAIR AND NAILS

Condition	Description	Genes Required
Baldness	*a.* Pattern—almost exclusively in males. Maturity. (See text.)	● D (Men only)
	b. Patch baldness—small bald area on scalp; may spread. Birth or puberty.	● D(q)
	c. Congenital—Hair defective or never developing. Various types, associated with teeth, nail or scalp defects.	●● R ● D (or S-L)
	d. Susceptibility to scalp infection (*seborrhea*) leading to baldness. In adults, mostly men.	
Defective Hair	*a.* Infantile down remaining through life.	● D
	b. Beaded hair. May lead to baldness. Infancy.	● D(q)

Condition	Description	Genes Required

HAIR AND NAILS (*Continued*)

Defective Hair
(*Continued*)

c. Excessive long, soft hair on face and elsewhere. Other effects. ("Dog-face".) Childhood. — ● D(q)

d. Defective hair with abnormal nails. Mostly among French Canadians. Puberty. — ● D

e. Follicle defects, causing hair-loss, goose-flesh; frequent growth and mind defects. Several types. Birth or childhood. — ● D(q) (or S-L)

Woolly Hair — Short, tightly-curled (not to be confused with Negro hair); may be any color. Infancy. — ● D

Premature Grayness — Head-hair only. No effect on life-span. Begins in adolescence. — ● D

White Forelock — (Or "Blaze".) (See Albinism, p. 197.)

Defective Nails

a. Nails absent, partially or wholly. — ●● R or ● D

b. Thick nails. Skin on palms, soles also thick. Birth. — ●+D+?

c. Thick nails, protruding at angle. Birth. — ● D

d. Small, thin, soft nails. Birth. — ● D(q)

e. Bluish-white spots on nails. Birth. — ● D

f. Flat and thin nails. Birth. — ● D

THE FOLLOWING "FORECAST" TABLES
SHOULD INTEREST YOU IF—

—You are still young, and there is some condition known in your family, generally appearing in later life, which you are worried may also appear in you.

—You are planning to marry, and are worried that some condition in either you or your prospective mate, or one that appears in your families, may be passed on to your children.

—You are married and already have children, and are worried that some condition may crop out in them later.

WHEN USING THESE FORECAST TABLES, BE AS
CERTAIN AS POSSIBLE THAT—

—The condition you have in mind is the *one listed* in our tables.

—That, where there are various ways in which it can be inherited, you know which gene mechanism applies in your case.

—That, where environment is a factor in its expression, you have ruled out the possibility that the condition has not been covered up, or that, even if the genes are transmitted, it might not be prevented from developing in a child.

—That, where a condition can also be caused by environment, the one you have in mind is of the *hereditary type*.

—That you have paid full attention to the question of *"onset"* (for instance, where a condition appears late, you cannot be sure that the genes are, or are not, present until the person reaches the required age).

IN NO CASE CONSIDER YOUR "FORECAST" CONCLUSIVE, OR TAKE ANY ACTION ON THE BASIS OF IT, WITHOUT CONSULTING COMPETENT MEDICAL AUTHORITY.

In All Cases It Is Best to Consult Your Family Doctor!

I. RECESSIVE GENE FORECASTS
●● R

(The most common form of "black" gene inheritance. Because of the vast number of persons that are carrying a "hidden" recessive gene for various conditions, *complete* assurance can never be given that any common recessive condition may not crop up in some child. But the possibility that it will crop up diminishes with the infrequency that it appears in the parents' families. The more prevalent the condition in the general population, however, the more likely it is to turn up unexpectedly—especially if the parents are closely related.)

WHERE THE CONDITION IS RECESSIVE	CHANCES CHILD WILL INHERIT IT:
1. IF BOTH PARENTS ARE AFFECTED*	Almost certainly
2. IF ONE PARENT IS AFFECTED, THE OTHER NOT BUT IF IN THE FAMILY OF THE "FREE" PARENT*—	
a. His or her father or mother is affected, or a child with the defect has already appeared:	Even chance
b. A brother, sister, or grandparent is affected:	Less than even chance
c. Some more remote relative is affected:	Possible, but not probable
d. No one, near or far, has been known to have the condition:	Very unlikely
3. IF NEITHER PARENT IS AFFECTED*, BUT	
a. The condition occurs *on both sides* in one of their parents, or in a brother or sister, or has already appeared in a child:	One-in-four
b. The condition occurs or has occurred in more distant relatives of the families of both:	Extremely unlikely, but yet possible
c. The condition is wholly unknown in the family of either:	Virtually nil

*NOTE FOR ALL ABOVE: Certain recessive conditions (childhood rheumatism, diabetes, etc.) may be strongly influenced in their expression by environment. The fact, then, that parents or their families are affected does not positively indicate whether, or to what extent, their child might develop the condition if the environment is favorable. Or the fact that the parents themselves do not show the condition, when it appears in others in their families, is not conclusive proof that they are free of the genes involved. All this applies to the "qualified" recessives following:

II. "QUALIFIED" RECESSIVE FORECASTS
●● R(q)

The chances of inheriting the *genes* are exactly the same as shown in Table I, but the chances of the *condition* actually appearing in the child may be altered by the circumstances stated in the preceding footnote. In general, however, the odds are somewhat lower than in simple recessives for each type of mating.

III. "RECESSIVE PLUS" FORECASTS
●●+R+

The situations are about the same as in Table I, but with the *probability lessened* in most cases.

IV. SEX-LINKED (RECESSIVE) FORECASTS

males ●
—— S-L
females ●●

(Where the "black" gene is carried in the "X" chromosome, and therefore acts as a dominant in the case of males, as a recessive in the case of females. Examples: Color blindness, hemophilia, nystagmus, enlarged cornea.)

	CHANCES CHILD WILL INHERIT:
1. IF BOTH PARENTS ARE AFFECTED:	Almost certainly in all their children
2. IF MOTHER IS AFFECTED, BUT FATHER IS FREE OF IT:	Certain for every son, but no daughter
3. IF FATHER IS AFFECTED, AND MOTHER IS FREE OF IT, BUT—	
a. Her father, mother or a sister has or had the condition:	Even chance in any child
b. One of her brothers is affected:	One-in-four for any child
c. One of her more remote relatives is affected:	Extremely unlikely, but yet possible
d. No known case in her family:	Virtually nil
4. IF NEITHER PARENT IS AFFECTED, BUT IT OCCURS IN THE MOTHER'S FAMILY (in the same situations as noted above):	No chance for any daughter, but for sons same odds as in 3-*a.b.c.d.* above

V. DOMINANT GENE FORECASTS
● D

(For all conditions which can be produced in either sex by one gene acting singly, as in acholuric jaundice, drooping eyelids, various hand defects, etc.)

	CHANCES CHILD WILL INHERIT THE CONDITION
1. *IF BOTH PARENTS ARE AFFECTED:	Very probable
2. *IF ONE PARENT IS AFFECTED, THE OTHER "FREE":	Even chance
3. WHERE NEITHER PARENT IS AFFECTED, BUT IT APPEARS IN THE FAMILY OF ONE OR THE OTHER:	
a. If the condition is always known to show itself when the gene is present:	Nil
b. *If the gene action is sometimes known to be suppressed by environment:	Some likelihood, but not great

*NOTE: In every case where the gene action is irregular, or influenced by environment, we have the situation following of

VI. "QUALIFIED" DOMINANT FORECASTS
● D(q)

In all "qualified" dominant conditions, such as mirror-reading, extreme far-sightedness, adult glaucoma, etc., the predictions are modified downward from those shown in preceding table, the forecasts depending upon the degree to which the gene expresses itself or is suppressed by environment.

VII. "DOMINANT-PLUS" FORECASTS
●+ D+

(Rare, as in dwarfism and rare defective enamels.) Relative probabilities are about as shown in Table V, but greatly reduced in most cases.

VIII. SEX-LINKED DOMINANT FORECASTS
● S-L D

(As in *thrombasthenia* type nose-bleed.) If mother has condition, ratios for *all* offspring, male and female, will be the same as in Table V-1, 2. When father has condition, *every* daughter, and only the daughters, will get it

CHAPTER XXVIII

HOW DO YOU KNOW THE BABY'S YOURS?

THERE used to be a jolly old judge in Milwaukee who specialized in doubtful paternity cases, or what the state so bluntly calls "bastardy actions."

By "specialized" we mean that he showed a special aptitude for trying these cases, and accordingly most of them were assigned to him. For one thing, he seemed fully aware of the fact that such actions permitted no strict adherence to legal procedure. The evidence offered—aside from the highly contradictory statements of the plaintiff and defendant—was hearsay and much colored by perjury. Recognizing that it was largely a matter of deciding who was lying and who wasn't, the judge viewed the proceedings as a family squabble in which he had to play the rôle of an impartial father.

One case in particular (of the many before him which we covered as a "cub" reporter) stands out in our memory. The young woman plaintiff had given rather convincing testimony, and the young man whom she named as the father of her child had taken the stand. Under a barrage of cross-examination he admitted having "sat up" with the young woman on the night in question, but insisted that his deportment had been blameless. No amount of forceful questioning could shake him. At this point the judge intervened.

"Tell me," the judge asked, "was there by any chance a *moon* shining that night?"

The young man thought a moment and innocently replied, "Why, yes, sir. I think there was."

The judge nodded with mock gravity, then sat back in his big chair and gazed at the ceiling, seemingly in deep thought. "Ah!" he said at last, and bent forward as if to take the entire court-

205

room into his confidence. "It's all very simple. *Some* man had to be the father of the child. Well, there was a moon shining that night. All we have to decide is whether it was this young fellow or the *man in the moon.*"

Now, any lawyer could tell you that such a remark coming from a judge was improper. But, as we said before, the entire procedure in doubtful paternity cases was (and usually still is) highly questionable. The "paternity" laws have little concern with the individual. They do not seek to compensate the mother nor to punish the errant father. Their primary purpose is to insure the state against the possibility of the child becoming a public charge.

The justice or injustice of the law, however, is not an issue here. What we wish to point out is that the whole matter of deciding parentage in disputed cases has been befogged with uncertainty, and that fortunately a fairer, and more scientific, approach is in sight.

The first constructive step has already been taken through the "blood" tests which are just beginning to be used in doubtful paternity cases. Here the law formally recognizes, and makes practical application, for the first time, of our knowledge of the gene mechanism of heredity.

What are the "blood" tests? They are based on the discovery that the blood of all human beings can be classified into *four hereditary groups*—which provides one of the clearest examples we have of Mendelian gene action. Only three "key" blood genes are involved in producing the four groups. These genes may be designated by the letters *A, B* and *O*. To describe their effects as simply and untechnically as possible, we may say that each of them produces different substances in the blood.

Gene *A* produces, principally, a substance known as "Antigen A."

Gene *B* produces, principally, "Antigen B."

Gene *O* produces neither antigen, but only certain milder substances.

Every one of us inherits two of these genes—a single one from each parent. We may therefore receive two genes of the same kind—*AA, BB,* or *OO*—or a mixed pair, *AB, AO* or *BO.* It is

YOUR BLOOD TYPE

Was inherited through a pair of any of these genes—two of the same kind or a mixed pair—one gene coming from each parent:

(Symbols)　　Ⓐ　　　　Ⓑ　　　　Ⓞ

Each gene produces different blood substances. Genes "A" and "B" are of equal strength, and when brought together, work independently. But Gene "O" is recessive; and if coupled with "A" or "B," does not function. Accordingly:

IF YOU RECEIVED GENES:	Ⓐ+Ⓐ or Ⓐ+Ⓞ	Ⓑ+Ⓑ or Ⓑ+Ⓞ	Ⓐ+Ⓑ	Ⓞ+Ⓞ
YOUR BLOOD TYPE IS:	**A** Containing "A" substance	**B** Containing "B" substance	**AB** Containing "A" and "B" substances	**O** Containing only "O" substance

ALTHOUGH LOOKING ALIKE, THE BLOODS ARE NOT COMPATIBLE, SO IN TRANSFUSIONS IT IS SAFEST TO MIX BLOODS OF THE SAME TYPE. BUT IN EMERGENCIES:

AB
BLOOD

—Containing both "A" and "B" substances, most easily receives the others

—But, because it also has something foreign to each, clashes most if infused, producing clotting

O
BLOOD

—Being "weakest," is least able to receive any of the others

—But can be transfused into the others with the least clotting

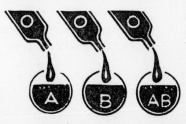

when the genes differ that their relative effects become apparent. How they work to produce the blood types is illustrated on p. 207.

As each of the bloods has its own peculiarities, they are incompatible with one another in greater or less degree. All this is of tremendous importance in connection with blood transfusions—much more important than in the infrequent cases of determining parentage. Until the discovery of the blood groups was made the medical world could not understand why in some cases the blood of even the closest relatives—mother and child perhaps—would not mix, and why transfusions were sometimes fatal. Now, of course, the mystery has been solved. We can see that it is just as possible for a mother to have one kind of blood and her child another kind, as it is for her to have brown eyes and her child blue eyes.

To return to the subject of determining parentage, the blood-group tests now enable us to make certain deductions. Previously in this book (in the "feature" forecasts and the "black" gene tables) we asked, "Given parents with certain characteristics, what can we predict about their child?"

Now our question is reversed:

Given a specific baby whose parentage (usually paternity) is in doubt, what can we determine about its parents?

Here is where the blood tests may provide definite clues. An actual case (in 1936) in the New York City courts will serve as the best illustration.

A young woman sued a prominent society man for a huge sum, claiming that on his promise to marry her she had borne him a son. Under authorization of the "blood test" statute, passed a short time before, the court assigned the blood specialist, Dr. Rufus E. Stetson, to make tests of the mother, the child and the alleged father. And this is what Dr. Stetson reported:

The mother's blood was of the O type. The child's was of the A type. This meant that as the mother could have given the child only an O gene, the A gene must have come from the father. The father would therefore have had to be of either A or AB type blood. But what Dr. Stetson found was that the accused man had O type blood—conclusive proof that he could not have been the father of that child. So without further ado the judge dismissed the action.

But suppose these first tests show that a man's blood is of one of the required types?—which would be more than likely. At this point an accused man has still another "out." In addition to the *A, B* and *O* genes, it has been discovered that there are two minor supplementary blood genes, the *M* and *N* genes. Every one carries two of these genes (one received from each parent); either two of the same kind, *MM* or *NN,* or a mixed pair, *MN,* in addition to the main ones. The *M* and *N* genes also produce substances in the blood which, while having no effect in transfusions (nor, so far as we yet know, any other important effect), nevertheless reveal themselves in tests. And it is by these additional tests that sometimes conclusive proof may be obtained.

Another actual happening (reported in the *Journal of Immunology*) will again serve as an illustration:

This was a most unusual case. A married woman came into court *to prove that her child was illegitimate*—that not her husband, but a lover, was its father. And it was her husband who was contesting the claim. True enough, the first tests, on the basis of the *A, B, AB* and *O* groupings, did show that he *could* have been the father. But unfortunately for him, and perhaps for the child, when the *M* and *N* tests were made it was found that he *could not have been* the father.

All the various situations in which blood tests may offer proof of non-paternity are presented in the tables on page 210. Note, however, that they are of value only when *negative*. Dr. Stetson informs us that of quite a number of such tests that he has made since the one mentioned (these others, however, being in cases that were never brought to court) only about 20 to 25 percent provided *disproof* of parentage. Where the results are positive, it does not mean that the accused man *is* the father. It only implies that he *could be,* as could be any of tens of millions of other men with the same type of blood.

Another important failing of the blood tests is that they cannot be made until the blood of the child in question is "set" and its

THE BABY IS NOT YOURS—
(Assuming that you're a man and that its paternity is in doubt)

—IF

THE BABY'S BLOOD IS OF GROUP	THE MOTHER'S BLOOD IS OF GROUP	—AND *YOUR* BLOOD IS OF GROUP
O	No Matter Which	AB
AB	No Matter Which	O
A	O or B	O or B
B	O or A	O or A

OR, REGARDLESS OF THE ABOVE, THE BABY IS NOT YOURS IF—

THE BABY HAS SUPPLEMENTARY BLOOD TYPE	THE MOTHER	—AND *YOUR* SUPPLEMENTARY TYPE IS
M	No Matter What	N
N	No Matter What	M
MN	N	N
MN	M	M

blood type revealed, which may not be until a year or more after birth.

When the blood tests fail, genetics now makes possible many other tests, gradually being recognized by the courts. An immediate source of evidence is provided through distinctive surface abnormalities which are known to be clearly inherited. This was first recognized by a Norwegian court in the case of an illegitimate child who had the hand abnormality known as *brachyphalangy,* in which the middle finger joints are missing. The mother, normal, accused a certain paperhanger in her community of being the child's father. He was brought into court. "Let's see your hands!" the judge ordered. And when the unfortunate man held up his stub-fingers (a condition in which he was unique in the entire community) the court promptly adjudged him the father.

Any other inherited surface abnormality in a child caused by a dominant gene—which, if not revealed in the mother must have come from the father—can provide similar evidence. The "Mongolian" spot in a child, where the mother is without question "pure" White might be evidence against an Oriental or Indian accused of being its father. Many conditions listed in the "feature" or "black" gene chapters could also provide evidence, but most of these conditions occur so rarely that they are of little general value. Nevertheless, even through the common genes in plentiful circulation, we have at our disposal many valuable clues.

By considering *combinations* of various characteristics instead of merely single ones, a new field is opened for establishing parentage. A child is blue-eyed and blond. The mother is blue-eyed and blond. The reputed father is blue-eyed and blond. That proves nothing. But we find also that the child has curly hair—its mother has straight—but the *reputed father also has curly hair.* The child is freckled—its mother isn't—*but the reputed father is freckled.* The child has a Hapsburg lip—its mother hasn't—*but the reputed father has this peculiarity.* By means of various points of genetic similarity, or dissimilarity, in *combination,* evidence could be built up for or against parentage. But you might say, "This is merely circumstantial evidence!" True enough, but if you think about it, there has never been and can never be anything *but* circum-

I. "PATERNITY" DECISION BASED ON A NOT UNCOMMON DEFECT, PLUS OTHER CHARACTERISTICS

Child "A", about six months old, has drooping eyelids (*ptosis*). Its mother is free of the condition, but Man "X" alleged to be the father, is found to have the condition. This in itself is insufficient proof of paternity, for drooping eyelids occur quite frequently in the population. But a comparison of other traits in the child, the mother and the man reveal the following:

CHILD "A" HAS	MOTHER HAS	MAN "X" HAS
Black Hair	Blond Hair	Dark Hair
Blue Eyes	Blue Eyes	Blue Eyes
Curly Hair	Straight Hair	Curly Hair
Affixed Ear-lobes	Free Ear-lobes	Affixed Ear-lobes

Because in each trait there is evidence that he could have contributed to the child the required gene, *Man "X" is in all probability the father.*

II. DECISION BASED ON SIMILARITY OF COMMON TRAITS WHEN "BLOOD" TESTS ARE NOT CONCLUSIVE

Child "B", about a year old. Two men, "Y" and "Z" are equally under suspicion of being the father.

	CHILD	MOTHER	MAN "Y"	MAN "Z"
Blood	A	A	B	O
	MN	M	N	N
Eyes	Green, Slant	Black, Slant	Brown, Straight	Blue, Slant
Eyelashes	Very long	Short	Short	Very long
Hair	Blond	Black	Black	Red

With regard to blood type, the premise is that the child must be carrying a hidden *O* gene, otherwise both men should have been ruled out. On this assumption, then, the odds would be greater that Man "Z" contributed this gene to the child. (In the matter of the "N" gene both men are equal.)

In all the other traits, however, the odds are also higher that Man "Z" contributed the required genes. Accordingly, *Man "Z" is in all probability the father of the child.*

stantial evidence in questions regarding the paternity of a child.

We have confined ourselves largely to cases of doubtful paternity, because these are the ones usually at issue. Rarely now, with infants so scrupulously identified at birth, are "changelings" possible. Nevertheless, all the tests here mentioned can be used with regard to the mother, or even with regard to both parents, should the need arise.

Genetic knowledge, at its present stage, may or may not offer definite proof of parentage in many cases, but it can certainly help to throw light on almost any case. With the knowledge increasing rapidly, more and more clues will be made available. In these days when experts can tell that a given hair came from a given head, that a certain rung in a ladder came from such and such a tree in such a forest, that a certain bullet was fired from a specified revolver, that a brush-stroke on a painting was made by the hand of a certain old master dead four hundred years, it would be strange if we should continue unable to determine whether a child, with a host of characteristics differentiating it from other children, did or did not stem from such and such a parent.

We have every reason to anticipate the discovery before many years of other hereditary factors in the blood and perhaps in the glandular secretions, of many more feature and structural genes, of the establishing of hereditary factors in fingerprints, palm and foot patterns, and of the identification of so many additional clues that doubtful paternity cases will become among the easiest to decide.

CHAPTER XXIX

ACHIEVEMENT: BIRTH OR LUCK?

WITH this chapter we enter a new phase in our book. Up to this point we have been considering human beings as mechanisms. Now we begin thinking of you, and all the rest of us, as social animals.

As mechanisms we have seen that every one of us is created differently from any other individual, that a great deal of how each of us looks and functions physically is determined by heredity. Now we ask whether the differences in *social behavior* among individuals may not also be greatly influenced by heredity.

Are some individuals *predestined* to success, and others to failure, by their *inherent* natures? What keeps large masses of people submerged at the same low social level, and enables others to emerge from the depths and reach the heights? Why, in the very same family, is one person stupid, one brilliant; one son a law-abiding citizen, the other a criminal; one member kindly and happily adjusted, the other mean and anti-social? Are these differences due mainly or in part to different combinations of genes, as are the different features of members in the same family? Or are they due *entirely* to environmental influences?

Genetics can already throw much light on these questions. But as you will soon see, answers regarding the social traits of human beings can be given with no such surety as were those regarding our surface characteristics and organic make-up. For we may say at once that we are now venturing into uncertain territory. Previously we confined ourselves to the presentation almost exclusively of scientific facts. But from this point on, as we begin to analyze the rôle of heredity in such variable and intangible human characteristics as mentality, personality, talent, temperament, crimi-

214

nality, sexual behavior, etc., we will find our facts becoming more and more diluted with theory.

Our genetic evidence, like a stream of clear, fresh water flowing into an arm of the sea, now begins to intermingle with theories of psychology, anthropology, sociology, economics and even politics. And it will be increasingly difficult to sift out the facts from the theories—theories which, even in the case of leading authorities, are often tempered by unconscious prejudices or emotional reactions.

The social phases of human heredity are viewed through varied lenses, sometimes rose-tinted, sometimes dark or almost opaque, so that the outlook ranges from bright to dismal; again, the lenses may be concave or convex, offering to some a long view, to others a short view. The very directions which researches into human genetics may take, and the findings arrived at, may differ in the degree that the investigators themselves differ in personality, background and emotional make-up. The descendants of *Mayflower* stock and the offspring of recent immigrants, the hidebound reactionary and the confirmed Marxist, the Russian, English, German and American biologists as groups often react differently toward the same evidence.

Thus, you also will find yourself taking sides in the ensuing chapters. If you are socially and financially secure, and come of a worthy family, your reactions will be different from those of the man at the bottom or of insignificant stock. You may say of this, "That sounds unreasonable," or of that, "I don't believe it." And there may be no denying you the right to say it, for often the problems we are coming to are so involved, the play of heredity and environment so tangled, that no absolute and definitive answers can yet be given.

Further, you may find yourself chafing, as we did in our own researches, at the constant procession of "ifs" and "buts" which dot the ensuing discussions. But remember, genetics is a new science, and its application to human behavior is most recent of all. The experts are feeling their way cautiously into the new fields. Few wish to commit themselves definitely on controversial points, for nothing is so damaging to a scientist's reputation as the espousal of a theory that is subsequently upset. Accordingly, many statements and findings are presented with more qualifications than they deserve, giving the impression of greater doubt than really exists.

So we frankly advise you that from now on in our book, with regard to conclusions, you will be more and more "on your own."

CHAPTER XXX

THE BATTLE OF THE "IQ's"

HERE are two orphaned infants, available for adoption at a placement bureau: They look the same and are "guaranteed" to be equally sound and fit. You are eager to adopt one, and as there is apparently no choice, you are about to toss a coin to decide.

BABY "A"

Then the matron tells you that Baby "A" is the offspring of a charwoman and an illiterate day-laborer.

Baby "B" is the offspring of a young woman writer and a young physician.

Would you still feel there was no choice?

BABY "B"

Or would you pick Baby "B" on the chance that *it had inherited a higher degree of mentality?*

Around this question, or others closely related, centers one of the greatest controversies in the study of human heredity. There are authorities who say that no evidence exists which would justify a choice in favor of Baby "B." There are many others who disagree with them.

What is the basis for the arguments pro and con? Let us start at the beginning.

We have seen that various types and degrees of *abnormal* intelligence—idiocy, insanity, etc.—can be inherited, but this tells us as little about the normal mental process as the throwing of a monkey-wrench into any complex machine would tell us about its normal workings.

In lower animals, true enough, we know that a normal mouse inherits a certain type of brain, a cat another type, a dog still another, etc. Also, that within each species itself there seem to be degrees of brain activity. In dogs, breeds vary in alertness; in mice, geneticists have bred strains, one dull, one bright.

If degrees of "normal" intelligence are inherited among other animals, why not among human beings? There's the rub! For should we prove that gradations of human intelligence we see about us in the workaday and social world are conditioned to any great extent by heredity, then we'd be faced with the possibility that dulness, mediocrity and superiority are *inherent* in individuals, and that failure and success may be to a large extent *predestined*.

No wonder that beneath the placid surface of scientific research on this subject a struggle is going on between the "hereditarians" and the "environmentalists." The "hereditarians" are out to prove that certain individuals come to the top, like cream in a milk bottle, because of *inherent superiority*, thus tending to form classes at various intellectual levels. The "environmentalists" challenge this analogy. They are set on proving that if we *shake the bottle and equalize the environment*, the levels of mentality in which classes of people now appear to be stratified would disappear.

How are we to settle this?

Our great difficulty in analyzing intelligence is that it can be measured only by arbitrary standards, such as those set up by the current intelligence tests. We saw in the chapter on "Sick Minds" how the tests are used to determine degrees of mental defectiveness: the idiot scoring an IQ of under 25; the imbecile, 25-50; the moron, 50-70. Those who score from 70 to 80 are placed on the borderline. Above that, now, we come to non-defective mentality, with the ratings as shown in the accompanying table.

80– 90	dull
90–110	normal
110–120	superior
120–140	very superior
140 or over	genius [1]

[1] Used in a technical sense, and not implying that individuals with this score are "geniuses."

As between a person with an IQ of 90 and a person with an IQ of 130 there can be little doubt that the tests do indicate a marked difference in mental capacity. But with regard to the lesser gradations, those closer to the normal range, there is disagreement as to the significance of IQ scores. The same person may score 108 one day when he isn't feeling well, and 113 the next day; or he may be given one score by one examiner and a lower or higher score by a different examiner. It has also been claimed that the tests are not equally fair to all, that they are not consistent at the different ages and that they measure "classroom" intelligence rather than general intelligence.

Despite the foregoing and other criticisms, the standard intelligence tests are considered sufficiently reliable so that they are in wide use throughout our educational system. If you live in New York City (as one of many places) and you have a child, that child will be placed in a class with backward pupils, or average pupils, or superior pupils, on the basis of its IQ. If you are seeking admission to some highly selective university, medical college, dental college, law school, etc., your IQ might decide your acceptance or rejection. And in various corporations and research institutions your IQ may be a factor in winning a job.

For all practical purposes, then, the intelligence tests must be seriously considered. But how significant they are when used to study the *inheritance* of intelligence is another matter. For only if the IQ scores are proved to reveal a fixed capacity—born in the individual and but little affected by environment—can they have meaning to the geneticist. In other words, inasmuch as all the studies made to date of the inheritance of intelligence are based on IQ scores, the interpretation of these studies must depend upon the importance attached to the intelligence tests and to their actual or implied weaknesses.

Here is where the authorities fall out. You will not be surprised to learn, therefore, that the findings of various studies made on the same questions may differ markedly. All we can do is to summarize what we consider the most valid studies, theories and opinions on all sides, leaving you to form your own conclusions.

Let us now follow the procedure of the investigators. First they ask themselves questions. Then they set out to find the answers. We'll start with this:

1. *Do people of different "classes" show different degrees of intelligence?*

As measured by intelligence tests, yes. Extensive studies reveal that the higher up the social and economic scale one goes, the higher is the average IQ. That is to say, unskilled laborers and farmhands as a group have lower IQ's than skilled laborers and farmers; above these rank skilled factory workers, "white-collar" workers and small business men; above these, semi-professional people, bigger business men and managers, and at the top of the IQ structure are the professional men. Obviously, however, there is much overlapping among the groups, some unskilled workers having higher IQ's than those in levels above, and some professional men having lower IQ's than those in levels below.

Bearing in mind that we are speaking always in *general terms* and allowing for individual exceptions, it would seem that lower intelligence goes with lower work. But does this mean that the unskilled laborer has a very low IQ because conditions have thwarted his mental development, or does it mean that he is an unskilled laborer because he has a low IQ? Which came first, the low condition or the low IQ?

We ask another question:

2. *Are the intelligence levels of children related to those of their parents?*

Yes. Children of a group of parents of high intelligence almost uniformly—on the average—are reported as having greater mental capacity than children of parents of low intelligence.

Studies in Boston (Stuart M. Stokes) and in New York (Lita Hollingworth) indicate that rarely, if ever, where both parents are of inferior mentality, does a superior child result.

Comparing offspring of parents at various social and economic levels, it is found that children of unskilled laborers have the lowest IQ's, children of professional men the highest, with those of the groups in between being similarly correlated (as shown in our accompanying diagram).

We must note, as with their fathers, that the differences be-

tween adjacent groups of children are not radically great, the entire
range in IQ's, from lowest to highest, averaging within twenty
points.

A criticism regarding the above data is that the comparison

HEREDITY?

Average
IQ
of child

PROFES-
SIONAL   ----------------------------> 116

SEMI-PROFES-   --------------------------> 112
SIONAL AND
MANAGERIAL

CLERICAL,   ----------------------> 107.5
SKILLED
TRADES, RE-
TAIL BUSINESS

SEMI-SKILLED,   ------------> 105
MINOR CLERICAL,
MINOR BUSINESS

SLIGHTLY   ------> 98
SKILLED

DAY LABORERS,   -> 96
URBAN AND
RURAL FARMERS

FATHERS'
OCCUPATIONS

(Based on studies by Terman and Merrill, reported in
"Measuring Intelligence")

made is not of the intelligence of children and fathers, but of the
IQ's of children compared with the *assumed* intelligence of their
fathers as reflected by occupational rank. If, as is claimed, the
intelligence tests are weighted in favor of "book learning," children from homes of poorly educated workers would be retarded

in comparison with those from better educated circles. An additional criticism is that the different occupational groups do not have the same ethnic make-up, the unskilled and "lower" groups having a larger proportion of foreign-born and Negroes, and that children from such parentage are therefore at a further disadvantage because the intelligence tests are presumably designed for native Whites.

So again we might draw two conclusions: (a) that the children of parents in the lower intellectual levels have *inherited* their lower mentality; or (b) that the lower mentality has been thrust upon them by inferior environment.

Which is right? We go on:

3. *When children are taken away from their parents in infancy and reared elsewhere, do their IQ's still show the influence of their heredity?*

According to some studies, yes; to others, no.

Tests have been made in various places of large numbers of illegitimate children placed in institutions or adopted soon after birth. The fathers of these children were of all classes. In the institutions the environment for all children was the same. Yet it was reported that the IQ's of the children bore almost the same relation to the levels of their fathers (whom most had never seen) as IQ's of children on the outside.

Studies of children adopted and reared in private homes conflict in their findings. Some report that the IQ's of adopted children accorded very closely with the levels of their fathers, and were but slightly influenced by the levels of their foster parents.

But from the University of Iowa where studies are being made of about 150 waifs, of generally inferior parentage, adopted into superior homes, comes the report that the IQ's of these children follow not the low levels of their true parents but the higher intelligence levels of their foster parents.

(Discrepancies in the foregoing and other studies of adopted or orphaned children have been attributed to various factors, among them: that investigators have taken different directions and studied differing groups of children under not fairly comparable circumstances; that "superior" couples tend to select, or to be offered for adoption, the brightest infants; that the paternity of illegitimate children may be in doubt; that orphaned and illegitimate children receive a worse physical start than others; and that even the most conscientious foster parents might not rear an adopted child in the same way they would their own. It is also claimed that where an average difference of 6 or 7 points is reported, this is not statistically conclusive.)

We'll leave this question open and go on:

4. *When children are transferred from bad environments to better homes or institutions, do their IQ's improve?*

The evidence on this point is also variable. In one study (Rogers, Durling and McBride, 1928) a group of American girls aged four to thirteen, taken from bad environments, were tested before and after being placed in improved environments. Their IQ's were not found to have been changed. In another study, made in Glasgow, Scotland (Dawson, 1934), children taken from slums and sent to a better environment also showed no improvement in IQ.

Contrariwise, a study made at the Hebrew Orphan Asylum in New York (Donah B. Lithauer and Otto Klineberg, 1933) showed that children taken from disrupted homes increased their IQ's by an average of about 6 points when being placed in a more stable environment. (Here, however, the change was largely one in psychological atmosphere.)

Several other studies on the effects of change in environment also report some increase in IQ, but none averaging more than about 7 points.

5. *How far can training mold intelligence?*

Again, studies in orphanages revealed that children reared from early age under almost uniform conditions showed the same degrees of differences in IQ as children on the outside reared under divergent conditions. This would suggest that there were inherent mental differences in the children to begin with.

At the State Teachers College at Jersey City, 140 primary school children were studied before and after they were given the very best training possible. It was found that there was no significant improvement in their IQ's, regardless of the length of training. (Edna E. Lamson, 1938.)

On the other hand, Dr. Wellman of the University of Iowa reports findings that IQ's of children can be raised materially if they are subjected in *early life* to stimulating schooling. Commenting on the criticism that intelligence tests made of very young children (the point of departure for her study) are unreliable, she has written to us: "I believe this is an erroneous conclusion which has arisen from the fact that changes in IQ occur. I do not believe we should discredit the measuring instrument because changes are registered, any more than we should discard a thermometer because temperatures vary."

Continuing, we may ask:

6. *Does heredity unalterably fix the intelligence of an individual?*

We turn once more to our human laboratory subjects, twins. If heredity alone determined one's intelligence, then identical twins, with exactly the same genes, should always have exactly the same IQ's. But they don't. IQ's of identical twins do often differ, although on an average *they are much more alike than those of fraternal twins,* and decidedly more alike than those of ordinary brothers and sisters in the same family. Most interesting are the comparisons reported (by Professor H. H. Newman and others) of identical twins who were separated in early life and reared in different environments. In several instances their IQ's were found to differ by as much as 18 points, but on an average the IQ's of identical twins even when reared apart are found to be as alike as, or slightly more alike than, those of fraternal twins reared together. Moreover, while identical twins become neither more nor less alike in intelligence as they grow older, fraternal twins become increasingly different in IQ as time passes.

Fascinating to watch will be the mental progress of the Dionne quintuplets. While their IQ's have not yet been announced, the little girls as a group are reported to be somewhat retarded (which was to be expected because of their underdevelopment at birth). But of greatest importance to us is the fact that there are differences among them in mental achievement and behavior responses which seem to be correlated with the physical differences we have previously discussed. Marie, physically the weakest, ranks the lowest in mental achievement and responses; Emilie, her "other half," is next lowest;

AVERAGE DIFFERENCES IN IQ

BETWEEN

IDENTICAL TWINS REARED TOGETHER:

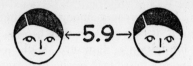

IDENTICAL TWINS REARED APART:

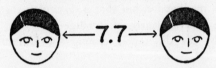

FRATERNAL TWINS REARED TOGETHER:

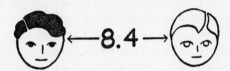

ORDINARY BROTHERS AND SISTERS
(a) Reared together:

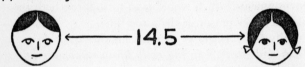

(b) Reared apart:

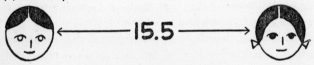

UNRELATED ORPHAN PAIRS
(a) Reared together:

(b) Reared apart:

(Based on tables from "Heredity and Environment," by Gladys C. Schwesinger)

225

Yvonne ranks the highest and Cecile and Annette alternate for second place.

How great the IQ differences among the quintuplets are we do not yet know, but if as time goes on they become marked, we will have a striking illustration of how even slight inequalities in environment may modify hereditary intellectual capacities. The other twin studies, however, have already proved that *heredity does not* unalterably fix intelligence, but that it does play a great part in determining the general degree of intelligence.

Suggested by the differences among the Dionnes is our next question:

7. *Does a poor body produce a poor mind?*

Or, conversely, does a healthy body make a healthy mind?

To the surprise of most of us, there is little proof on this point.

In the population at large, there is a general tendency for more intelligent children to have fewer constitutional physical defects and less disease than children of lower intelligence. But it may be not the poor bodies that produce the poor minds, but the fact that the less intelligent children are usually found to come from less favorable environments, which would tend to suppress both their bodily and mental development at the same time.

To clarify this further, we may ask another question:

8. *Does malnutrition during early life permanently affect the intelligence of children?*

One of the classic studies was made in Germany to see whether the extreme undernourishment of the children during the World War had lowered their IQ's. It was reported that even where children had been literally starved for two or three years, their basic intelligence rarely appeared to be affected.

Malnutrition, by the way, is not a synonym for starvation, and is not something confined to the poor. It refers to any defective nutrition or failure of the individual to assimilate food properly, and occurs among the very wealthiest children as well as the poorest. Dealing, then, with malnutrition rather than starvation, various investigators (Hunt, Dowe and others) have concluded that "undernourished children, whatever their other handicaps, are no whit inferior mentally to well-nourished children of the same race and social status." Also, it was found that when undernourished children are fed properly, their physical condition may improve greatly, their intelligence very little.

9. *Does disease retard mental development?*

If we eliminate, obviously, mental diseases, the answer appears to be sometimes Yes, sometimes No.

Consider *adenoids* or *bad tonsils.* Popular belief is that when dull-witted Johnny Jones, who has a bad case of adenoids, gets them removed, he will brighten up immediately. But studies show that after children have had adenoid or tonsil operations, *there is no increase in their basic intelligence.*

In *hookworm,* directly correlated with poverty among children of the South, the more serious the condition, the lower the intelligence. But again the possibility is that the disease is severest where the conditions would ordinarily be most unfavorable for mental development.

Syphilis, ominous as this disease is, has not yet been shown to have any effect of itself on *intellectual capacity,* unless, or until, the disease causes some severe breakdown or mental derangement.

No disease which does not attack the central nervous system is known to diminish intelligence. A few diseases such as spinal meningitis, epilepsy, hardening of the arteries (*arteriosclerosis*) and brain fever (*epidemic encephalitis*) may lower the sufferer's IQ, but not invariably.

Many physical defects do, however, adversely affect intelligence. *Deafness* might retard a child's mental development by two or three years, and defects of the eye (which retard the capacity to learn) are also known to affect intelligence. *Accidents* may directly affect the brain; and as we've already seen, certain harmful intra-uterine influences (alcoholism or drug addiction of the mother, injuries attending birth, etc.) may even produce idiocy in a child. But, on the other hand, history is starred with individuals who rose to the greatest heights despite every sort of physical and even psychotic handicap, sometimes dating from birth, sometimes suffered later. (This will be enlarged upon in our later discussion of "genius.")

Among normal, healthy individuals we find it quite impossible to establish any correlation between basic physical characteristics and basic mentality. For instance:

10. *Does head size have any bearing on mentality?*

Not that we can discover. Disregarding imbeciles and "pinhead" idiots, exhaustive studies fail to prove that loftier foreheads mean higher IQ's (as the late Arthur Brisbane, who himself had a high-domed forehead, so frequently maintained). Eskimos have bigger heads than Whites, and the skulls of some prehistoric men had a bigger cranial capacity than the record head of modern times, that of Ivan Turgenev, the Russian novelist (2,030 cubic centimeters). Studies of brain size among men of different occupations, ranging from scientists to unskilled laborers, have likewise failed to reveal that there is any special correlation between one's brain dimensions and one's achievements.

In women, their smaller heads, as compared with those of men, have been cited as the reason for their "lower mentality." But that statement is open to question. Which brings us to this:

11. *Are women mentally inferior to men?*

No!—at least, according to IQ scores.

Undoubtedly women think in different ways than do men about many problems. This may or may not be due largely, if not entirely, to differences in the way the sexes are reared and conditioned. But regarding "quantitative," or measurable differences in the mentality of the two sexes, Professor Lewis M. Terman, one of the highest authorities in the field, has this to say:

"Intelligence tests . . . have demonstrated for all time the falsity of the once widely prevalent belief that women as a class are appreciably or at all inferior to men in the major aspects of intellect. The essential equality of the sexes has further been shown by psychometric methods to obtain also in various special fields, such as musical ability, artistic ability, mathematical ability and even mechanical ability. The enfranchisement of women and their invasion of political, commercial and other fields of action formerly reserved to men have accorded increasingly convincing evidence that sex differences in practical abilities are also either nonexistent or far less in magnitude than they have commonly been thought to be."

From the standpoint of intellectual achievement, it need hardly be disputed that women still rank below men. This might be explained by their social limitations, or perhaps by physical limitations. It has been suggested that because women mature earlier (correlated with the earlier onset of puberty) they become mentally "set" sooner. This would seem to be borne out in literature, the theater and a number of professions where women achieve fame at an earlier age than men, but do not as a rule progress as far. As we write this, Dr. Richard J. Block of New York reports that he has found chemical differences between male and female brains. But this we know: There cannot be any difference in the "mental" genes that men and women carry, with the reservation that if there are any "mental" genes in the X chromosomes, women receive more of them than do men.

The difficulty in measuring comparative intelligence of any two dissimilar masses of people is brought out by our next question:

12. *Do different races and nationalities have different degrees of mentality?*

This, too, cannot be answered with scientific certainty. We may be able to measure comparative intelligence of individuals *within* the same country and within the same race, but the question arises as to how fairly we can apply IQ tests, devised by investigators of one country for their own kind, to those of an entirely different country and civilization. To remedy this, psychologists are working on new tests of a non-verbal nature which may be universally applicable.

At present we can only go by what has been learned about children brought up and educated under relatively the same conditions. In California, then, Chinese and Japanese children were found to have just as high IQ's as American and European children. The children of Jewish immigrants were found to score higher than those of other immigrant stocks. Negro children, tested in various parts of the United States, average much lower in their IQ's than do Whites. But let us not forget that the conditions and opportunities among the Negroes are greatly inferior to those of the others tested. Negro children in the North, with better opportunities, score higher IQ's than do those in the South—in New York City the average among them being about 7 points higher.

That this is not due to selective immigration has been brought out in a study by Professor Klineberg.

By now you have seen that while the "intelligence" studies have thrown doubt on many points previously taken for granted, few, if any of our main questions, have been answered decisively. So you may ask:

13. *Why cannot science tell us something more definite about the inheritance of intelligence?*

First, because we haven't determined what we mean by "intelligence." The intelligence tests, as we have already pointed out, were devised by educators chiefly for their own domain, the realm of the classroom. But academic intelligence and practical intelligence as judged in the larger world outside are not necessarily the same.[1] Often the tasks and problems of everyday life demand mental attributes that the standard intelligence tests do not reveal—character, will-power, intuition, humor, understanding, ability to get along with people, and so on.

Before we can make accurate studies of the inheritance of intelligence, we must be clear as to what we are studying. Further, we must have a way of measuring *inherent* mental capacity, stripped of environmental influences and by standards which can be fairly and uniformly applied to people of all ages, types, races, backgrounds, occupations and degrees of education. In these respects the existing tests fall short. However, even if they were scientifically acceptable, the present intelligence tests have not been in existence long enough so that we could yet have any comparative records of IQ's of parents and children at the same ages and successive stages through to maturity. Possibly when the present generation of school children grows up and produces families we may be able to make some fairly accurate genetic studies without waiting for more acceptable tests.

Meanwhile most geneticists, while agreeing that differences in intellectual capacity among humans may be inherited, shy away from further commitments. Several have toyed with theories of

[1] Mendel, father of genetics, twice failed in an important examination in botany at the University of Vienna, largely because he had been self-taught and his academic knowledge was deficient.

the genes involved in producing intelligence, and have even made guesses as to the types and numbers of these genes. But certainly no geneticist would yet venture to predict what ratios and degrees of intelligence to expect in the children of parents with such and such IQ scores.

Which brings us back to the beginning of this chapter, and our final question:

14. *What, then, is one to decide regarding a choice on the basis of intelligence between Baby "A," the offspring of a charwoman and a day-laborer, and Baby "B," the offspring of a young woman writer and a physician?*

As we cannot find the answer in scientific fact, we might look for guidance to the opinions of leading authorities (geneticists, anthropologists, psychiatrists and psychologists) who have given detailed attention to all the evidence we have summarized. To the best of our knowledge, these opinions would take two main and divergent directions:

1. There are those who would say that *no choice is justified,* because:

"—We have no *proof* of the extent to which intellectual attainments are due to heredity or to environment. Even with the use of the present 'intelligence' tests, faulty as they are, it is clear that what we call 'intelligence' is greatly influenced by education and conditioning. We have no right, therefore, to compare by the same tests people whose environments are radically different and to consider that their relative scores have any bearing on their relative inherited mental *capacities.*

"—Assuming that there are genes which produce degrees of intelligence, in view of the complexity of the mental processes there would obviously have to be a great many of such genes; which makes it difficult to conceive how, with the constant intermingling that has taken place among people of all levels, 'superior' and 'inferior' intelligence genes could have become noticeably segregated in different proportions within our different occupational groups, especially in so short a time.

"—Therefore we have no basis for assuming that parents in the unskilled laboring group carry, or will transmit to their offspring, genes for intelligence inferior to those of parents in the professional class.

"Accordingly, we are justified in concluding with regard to the intelligence of the two hypothetical infants that there should be no choice between Baby 'A,' born of a charwoman and a day-laborer, and Baby 'B,' born of an authoress and a physician."

2. On the other hand, we know of authorities who would answer:

"—The view that, lacking clear scientific evidence of how intelligence is inherited, we are not justified in making deductions regarding it, is shortsighted and unwarranted. All the general findings of genetics point to the inheritance of degrees of intellectual capacity in the same way that other characteristics and capacities are inherited. Therefore,

"—Without knowing what the 'intelligence' genes are, we may still rightfully assume that there are some which make for greater intellectual capacity and others for lesser capacity.

"—Allowing for all possible powers of environment to depress or to raise intelligence, we know that many bright individuals born into lower social levels rise to higher levels, and many dull individuals born into upper levels sink to lower levels. With this process having gone on throughout civilization we may reason that in two large social groups differing radically in intellectual attainment, there would be more of the 'superior' genes in the superior group.

"—The average IQ difference of 20 points between offspring of the unskilled laboring classes and those of the professional classes cannot be dismissed as without significance unless it is ascribed *entirely* to differences in environment. There is no proof that this is so. Knowing that in the same environment, even in members of the same family, great differences in intelligence exist, the burden of proving that environment alone is responsible for all these differences rests on those who make the assertion.

"—At the very best, in the situation cited, one can only say that Baby 'A' might be expected to be as inherently intelligent as Baby 'B.' No one would venture to say, and not a single study has indicated, that children of unskilled laborers as a group would be expected to have a better intellectual heritage than those of professional people. On the other hand, many studies do indicate that there is a possibility, if not a probability, that the average child of professional people will turn out to be more intelligent than the average child of those in the lowest occupational groups.

"—The question thus becomes one of odds. Baby 'A' might indeed turn out to be more intelligent than Baby 'B.' But the odds are surely greater—although we cannot say how much greater— that Baby 'B,' offspring of the authoress and the physician, would have inherited the better mental equipment.

"Therefore, everything else being equal, on the basis of intelligence there should be a choice in favor of Baby 'B.' "

So here are two clearly conflicting interpretations of the same set of facts. How are you, the layman, to decide? For remember, the two theoretical babies are before you, and you can take only one of them.

You might beg the question by saying, "We are dealing, after all, not with objects but with human beings, helpless infants. So long as there is uncertainty, the humane thing to do, and the democratic thing to do, would be not to condemn Baby 'A' as inferior purely on theoretical grounds, but to give it the benefit of the doubt and consider it as equal." There is merit in this viewpoint, but our problem here is not a humanitarian one but essentially a scientific one. You are called on to decide, solely on the basis of the evidence, whether the offspring of the one set of parents would be likely to turn out more intelligent than the offspring of the other set of parents.

If you conclude that the facts presented are not conclusive enough to warrant a choice, and that you should leave the selection entirely to a toss of the coin, we can assure you that there are high-ranking authorities who will approve your stand.

But if you prefer to be guided by the weight of opinion, at least in a numerical sense, we may say this:

It is our belief that the *majority* of qualified experts of all kinds would subscribe to the second viewpoint previously stated, and would unequivocally advise you to keep your coin in your pocket and to choose Baby "B," child of the authoress and the physician.

CHAPTER XXXI

MUSICAL TALENT: Part I

(*An Original Genetic Study*)

A LITTLE boy, hugging a violin, walks out onto the stage at New York's Carnegie Hall. There is a flutter of applause from the thousands of persons filling the auditorium. The little boy tucks his violin under his chin and begins to play. The audience, skeptical, watches, listens. A tiny hand sweeps the bow back and forth, tiny fingers fly over the strings, streams of melody, now shrill, now full-throated, cascade forth. Already, in those first minutes, many mature musicians out front know that in all their years of study and work they have not been able to achieve such mastery. Soon they, and the others, forget that this is a little boy who is playing. As if drawn by invisible bonds, they are carried out of the hall, into the night, higher and higher, so high they can scarcely breathe. Then suddenly there is a burst of notes like a rocket's shower of golden stars . . . the music stops . . . a sensation of dream-falling . . . and they are all back again in Carnegie Hall, incredulously storming with their bravos a little boy—a very little boy who in a few hours may be crying because he isn't allowed to stay up and play with his toy soldiers.

The scene has been enacted a number of times in each generation, but not too many times, for little boys like this do not appear often. It may have been elsewhere than Carnegie Hall—in Paris, London, Vienna—possibly in your own town. And sometimes it was not a violin that the child played, but a piano. So Chopin, Mozart, Mendelssohn, Liszt, Schumann, César Franck, and of living musicians, Heifetz, Hofmann, Kreisler, Rosenthal and Menuhin, among many others, revealed their genius to the world as children.

In no other field of human achievement do the young so strikingly scale the heights. Not even in the other arts—painting, sculpture, literature—is there any such early ripening of genius which enables a child to compete on equal terms with adults. How can we explain this? Is it due to a divine spark, an inexplicable gift? Is it the practical result of unusual environment and training? Or is it merely another something with a physical basis, produced by genes and *inherited* as are other unusual characteristics?

Scientists began wondering about this long before modern genetics offered any clear approach to the subject. Many studies of musical genius were made in the past. The fact that this form of genius ran in certain families was apparent in the case of the Bachs, Mozarts and Webers, and of the families of Beethoven, Brahms, Schubert and Liszt. Most notable of these were the Bachs, in which genius was traced in an unbroken line through five generations of males. Johann Sebastian Bach himself sired five noted musicians. Johann's father and his father's brother were identical twins who were reported to be markedly similar not only in the way they played, but in their speech, temperaments and physical characteristics. (Even their deaths came close together.)

But these striking examples were not in themselves evidences of heredity, as we know now. Where musical achievement did run in families one could easily argue that it was due to environment, precept and training—just as "banking" achievement ran in the Rothschild family—for in previous times, much more than today, sons tended to follow the calling of their fathers. But—and there is that ever-present "but"—even in former times, where a father was outstanding in some field that called for unusual ability *not every* son was chosen to follow in his footsteps. Only those sons who showed the required talent or aptitude were trained to carry on. So we come back to the question, "Where does talent come from?"

With the question still so much in doubt, we felt that perhaps we could learn something if, instead of again stirring up the ashes of bygone personages, we inquired into the careers of great musicians of our own time. And thus was inspired a detailed study made especially for this book, in which, we are happy to say, we received the fullest cooperation of the artists themselves and of leading figures in the musical world.

Our study was carried on among three groups of artists, in two fields of music, instrumental and vocal (the reason for distinguishing between the two fields soon to be apparent):

1. Thirty-six outstanding instrumental musicians of the world— that is, those universally conceded to be leading figures on our present-day concert platform.

2. Thirty-six principals of the Metropolitan Opera Company (season 1937-38) concededly representing a large proportion of our best-known and most talented singers at this writing.

3. Fifty students of the Juilliard Graduate School of Music, comprising a highly selected group of younger musicians and singers, many of whom are already active in the professional field.

In all three groups direct questions were asked and answered by each artist personally (with two exceptions: one, of Arturo Toscanini, where, in his absence, the data were supplied by some one very close to him officially; and in the case of Yehudi Menuhin, where the data came from his father). The result is a rather imposing array of facts which we will present in detail because, aside from what they may prove, they afford you a splendid opportunity for seeing how genetic studies are made, evidence analyzed and conclusions derived. In fact, we hope that you will study the data carefully and try to form your own conclusions before you look for ours.

THE VIRTUOSI INSTRUMENTALISTS: We come first to the noted figures in the instrumental field. You will see that our list includes a large majority of those likely to be known to you. (Space did not permit us to include every one, and here and there a few outstanding individuals whom we wished to include could not be reached, or for some personal reasons did not wish to be represented in these studies.) Whatever may be said about the relative worth of these artists, we feel sure that the talent of each one is beyond question. They have risen from the ranks of tens of thousands of musicians, from many countries and many backgrounds. Week after week and year after year they have faced the most critical of audiences, and have continued to be acclaimed. So we may well say that as a scientist first tests his materials before he begins his study, here is a group of persons as thoroughly tested for the same characteristic, basic musical talent, as any that could be assembled.

What now can we learn from these artists about the source of their talents? From our first table (see ff. pages) certain facts are immediately apparent:

TABLE I: *The Musicians Themselves.* The average age at which talent was expressed was under five. It might be said, "Ha! You'd expect a musician to say that his talent was expressed early!" But this is quite clearly answered by the next fact.

The professional débuts were made at the average of thirteen. By "professional" début is meant, in the sense that it is used by most of the musicians, not the mere first public appearance, or even the first paid performance, but the formal launching of their careers. Note the four débuts after twenty-one—Brailowsky, Gieseking, Rodzinski and Smeterlin. Brailowsky, for instance, had already given minor concerts before his professional début, and the others had also performed publicly. Inquiry revealed that *in all four cases their musical careers were delayed by service in the World War* and by these other factors: Smeterlin's father had first "sent him off to be a Latin and Greek scholar"; Rodzinski (although his impulse toward music was not expressed until late) had started out with the study of law; and Gieseking, definitely of "prodigy" caliber, was retarded in making his début by the fact that his father, a physician, did not believe that careers should be begun in childhood.

Except for these four the professional débuts of the others were made in their 'teens, with many of them achieving fame at an age when other children were still in grade school.

To put it another way, our facts indicate quite definitely that *great achievement in this field is correlated with an extremely early start.* But what is the reason for that early start—something from outside of the individual or something inside of him?

Wherever such a question occurs, the first thing the geneticist does is to explore thoroughly the family backgrounds of the individuals. If there is any presumption that an unusual condition has

MUSIC TABLE I—THE INSTRUMENTAL ARTISTS

MUSICIAN (Figure in parentheses: Year born)	TALENT FIRST EXPRESSED		PROFESSIONAL DEBUT	MUSICAL TALENT IN FAMILY (Star denotes professional or unusual ability)				
	Age	How	Age	Mother	Father	Bros. & Sists. (Tot. No.)	Tal-ented	Other Near Kin
JOHN BARBIROLLI (Cond.-cellist) ('99)	4	Playing violin and cello	12	No	Yes*	(2)	2 **	Grt'uncle* Cousin*
HAROLD BAUER (Pianist) ('73)	3	Unusual response to music	10 (violinist)	Yes	Yes	(3)	3	.....
ARTUR BODANZKY (Conductor) ('77)	6	Trying to play piano	20 (1st violinist)	No	Yes	(3)	2	.....
ALEXANDER BRAILOWSKY (Pianist) ('96)	6	In piano lessons from father	23 (War Delay)	No	Yes*	(1)	1*	.....
ADOLF BUSCH (Violinist) ('91)	2½	Began to play violin	3½	Yes	Yes*	(7)	4	Grandf.*
GUILA BUSTABO (Violinist) ('19)	2	"Tweaking" violin strings	4 (Chi. Symp. Orch.)	Yes	Yes*	(1)	1*	Grandf.* Grandm.*
WALTER DAMROSCH (Cond.-pianist) ('62)	6	Playing piano	19 (as cond.)	Yes* Singer	Yes* Cond.	(4)	4 ***	Neph.* Gr'nephs.
MISCHA ELMAN (Violinist) ('91)	5	First public appearance	13	...... (Appr.)†	Yes	(3)	3 ***	Grandf.*
WALTER GIESEKING (Pianist) ('95)	4	Pl. piano untaught; "prodigy" qualities	25 (War Delay)	Avg.	Yes	(0)	......	.....

† "Appr.", under ...... or the word "No" signifies no playing talent, but marked response to music.

238

Name		Playing violin as father's pupil	10 (11, composer)	Yes* Singer	Yes* Cond.	(4)	4 ****	Gr'p'rs*** Many**
EUGENE GOOSSENS (Cond.-violinist-comp.) ('93)	5	Playing violin as father's pupil	10 (11, composer)	Yes*	Yes*	(4)	4 ****	Many**
PERCY GRAINGER (Pianist-composer) ('82)	3½	Singing; composing at 7½	10	No	Yes*	(0)	....	.....
JASCHA HEIFETZ (Violinist) ('01)	3	Acute musical ear	9	No	Yes	(2)	2 **	Uncle
MYRA HESS (Pianist) ('90)	4½	Read all available music for piano	17	Yes	No	(3)	....	.....
ERNEST HUTCHESON (Pianist) ('71)	3	Possession of absolute pitch	5	No	Yes	(3)	1*	.....
JOSÉ ITURBI (Pianist-cond.) ('95)	5	Interest in piano	17	No	No	(2)	1*	Niece
FRITZ KREISLER (Violinist-comp.) ('75)	4	"Playing violin" with two sticks	12	No	Yes	(2)	1*	.....
JOSEF LHEVINNE (Pianist) ('74)	4	Absolute pitch, singing, accomp'g	15	No	Yes	(7)	3 ***	.....
YEHUDI MENUHIN (Violinist) ('17)	1½	Response to violins at concerts	8	(Appr.)	(Appr.)	(2)	2 **	.....
NATHAN MILSTEIN (Violinist) ('04)	7	Delighted in music at earliest age	16	(Appr.)	Yes*	(5)	2	.....
ERICA MORINI (Violinist) ('06)	3½	Pronounced interest in music	10	Some	Yes	(6)	1	.....
GUIOMAR NOVAES (Pianist) ('96)								

(Received too late for tabulation. See p. 245.)

MUSIC TABLE I—THE INSTRUMENTAL ARTISTS—(Continued)

MUSICIAN (Figure in parentheses: Year born)	TALENT FIRST EXPRESSED		PROFESSIONAL DEBUT	MUSICAL TALENT IN FAMILY (Star denotes professional or unusual ability)				
	Age	How	Age	Mother	Father	Bros. & Sists. (Tot. No.)	Tal-ented	Other Near Kin
EUGENE ORMANDY (Conductor) ('99)	1½	Knew all records on father's hurdy-gurdy	7	No	Yes	(1)	1*	....
GREGOR PIATIGORSKY (Cellist) ('03)	Very young	Playing in local cinemas at 9	15 (1st cellist)	Yes	Yes	(6)	4	....
SERGE PROKOFIEFF (Pianist-comp.) ('91)	4	Playing piano, composer at 5½	17	Yes	...... (Appr.)	(0)	......	Cousins
SERGEI RACHMANINOFF (Pianist-comp.) ('73)	4	Began playing piano	19	Yes	Yes	(5)	1	Grandf.*
ARTUR RODZINSKI (Conductor) ('94)	20	(Delay 1st by law study, then War)	26 (Opr. cond.)	Very little	No	(1)	......	....
MORITZ ROSENTHAL (Pianist) ('62)	7	Had at this age absolute pitch	10	No	No (Appr.)	(5)	2 **	....
ARTUR RUBINSTEIN (Pianist) ('89)	1½	Using "song" language. Absolute pitch at 3	6	No	No (Appr.)	(6)	......	....
ARTUR SCHNABEL (Pianist) ('82)	6	Emulated sister's piano playing	10	No	No	(2)	1	Cousins Niece

Musician	Avg. Age Talent Expressed:	Avg. Age Professional Debut:	Mothers	Fathers	Bros. & Sists.	Reporting talent in other near kin:
TOSCHA SEIDEL (Violinist) ('99)	Had tantrums when uncle played wrong — 3	14	No	No	(1)	....
RUDOLF SERKIN (Pianist) ('04)	Tried to imitate brother's playing — 2	6	No	Yes	(7) 5	....
RUTH SLENCZYNSKI (Pianist) ('25)	Sense of pitch; distinguishing scales — 9 mos.	4	No	Yes*	(2) 2	....
JAN SMETERLIN (Pianist) ('92)	Played concerto with orch. at 8½ (War Delay) — 7	27	No	No	(2)	....
JOSEPH SZIGETI (Violinist) ('92)	Singing, trying to play violin — 3½	13	Fairly	Yes*	(1) 1	Grandf.* Many**
ARTURO TOSCANINI (Conductor) ('67)	Began study. (See text) — 9	14 (19 as cond.)	No	No	(3)	Niece*
ALFRED WALLENSTEIN (Cellist-cond.) ('98)	Tuning his first cello, showing absolute pitch — 7	11	No	Yes	(2) 1	....
EFREM ZIMBALIST (Violinist) ('89)	Began playing violin — 7	18	No	Yes*	(6)	....
TOTALS: 36 MUSICIANS	4¾ yrs.	13¼ yrs.	Talntd. 10 Some T. 7 — 17	Talntd. 25 Some T. 4 — 29	Total 110 Talntd. 55	13

241

a hereditary basis, there should be a much higher than average incidence of the condition among the parents, brothers and sisters and near relatives of the individual. So we turn to:

The Instrumentalists' Families: First, were the parents musically talented?

Of the mothers, half are reported as having musical talent or "musicality" of some kind. (At this point we may explain that the question of evaluating talent in relatives was left to the artists themselves; but both the data, and "check-ups" here and there with others, have convinced us that fair and honest appraisals were made —so far as such appraisals can be made without scientific tests. Above all, the reputations of the artists, and the fact that their reports are here presented for all to see, should give assurance that their judgments are authoritative.)

We may note also that sometimes where a parent or other relative was not credited with *performing* talent, the musicians took pains to report "appreciation" or "response." This refers to an "ear" for music, which often may indicate latent talent that for lack of training or for other reasons may not have had a chance to express itself.

Of the fathers, three-fourths were musical, at least nine being professional musicians and several (including the fathers of Damrosch, Goossens and Barbirolli) being outstanding.

Considering mothers and fathers together, in only five instances were both parents reported as unqualifiedly not talented—Iturbi, Schnabel, Seidel, Smeterlin and Toscanini. (The interesting case of Arturo Toscanini will be dealt with later.)

What of the brothers and sisters?

We find talent in *half of the total number of brothers and sisters.* Several (including Leon Goossens, Amparo Iturbi and Hephzibah Menuhin) are concert artists of note. In only five instances where there is more than one brother or sister do we find no others with talent.

As for the other near relatives, talent was reported in one-third of the cases. As a whole, Barbirolli, Busch, Bustabo, Damrosch, Goossens, Elman, Szigeti and Rachmaninoff may be said to have stemmed from distinctly musical lineages. To complete our study of familial talent we have still another question:

What of the children of musicians?

With six exceptions at this writing, all the musicians are married, and of these thirty—all men—only eighteen have children, with a total of thirty-seven among them.

Are these children usually talented? We have compiled the answers of the fathers themselves, in TABLE II (page 244).

TABLE II: *Offspring.* Here we have included "talent" data about the wives of the musicians also, because obviously they must be considered equally in regard to the children's heredity. With only three stated exceptions, all of them are also musical, many being professional musicians. (Mrs. Lhevinne is a distinguished concert pianist in her own right; Mrs. Zimbalist was Alma Gluck, a former opera star; and Mmes. Prokofieff and Schnabel are also singers.) In half the cases, also, there were musicians in the wife's background.

On the whole, we can consider that from both sides the prospects were exceptionally favorable for the expression of talent in the children, either through environment or heredity. Has the promise been fulfilled?

Three-fourths of the children are cited as talented, or if still very young, as showing musical aptitude. That the parents are not too prejudiced is indicated by the several instances where *no* talent is reported, and in the several instances where one child is cited as talented, the others not.

A truly musical family is that of the Schnabels, all three of the children having shown marked talent, one son, Karl Ulrich Schnabel, now rivaling his father as a pianist. Also worth watching in the future is the Serkin child, whose grandfather is Adolf Busch.

Looking back over three, and in some instances four, generations of our musicians, there is unquestionable proof that musical talent "runs" in these strains. But, we hasten to add, *this in itself is no evidence that the talents were inherited,* for everything might still be accredited to environment. However, had we not found the high familial incidence, then the case for heredity would have

MUSIC TABLE II
CHILDREN OF INSTRUMENTAL ARTISTS

MUSICIAN	WIFE		CHILDREN	
	Musical?	*Her Family?*	*Number*	*Musical?*
ARTUR BODANZKY	Yes	Yes	2	Both, to a degree
ADOLF BUSCH	Yes	Yes, f.* Grandf.*	1	Yes
WALTER DAMROSCH	No	No	4	All 4
WALTER GIESEKING	Yes	Yes	2	Both
EUGENE GOOSSENS	Yes	No	4	1 yes,* 3 no
JASCHA HEIFETZ	Yes (Florence Vidor)	Grandf.*	2	Both
ERNEST HUTCHESON	Yes	Yes (many)	2	Both
JOSÉ ITURBI	?	....	1	Talented
JOSEF LHEVINNE	Yes* (Pianist)	No	2	Daughter, yes; son, no
SERGE PROKOFIEFF	Yes* (Singer)	Yes (both parents)	2	Both talented but not trained
SERGEI RACHMANINOFF	Yes	No	2	Both
ARTUR RODZINSKI	No	....	1	No
ARTUR RUBINSTEIN	Yes	f. cond.*	2	(4½, 3½) Both
ARTUR SCHNABEL	Yes* (Singer)	Yes (many)	3	All. Karl Ulrich, pianist; other son actor, singer; daughter, composer.
RUDOLF SERKIN	Yes	Yes (A. Busch)	1	Yes (2½)
JOSEPH SZIGETI	No	No	1	Yes, but chiefly critical ability
ARTURO TOSCANINI	Yes	Some	3	1 daughter, critical ability only
EFREM ZIMBALIST	Yes* (A. Gluck)	No	2	No

TOTALS—*Wives:* Talented, 14; Not, 3; ?, 1.
Children: Of 37, 27 Talented.

fallen down at once.[1] So, still keeping our minds open, let us continue to the second part of our study—that of the Metropolitan Opera singers.

THE METROPOLITAN SINGERS. Every one has heard, with regard to this or that vocally gifted person, "She inherited her voice from her mother" (or he from his father, etc.). To throw light on whether this is so or not, we present now the genetic backgrounds of exactly the same number of vocal artists as we did of instrumental artists.

The vocal study was confined to one brilliant group—the principals of the Metropolitan Opera Company. Originally we had planned to select singers from the field at large, but it quickly became evident that vocal artists cannot be evaluated with any such clarity as can instrumentalists, and that, had we sought to exercise our own judgment, we would have been beset with numerous difficulties.

The simplest procedure was to make a "unit" study of an outstanding group, obviously the Metropolitan ensemble, whose singers include a majority of the best-known vocal artists now appearing before the public. These, too, like the instrumentalists, have come from many countries, and have risen to the top through the ranks of tens of thousands of other singers.

We are well aware that there are many distinguished singers outside of the present Metropolitan cast; and if we think in terms of *basic* ability rather than public recognition, there are probably

[1] As we were going to press we received from her native Brazil these data sent by Guiomar Novaes:
Talent expressed: At age of less than four, playing by ear.
Professional début: Age of 8.
Mother: Pianist and her first teacher.
Father: Not musical, but a poet.
Brothers and sisters: Seventeen. None talented, but some appreciative.
Other near kin: None with any exceptional talent.
Note the remarkable fact that Mme. Novaes has, or had, *seventeen* brothers and sisters, *none* of whom showed musical talent. She points out, however, that some are "appreciative." We regret that time did not permit us to ascertain how many were meant by "some," and to what extent circumstances might have suggested that there was latent talent in these which had been suppressed.
Mme. Novaes reports further that she is married to a musical man of a musical family, and that the happy result is two children who are both musical.

MUSIC TABLE III—THE METROPOLITAN OPERA SINGERS

VOCAL ARTIST	VOCAL TALENT IN FAMILY (or Musical Talent)					
	Age Talent Shown	Training Begun	Mother	Father	Bros. & Sists.	Other Near Kin
ROSE BAMPTON (Dram. Sopr.)	15	16	No	No	(2)	·····
LUCREZIA BORI (Soprano)	5	12	Yes	No	(2)	Uncle
KARIN BRANZELL (Contralto)	12	16	Yes	Yes	(2)	·····
HILDA BURKE (Lyr. Sopr.)	3	16	Yes	Yes	(0)	Grandf.* 3 Uncles*
GINA CIGNA (Dram. Sopr.)	Very young	16	No	No	(0)	·····
SUSANNE FISHER (Soprano)	8	16	Yes	Yes	(2)	Several
KIRSTEN FLAGSTAD (Dram. Sopr.)	12	16	Yes* (Mus.)	Yes* (Cond.)	(3) ***	Many mus. & singers
DUSOLINA GIANNINI (Dram. Sopr.)	3	14	Yes (Mus.)	Yes*	(3) **	Many mus. & singers
HELEN JEPSON (Soprano)	9	19	Yes	Yes	(1)	2
MARJORIE LAWRENCE (Dram. Sopr.)	5	18½	Yes	Yes	(5)	4 Uncle, aunt, cousin

LOTTE LEHMANN (Lyr. Sopr.)	Very young	16	Yes	Yes	(1)	1	Aunt
QUEENA MARIO (Lyr. Sopr.)	8½	....	Yes	?	(5)	3	....
GRACE MOORE (Lyr. Sopr.)	12	16	No	No!	(4)	:	....
EIDE NORENA (Lyr. Col. Sopr.)	Very young	16	Yes	Yes	(3)	3	Grandm
ROSE PAULY (Dram. Sopr.)	10	14	No	No	(0)	:	....
LILY PONS (Col. Sopr.)	4		Yes	Yes* (Mus.)	(2)	2**	....
ROSA PONSELLE (Dram. Sopr.)	5	16	Yes	Yes	(2) Sister	2*	....
ELISABETH RETHBERG (Dram. Sopr.)	Very young	16	Yes	Yes	(5)	1	....
BIDU SAYAO (Lyr. Col. Sopr.)	11	15	No	No	(1)	:	Uncle
GLADYS SWARTHOUT (Mezzo-Sopr.)	11	13	No	No	(1)	1	....
Average	8 yr. 4 mo.	15 yr. 7 mo.	14 Yes	12 Yes 1?	(44)	25	10

247

MUSIC TABLE III—THE METROPOLITAN OPERA SINGERS—(Continued)

VOCAL ARTIST	Age Talent Shown	Training Begun	VOCAL TALENT IN FAMILY (or Musical Talent)			
			Mother	Father	Bros. & Sists.	Other Near Kin
PAUL ALTHOUSE (Dram. Tenor)	6	7	Yes	Yes	....	.....
RICHARD BONELLI (Baritone)	17	17	Yes	Yes* (cond.)	(3) 1	.....
MARIO CHAMLEE (Lyr. Tenor)	19	20	No	Some	(7) 2	Grandf.
RICHARD CROOKS (Lyr. Tenor)	9	9	? (Untr.)	No	(4)	.....
CHARLES HACKETT (Lyr. Tenor)	5	17	Yes	Some	(6) 3 ***	.....
FREDERICK JAGEL (Tenor)	8	19	No	No	(2) ..	Grandps.*
JAN KIEPURA (Lyr. Tenor)	16	20	Yes	Yes	(1) 1*	.....
CHARLES KULLMAN (Tenor)	8	14	No	No	(1) 1	Grandf.
EMANUEL LIST (Basso Prof.)	5-6	26	Yes	?	(2) ..	.....
G. MARTINELLI (Tenor)	18	23	No	No	(14) ..	.....

	A	B	C	D	E	F	G
NINO MARTINI (Lyr. Tenor)	7	18	Yes	Yes	(3)	1	.....
LAURITZ MELCHIOR (Heroic Tenor)	Very young		Yes	Yes	(6)	3	Niece*
EZIO PINZA (Basso)	?	19	No	?	(3)	1*	.....
FRIEDRICH SCHORR (Baritone)	17	19	No	Yes	(4)	2	Several*
JOHN CHAS. THOMAS (Lyr. Baritone)	8	19	Yes	Yes	..	:	.....
LAWRENCE TIBBETT (Baritone)	16	17	Yes	No	(3)	3	2(?)
Average—Males	11yr.5mo.	17yr.7mo.	9 Yes 1?	9 Yes 2?	(59)	18	6
Females	8yr.4mo.	15yr.7mo.	14 Yes	12 Yes 1?	(44)	25	10
Average for all	9yr.9mo.	16yr.7mo.	23 Yes 1?	21 Yes 3?	(103)	43	16

very many talented artists whom we have excluded. But by and large, we believe that our list is a representative selection of vocal artists whose backgrounds can be intelligently compared, for the purpose of this study, with the data regarding our instrumentalists.

TABLE III: *The Singers Themselves.* Perhaps the first fact that will strike you is the preponderance of women in the "vocal" table compared with the mere four in the instrumental tables. Unbalanced as this may seem, the comparative ratios actually are about those which prevail in the field at large. That is to say, women predominate among the better-known singers, whereas in the instrumental field there are exceedingly few women in the front ranks.

Second, we see that the age at which vocal talent appeared (according to the artists' own statements) averaged about eight and a half years in women, and eleven and a half in men. We may compare this with the appearance of talent at the average age of less than five among the instrumental artists.

Note also that we did not ask for "age at professional début" in the vocal field, but "when training was begun." The principal reason was that "professional début" in the singing field is much more variable in its meaning than in the instrumental field. (Another reason: Many vocal artists are reluctant to give any figures which would be a clue to their ages.) To be on the safe side, therefore, we confined ourselves to the age at which training began, which in some cases was but a short time before the professional début, in others quite a number of years earlier. Nevertheless, by indirect comparison a significant fact stands out:

The average age when training began in the vocal field was *directly correlated with the period terminating puberty.* (Fifteen and a half for the female artists, seventeen and a half for the males.)

Here is a striking environmental factor in the vocal field that does not occur in the instrumental field, namely, the purely physical requirement that the voice must first weather the rigors of puberty and be "set" before it can be trained. Thus, averaging male and female singers, *vocal training did not begin until the age of sixteen and a half—more than three years after the average instrumentalist had already been launched on his or her career.*

The Singers' Families: Turning to the family histories of our vocalists, we find, however, that they tell very much the same story as do those of the instrumentalists. A larger number of mothers and a slightly smaller number of fathers are reported as talented, but the average for both parents together is about the same. Also, while there are not quite as many brothers and sisters with talent, there are still almost half.[1] In other near kin (grandparents, uncles, aunts, cousins, etc.) the talent count is about the same for the singers as for the instrumentalists.

Again we have clear evidence that where there is a high degree of musicality in individuals—this time expressing itself in singing—there is an unusually high incidence of talent in their families.

Now to our third group.

THE JUILLIARD GROUP. With the aid of Ernest Hutcheson, the noted pianist previously listed who is president of the Juilliard School of Music, the third part of our study was conducted among graduate students of this distinguished institution.

"Students" may convey an erroneous impression of this group, for all of them have won their spurs as unusually talented individuals, and many are professional musicians. Ranging in age from the required minimum of sixteen up to the maximum of thirty, they were chosen from a great many applicants. How keen is the competition for admission into the Juilliard Graduate School may be gathered from the fact that there is no tuition and that private instruction by leading concert artists and music teachers is provided without cost.

All those included in this group, therefore, may be accepted as among the most talented of the new generation of musicians in this country. We say "new generation" because, although some may be as old as some of the celebrities in our virtuoso groups, their average age puts them almost a generation behind; and profes-

[1] The large quota of *fourteen* non-talented brothers and sisters reported by Martinelli may have tended to reduce the percentage somewhat, but not greatly, as we shall explain later. Another factor might have been that we queried the singers primarily regarding vocal talent, and although we suggested also that other musical talent be named, it is possible that some may have reported an unqualified "No" for relatives who could not sing but were otherwise musical.

sionally, also, they may on the whole still be considered "juniors" compared with the others. We therefore have the interesting opportunity of comparing musically gifted groups of different generations, chronologically and professionally.

Data from fifty Juilliard students were secured, our returns being taken just as they came in, with the number limited only by the fact that our impending publication date made it necessary to halt. Although these constitute somewhat less than one-third of the graduate student body, in the opinion of the school authorities they represent a fair and accurate sampling.[1]

Both instrumentalists and vocalists are included in this group, but the instrumentalists are in the great majority. As it happens (quite by coincidence) there are thirty-six of them, exactly the same number as in each of the other two major groups. An easy numerical comparison is therefore made possible between the Juilliard instrumentalists and the "senior" instrumental artists, with the one interesting difference that half the Juilliard group are young women. Space limitations here preclude our listing the Juilliard students individually. We therefore, in Table IV, give merely the summaries.

Age Talent Expressed: The average age at which the Juilliard instrumentalists revealed talent was about 5¾ years—somewhat less for the girls, somewhat more for the boys. This is about a year higher than among the major instrumentalists, but shows, nevertheless, the early appearance of talent. (The "professional début" question was naturally not asked because most of the Juilliard group have still to begin their formal careers.)

Talent in Family: Two-thirds of all the parents are reported as having musical talent, a somewhat higher proportion than among

[1] The following are the members of the Juilliard group represented in the study: Maro Ajemian, Hinda Barnett, Emma Beldan, Edna Bockstein, Sophie Bostelmann, Eleanor Brownell, V. Condon, Diana Dipson, Leah Effenbach, Sue Elson, Ruth Freeman, Gertrude Gibson, Jane Glenn, Mary Eliz. Henderson, Drusilla Huffmaster, Rivka Iventosch, Eugenie Limberg, Miriam Mann, Estelle Andron, Elizabeth Morgan, Esther Schure, Vivienne Simon, Maxine Stillman, Barbara Pentland, Berenice Robinson, Helen Van Loon, Richard Browning, Dean Dixson, James de la Feunte, Edmond de Luca, Wendel Diebel, Michael Field, William Gephart, Norman Goldblatt, Leonid Hambro, John Calvin Jackson, Charles S. Kent, Richard Korn, Frederick Loadwick, Billy Masselos, Walter Mourant, Carl Nicholas, Peter Page, Charles S. Rugg, Robert Stevenson, David Stiner, Elie Siegmeister, Bernhard Tiede, Earl C. Voorhies, Harry Wilson, Joseph Wood, C. Wister Yearsley.

MEMBERS OF GRADUATE SCHOOL OF
JUILLIARD INSTITUTE

	INSTRUMENTALISTS (36)		VOCALISTS (14)		TOTALS (50)
	Females (18)	*Males* (18)	*Females* (8)	*Males* (6)	
Average Age Talent Expressed:	5	6	5	8½	5¾ yrs.
Talent in Mothers:					
(a) Definitely Yes	13(72%)	10(56%)	5(63%)	4(67%)	32(64%)
(b) Some Talent or Musicality	3	1		1	5
(c) Totals of Both	16(89%)	11(61%)	5(63%)	5(83%)	37(74%)
Talent in Fathers:					
(a) Definitely Yes	10(56%)	8(44%)	3(38%)	3(50%)	24(48%)
(b) Some Talent or Musicality	2	2		1	5
(c) Totals of Both	12(67%)	10(56%)	3(38%)	4(67%)	29(58%)
Brothers and Sisters:					
Number in Families	31	30	6	5	72
(a) Definitely Talented	21(68%)	13(43%)	4(67%)	3(60%)	41(57%)
(b) Some Talent or Musicality	6	3	1		10
(c) Totals of Both	27(87%)	16(53%)	5(83%)	3(60%)	51(71%)
Talent in Other Kin:					
(a) Those reporting talent in one or more grand-parents	7(39%)	9(50%)	5(63%)	5(83%)	26(52%)
(b) Those reporting talent in near kin of any kind, including grand-parents	13(72%)	13(72%)	6(75%)	5(83%)	37(74%)

the major artists but chiefly due to the much greater number of musical mothers reported.

Among brothers and sisters, again more than two-thirds are listed as musical, likewise a higher proportion than among the major artists. (An interesting revelation is that the total number of children in the families of this newer generation is about half the size of those in the senior groups—a significant indication of a drop in birth-rate.)

Further, we find more than twice as many of the Juilliard instrumentalists reporting musicality in their grandparents or other near kin as either of the two major groups. Can it be that there actually is more musical talent in the backgrounds of these "junior" artists than among the families of the outstanding major artists? We will come to that presently.

The Juilliard Vocalists: As our study here (at the time we were forced to halt) netted only fourteen individuals, a detailed analysis of their backgrounds would not be too significant. Nevertheless, all the important facts with regard to early appearance of talent, high incidence of talent in parents, brothers and sisters and near kin is consistent with the data of their fellow Juilliard students. While talent appeared earlier among them than among the Metropolitan singers, it is interesting to note that, comparing the two sexes, there is the same later manifestation of talent among the males as there was in the Metropolitan group.

.   .   .   .

The thought may have occurred that the records of the individuals we studied were by some chance not representative of musical artists in general. We, therefore, dipped at random into the backgrounds of other contemporary virtuosi. We found the stories the same: Josef Hofmann (his father a conductor, his mother an operatic star), making his début at six; Ignace Paderewski, born in a small Polish town, playing piano at three, taught by a musical mother; Feodor Chaliapin, rising to operatic triumph from a childhood of abject poverty in Russia during which his training consisted chiefly of apprenticeships at cobbling and carpentry; Georges Enesco, in Roumania, repeating in early childhood the songs of gipsies, making his violin début at eleven; Emanuel Feuermann, in Austria, from a highly musical family, showing precocity at the cello and also making his début at eleven.

No, the data from those we have studied are representative of others in the world of music. So now, as we look at our "evidence," we may ask in the words of Sherlock Holmes, "What do you make of it?"

CHAPTER XXXII

MUSICAL TALENT: Part II

(*An Original Genetic Study*)

WHEN we begin to analyze the assembled data regarding the 122 musically gifted individuals represented in our study, we are struck by this fact: in all of these three unrelated groups—whether the individuals are instrumentalists or singers, males or females, young or old, foreign or American, famous or still to make their mark— the general story is the same (see Table V, page 259).

Nevertheless, before we jump to any conclusions about heredity, we must first find out what we can or can't attribute to environment. For instance, take the fact that the talents of almost all, with a few exceptions, appeared in early childhood. Could not this have been the result of "conditioning"?

A similar question occurred more than twenty years ago to Prof. Carl E. Seashore of the University of Iowa, when he set out to study musical *aptitude*. (This, however, as will be explained later, is not quite the same as musical talent.) First, he had to find some standards of measurement, so he "broke down" musical apti- tude into what he considered its components—sense of pitch, sense of time, sense of intensity (or degrees of loudness and softness), sense of consonance (or harmony), sense of rhythm, and tonal memory. For each of these "senses" he devised tests to discover to what extent they might be inherent in persons, and to what extent they could be cultivated.

In the years that have followed he and others (notably Prof. Hazel M. Stanton in this country, Prof. Jon Alfred Mjoen of Norway, and Prof. J. Philiptschenko of Russia) have used the Seashore tests or similar tests to measure the musical aptitudes of many thousands of individuals. Children in public schools, students

256

in music schools and adults at large were tested before and after periods of training. And this seems to have been revealed:

The various "senses" required for musical aptitude do have a constitutional basis.

In other words (according to the Seashore studies) the sense of pitch is *innate*—developed quickly in the individual—and cannot be materially improved by training, nor can the "elemental" sense of time be improved; the sense of intensity cannot be imparted by training, apparently because it seems to depend mainly upon delicacy of ear structure; and the senses of harmony and of rhythm can be developed only to the extent made possible by the individual's inherent capacities. Prof. Stanton reported that by the time a child is ten years old its future musical performance can be clearly determined, and at sixteen an individual is musically "set."

Prof. Seashore gathered that for each of the musical "senses" there is a mental process. (Recently Dr. F. A. Gibbs of Harvard announced evidence of the location of brain cells which are concerned with recording sounds of different pitch.) It has also been shown that the different "musical" senses may be independent not only of one another, but of other mental factors. That is to say, an individual with an acute sense of pitch might have no sense of rhythm, or one with a sense of rhythm may have no sense of harmony; and—as many of you who read this may know all too well—a highly intelligent person may be almost devoid of musicality, while a nitwit may be highly musical. (There are many cases of feeble-minded persons who are good musicians, although, of course, never virtuosi.)

These findings would tend to prove that there is something *in* people, from childhood on, which determines or influences the degree of their musical aptitude. But this brings us to the point that musical aptitude does not necessarily imply true talent in the sense that musicians would understand it. A person may have well-developed senses of pitch, rhythm, time, etc., and yet be as mechanical as a nickel-in-the-slot player-piano. Aptitude is the basis for technique, but while technique is highly essential, by itself it cannot produce talent. This is true not only in music but in painting, writing and other arts.

Commenting on this point recently, Josef Hofmann said, "My hand is a bad one for the piano—too small, my fingers not long enough for everything—and my technique is limited. I have pupils who have far bigger technique than I."

For talent—and especially great talent—an additional "something" is required. This, in the opinion of Harold G. Seashore (Prof. Seashore's nephew), who has specialized in the study of great musical talents, is the "artistic deviation from the pure, the true, the exact, the perfect, the rigid, the even and the precise." He has shown (with unusual graph-recordings) that each virtuoso artist deviates from exactness and preciseness in a characteristically different way. Such artistic deviation must be dictated by extreme sensitivity, great emotion, and high intelligence. These qualities, we may assume, are probably some of the components of great talent. In addition, for the talent to reach full fruition, the artist must have unusual powers of muscular coordination and also the ability to concentrate.

When we add together, then, both the basic "aptitude" requirements and the added "talent" requirements, our next question is whether these essentials can be implanted in individuals by environment during early childhood, the stage at which they appeared among the artists we have studied. And this would imply some uniform influence in the early backgrounds of *all* the individuals.

But no such environmental uniformity can be found. True enough, the backgrounds of many of the musicians and singers were highly favorable for talent development, but then we also find individuals like Toscanini, Rubinstein, Seidel, Smeterlin, Schnabel, Iturbi, Grace Moore, Gladys Swarthout, Rose Pauly, Martinelli, etc., emerging from homes where neither parent was musical. In some instances the background might have been considered almost deadening for musical expression. Again and again we find evidence of talent cropping out with apparent spontaneity, as an orchid might suddenly appear in a field of dandelions.

Arturo Toscanini was born in a humble home in Parma, Italy. His father (a Garibaldi veteran) was a tailor, his mother an unpretentious homebody, neither being musical. No talent had ever been reported in grandparents, aunts, uncles or other kin, and there was none, moreover, in any of the other Toscanini children. There was therefore no reason to look for musicality in young Arturo. Yet by the time he was nine his tendency toward music had asserted itself sufficiently so that his parents sent him to the local conservatory. He soon "found" himself with the cello, and within a short time was winning honors. At fourteen he was conducting the school orchestra in pieces of his own composition and playing, professionally, in the town orchestra outside of school hours. At nineteen he made his début as a conductor at Rio de Janeiro.

Can something "special" in his environment be credited with having produced the genius of Toscanini?

Yehudi Menuhin's parents were also not musicians. His mother "dabbled" a bit on the piano, as any young woman might. His father couldn't read a note and to this day—as he lamented to us—

MUSIC TABLE V

SUMMARY—ALL THREE GROUPS

	Virtuosi Instrumental Artists (36 in all)	Metropolitan Opera Singers (36 in all)	Juilliard Graduate Students (50 in all)	Totals for All Groups (122 in all)
Average Age Talent Expressed	4¾ yrs.	9¾ yrs.	5¾ yrs.	6⅔ yrs.
Mothers Talented or Musical in Some Degree	17 (47%)	24 (67%)	37 (74%)	78 (64%)
Fathers Talented or Musical in Some Degree	29 (81%)	25 (69%)	29 (58%)	83 (68%)
Brothers and Sisters, Total	110	103	72	285
Talented or Musical in Some Degree	55 (50%)	43 (42%)	51 (71%)	148 (52%)
Number reporting Talent in Additional near kin	13 (36%)	16 (44%)	37 (74%)	66 (54%)

"can't even turn the pages for his son." The two, however, ardently loved music. They went to symphony concerts in San Francisco (where Mr. Menuhin was principal of a Hebrew school) and, the family budget not permitting a maid, took their baby with them. Soon they were aware that the infant was listening raptly to the music, but was especially drawn to the violins. One day they took him up to the conductor, Louis Persinger. He became interested in the baby, and as soon as Yehudi was old enough to finger a violin began giving him lessons. To what extent can environment claim credit for this brilliant young artist?

Artur Rubinstein was born in a poor home in Warsaw where no musical instrument was to be heard. Yet as a baby he began to sing little songs of his own making to express what he wanted or to designate various members of the family. He clung to his "song language" and could not be taught to talk until he was three. By that time musicians had taken note of this unusual child. Lessons began soon thereafter, and within a few years little Artur made his début.

Many stories of this kind lurk behind the terse sentences in our Table I. Eugene Ormandy, at $1\frac{1}{2}$ years, being able to distinguish each of the fifty or sixty records on his father's hurdy-gurdy. . . . Toscha Seidel, at the age of three having "tantrums" when his uncle, whom he describes as an earnest but not talented "fiddler," played the wrong notes. . . . Guila Bustabo, found "tweaking" the strings of her father's violin and not being made happy until she was given one of her own. . . . Alfred Wallenstein, who had already been playing the piano, instinctively tuning the first cello placed in his hands on his seventh birthday—a feat which any cellist would applaud.

Wallenstein, as it happened, had (as he still has) an acute musical ear or "absolute pitch"—the highest development of the sense of pitch—which might be described as a sort of "mental tuning-fork." This enables the fortunate musician or singer so endowed to "hit" any note accurately, or to judge the accuracy of any note, without the aid of any instrumental cue. Among others of our instrumentalists who revealed this gift in childhood are Hutcheson, Heifetz, Lhevinne, Rosenthal, Rubinstein and Miss Slenczynski.

KIRSTEN FLAGSTAD'S MUSICAL PEDIGREE

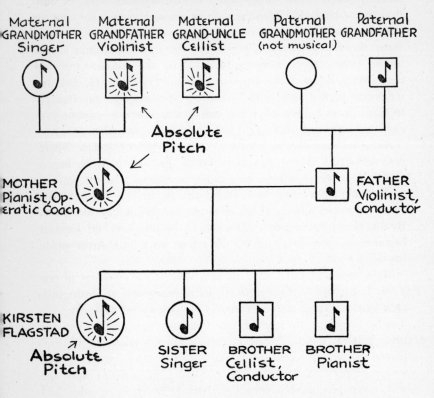

The latter is reported as also having been able to distinguish, at the early age of nine months, between major and minor scales.

Of the singers, there is the unusual case of Kirsten Flagstad, where absolute pitch is reported not only in herself, but in her mother, her mother's father and her mother's uncle. (This "pedigree of pitch" came to our attention through Prof. Mjoen, and is illustrated in the accompanying diagram.) Although "absolute pitch" is by no means a prerequisite for great musical achievement, it is, of course, a valuable asset. Many others in our lists report such acuteness of musical ear or the spontaneous manifestation of one of the other musical senses during their first few years of life.

The possibility that something unusual in the environment can have produced these early manifestations becomes more remote when we see that a home can be as musical as possible and yet no talent may appear, or it may appear in one child and not in another. Here is Efrem Zimbalist, married to the famous singer, Alma Gluck, and reporting that neither of their two children has talent. Again there are Toscanini's three children, only one of whom shows "musicality," and this only in the form of critical ability. There is Josef Lhevinne, whose wife is also a concert artist, and yet reporting that one child is talented, the other not. Our data provide numerous parallels, and any one in musical circles can add many other instances where children in the most musical homes "fail to respond."

It would seem very much, then, that one is, or is not born with great musical capacity. What do musicians and singers themselves think about this? Their opinions, of course, have no scientific validity, but they might prove interesting. So, with that thought in mind, we asked each one, "Do you believe that you inherited your talent?"

It is perhaps a mere coincidence that almost the same sized majority in each group answered "Yes." Some answered, "In Part,"

MUSIC TABLE VI

OPINIONS AS TO THE INHERITANCE OF MUSICAL TALENT

(Answers to the question: "Do you believe you inherited your talent?")

	Instrumental Virtuosi	Metropolitan Singers	Juilliard Students	Totals
Yes..................	18	19	28	65
In Part..............	3	3	10	16
No...................	7	9	10	26
Doubtful or No Opinion........	8	5	2	15
TOTAL ANSWERS.....	36	36	50	122

and a number were doubtful or offered no opinion. But about
20 to 25 percent answered quite definitely "No." (The "vote" is
tabulated in Table VI.)

One type of comment, however, is of special interest. Some of
the artists said that they didn't believe they *inherited* their talent,
but that they were *"just born with it."* Now, if a person is born
with talent, and it isn't due to heredity, then it must be due to
some *intra-uterine influence*. (In the way, for instance, that some
forms of idiocy are produced!) This would mean that musical
talent could be instilled by some shock, blow, nutritive agent or
chemical conveyed by the mother to the embryonic child. Do you
believe that? We are quite sure that no biologist does. When, in
fact, the situation was made clear to some of the musicians who
answered "inborn" they said, "I suppose, then, I must mean 'inherited.'"

So it begins to look very much as if musical talent *is* inherited.
But a mere guess isn't sufficient for the geneticist. He would like
to see some evidence of genetic ratios. That is to say, where a
condition exists in individuals or is presumed to exist, *it should
appear in their offspring in given proportions*.

So now we assemble some of our data in a new form. In all
our groups we have 122 matings represented between the parents
of the individuals studied. For our genetic study we will arrange
the matings in three groups:

(1) Where both parents are musical.

(2) Where one parent is musical, the other not.

(3) Where neither parent is musical. (Although, of course, having produced one highly talented child—the one represented in our
study—we assume that one of the parents at least is a "carrier" for
musicality.)

In our first computation we will eliminate the "doubtful" cases,
where judgment is uncertain regarding the talent of a parent or,
in a few instances, of a brother or sister.[1] Thus, we set to one side
the families of Elman, Menuhin, Milstein, Morini and Rodzinski,

---

[1] In all cases where a definite "Yes" or "No" was given by the artists, we have
accepted their estimates. The value of our data, or the importance attached to the
ensuing conclusions, must be governed by the faith placed in these estimates.

Pinza, List, Crooks, Queena Mario and Hackett, and about a half-dozen among the Juilliard group.

Our next step is to count *only the brothers and sisters of the individuals we have studied* because, if we included the artists themselves, we would be "loading" the evidence—giving each family a "send off" with one talented individual. The omission of this one need not upset the ratios, for if you recall, the laws of chance prescribe that the odds that any condition will turn up are always the same for the next child.

So now if musical talent is produced by genes, this should be evident: Where *both* parents are musical, we should expect a higher incidence of musical talent in their children than if only *one* parent is musical; and where one parent is talented, there should be more talented offspring than where neither parent is talented. *That is exactly what our figures reveal.* (See Table VII.)

In each of the groups different results from the three types of matings are clearly apparent. There were about 12 to 15 percent more talented offspring resulting from the "double talent" matings than from the "one parent talented" matings, and a strikingly small proportion produced where neither parent was talented.

To test our evidence further, we compiled the "doubtful" cases according to the fairest guess possible, and found that they yielded about the same ratios. Again, other more technical genetic calculations (grouping the families according to size, then including the artists themselves, etc.) also produced results consistent with the previous findings. And finally we tabulated the results of the marriages among our virtuosi instrumentalists—eighteen of whom, as you recall, had children. As almost all of these were "double talent" matings they offered no basis for comparison among themselves. But it may be noted that these matings produced almost the same percentage of talented offspring as did the similar matings among the Juilliard parents who are *of the same modern generation.*

The following deductions could therefore be made:

Where both parents were talented, in most matings one-half to three-fourths of the children were talented.

Where only one parent was talented, in most matings one-half of the children were talented.

Where neither parent was talented (referring only to parents whose capacity to produce a talented child had been demonstrated) the average of talented offspring was one-fourth or less.

With this strong indication that heredity is involved, we next ask, *"What type or types of genes could produce these ratios?"*

Remember, we are dealing with *talent,* not merely with "apti-

MUSIC TABLE VII

"TALENT" RESULTS OF DIFFERENT MATINGS

(Totals of other talented offspring produced by parents of the musicians and singers we have studied, in *addition* to these artists themselves. Further omitted are the results of those matings which were in doubt.)

	Where Both Parents Had Talent		Where Only One Parent Had Talent		Where Neither Parent Had Talent **	
	Number of Other Children *	Number With Talent	Number of Other Children *	Number With Talent	Number of Other Children *	Number With Talent
Bros. & Sisters of Instrumental Virtuosi (26 families)	31	22 (71%)	35	21 (60%)	27	4 (15%)
Bros. & Sisters of Metropolitan Singers (26 families)	42	26 (62%)	16	8 (50%)	25	2 (8%)
Bros. & Sisters of Juilliard Graduates (32 families)	21	19 (90%)	20	14 (70%)	14	4 (29%)
Totals for All Three Groups	94	67 (71%)	71	43 (60%)	66	10 (15%)

* In addition to the artists themselves.
** NOTE: It should be kept in mind that this refers only to the parents who had already produced a highly talented child.

tude." It is not unlikely that there are genes for each of the musical aptitude "senses" (of pitch, time, rhythm, etc.). But these genes are believed to be in such wide circulation that almost every one who can carry a tune, play the ukulele or harmonize in a barber-shop must have them in some degree. Nevertheless, as we have indicated, these ordinary aptitudes might not in themselves constitute talent. What we are after, then, are rare and "special" genes which might be acting either to intensify the effects of the common ones or to produce some unusual supplementary gifts.

Could a *single dominant gene* do this?

Apparently not, for if it could, as in any dominant condition, wherever there was a musical child the talent would also show in the parent that carried that gene. And as we've seen, many of our virtuosi reported neither parent talented.

Could one pair of recessive genes produce the talent?

Again, apparently not, for if musical talent were a simple recessive condition (like blue eyes or blond hair) wherever both parents were talented, *all* of their children would be talented. Our table would rule out this theory if we accept evidence that such matings have produced an average of 30 percent offspring without talent.

Evidently, then, the situation is more complex and demands that we look for multiple genes. Without taxing you further, we may say that the simplest multiple-gene mechanism which might explain the ratios would be that of *two different dominant genes*. In such a hereditary process both genes must come together to produce their joint effect. But where the double-dominant genes differ from a pair of simple recessives (like the blue-eye-color genes) is in this way: The simple recessive genes are exact duplicates of each other and only one of them can be received from the same parent. For any recessive condition to crop out, therefore, both parents would have to contribute the same gene to the child. In a *double-dominant* condition, however, as the two genes involved are of different kinds, one parent alone may give a child both of them. (All this is made clearer in the diagrams, pages 268-269.)

Thus, assuming for the moment that our hypothesis regarding the two dominant "musical talent" genes is correct, we could explain many puzzling facts in our study.

THE TOSCANINI FAMILY

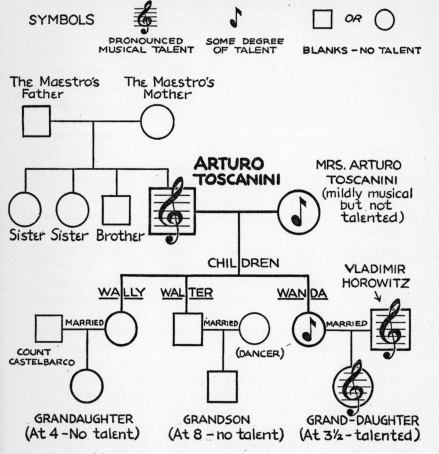

How could so great a talent as Toscanini's have emerged from so unmusical a background?

Our explanation might be that on the maestro's paternal side only one of the required genes had been carried, while on the maternal side the other one had been handed along—neither effective by itself. It may have taken many generations for both genes to be brought together through the mating of Father Toscanini

HOW MUSICAL TALENT MAY BE INHERITED
(An hypothesis)

Granted that a person has the ordinary "aptitude" genes (see text), the additional "something" required for musical talent may be produced by

TWO SPECIAL *dominant* "TALENT" GENES:

TALENT GENE (A) (SYMBOL)

TALENT GENE (B) (SYMBOL)

Each gene is ineffective by itself, but when both come together in the same individual the result is:

= MUSICAL TALENT

The ordinary "A" or "B" genes, which most persons carry, produce "blanks":

Thus, receiving a pair of genes ("talent" or ordinary) from each parent, individuals may carry any of the following

COMBINATIONS PRODUCING TALENT:
(All have the same effect.)

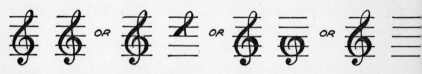

COMBINATIONS PRODUCING NO TALENT:

(While in each case above no talent will show in the individual, the more "talent" genes carried—as is also true of those with talent—the greater the chance that one's children will be talented.)

268

SOME POSSIBLE MUSICAL TALENT RESULTS
FROM VARIOUS MATINGS

(In each case it is assumed that the ordinary "aptitude" genes are also handed on to the children.)

1. BOTH PARENTS TALENTED
but of this same "talent-gene" type:

—Have an almost one-in-two chance of producing CHILDREN WITHOUT TALENT of these types:

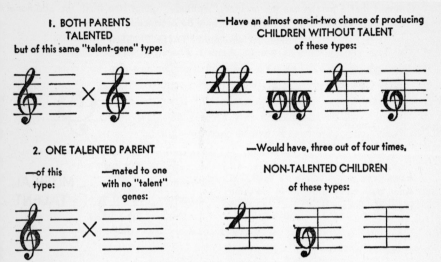

2. ONE TALENTED PARENT

—of this type: —mated to one with no "talent" genes:

—Would have, three out of four times,

NON-TALENTED CHILDREN

of these types:

BUT ALL CHILDREN TALENTED WOULD RESULT
FROM ANY OF THE FOLLOWING MATINGS:

3. BOTH PARENTS TALENTED

of these types

4. ONLY ONE PARENT TALENTED

—of this type   —mated to no matter what other type

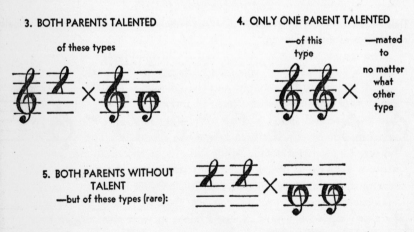

5. BOTH PARENTS WITHOUT TALENT
—but of these types (rare):

Through any of these matings (Nos. 3, 4 or 5) every child would receive the required two "talent" genes.

Note: In general, the more talented relatives there are on both sides, the greater will be the probability of children with talent.

and Mother Toscanini. Then the chance of the combination appearing in one of their offspring was one in four or less, and as it happened, out of their four children, Arturo was so favored.

Why has the maestro's talent failed to appear in his children?

The young woman whom Arturo Toscanini married had sung in a local choral ensemble, but whether or not she had unusual talent, or was presumably carrying the required "talent" genes, we do not know. Granted that she did have these genes, the odds would still be about even that a child of theirs might not receive both genes together. It would therefore not be surprising that out of three children, only one, the youngest daughter, Wanda, has shown any true musicality, and this only in the way of a keen critical sense. (Sufficiently acute, however, for her father to take stock in her comments on his performances.) But proceeding into another generation, this daughter is married to the pianist Vladimir Horowitz, and there is every indication that their little girl is highly talented.

With two dominant genes involved, as you can see by the diagram, almost any kind of talent combination could be possible in a family. Both parents talented (as the Zimbalists) might produce no talented children, or (as with the Lhevinnes) only one in two talented children; and neither parent talented (or at least, not outwardly so, as in the case of the Menuhins) might produce all talented children.

You may have wondered how Martinelli could have had fourteen brothers and sisters with no talent among them. So did we, and so did Martinelli. He thought and thought when our question was put to him and finally said, almost plaintively, "But what can I do? My brothers and sisters had no talent—not one!" (It was only by accident that Martinelli's own talent was discovered, and not until he was nineteen years old. While he was in service in the Italian army a keen-eared officer heard him singing in the barracks and arranged for his vocal instruction.)

Consulting our ratios, we can see that with two non-musical parents we need not have expected talent in more than one in four of the Martinelli family, which is to say in no more than three of the other children. It is not so surprising, then, that by the laws of chance, talent cropped out in only one. However, an additional possibility is that the ordinary "aptitude" genes might have been sparse in the Martinelli lineage, so that even given the "talent" genes, where one or more of the basic "aptitude" genes were missing, a brother or sister might still have shown no musicality.

While our data would seem to favor the hypothesis of two different dominant "talent" genes, plus certain "basic aptitude" genes, earlier investigators have suggested other gene mechanisms to explain the production of "musicality." About ten years ago the able Russian geneticist, J. Philiptschenko, reported the belief that *four pairs* of genes of different kinds were involved, both recessives and dominants, some acting to produce basic aptitude and others to intensify the effects. We are not sure, however, in view of the fact that Philiptschenko's studies were apparently not confined to so highly specialized a group as ours, whether he was dealing with mere musical aptitude or the *talent* we have in mind. Nevertheless, our findings need not be considered radically different from his.

In any case, while our conclusions must await confirmation by further studies in the field before they can make any pretense to finality, this much seems to have been settled (in refutation of earlier theories): Where both parents are highly talented, there is no guarantee that their children will be talented; and where neither parent is talented, there is still the possibility that they may produce a musical genius—*if they carry the required genes.* For, above all, to answer the main question raised by this study:

Musical talent is in all probability inherited through a number of genes acting together, and without the required genes there can be no musical talent.

This does not by any means dismiss the influence of environment. If the best musical environment cannot *create* talent, an unfavorable environment might well *suppress* talent. As the father of Yehudi Menuhin, Moishe Menuhin, said to us, "I am sure that there are many other young men now nobodies who might have become as great artists as my son if their talents had been immediately recognized by their parents and they had been given equal opportunities for training and development."

The "veto" power of environment is plainly revealed in our

data. We can see, as we trace backward into preceding generations, that wherever opportunity was more limited, less talent appeared. Most strikingly is this shown among women. We find that our virtuosi instrumentalists reported many fewer mothers, grandmothers and aunts with talent than did the Juilliard students, their juniors in both age and achievement. Certainly there could not have been any lesser amount of "talent" genes in the families of the world-famous musicians. The explanation must lie in the fact that their women forebears, most of whom had lived in humble surroundings abroad, had been given little chance for their talents to assert themselves. Among the women of a later day, as represented by the sisters of the artists, we find as many with talent reported as among their brothers.

But even today, while women may have an equal opportunity to show musical talent, this is far from saying that their achievements in music are equal to those of men. Very few women, as our Virtuosi Table bears out, are in the front ranks of the instrumentalists. Why? Erica Morini has this to say:

"In my opinion it is because only a few women have the great power of concentration, the strength and the energy required for such achievement. A complete absorption is necessary, and a readiness to give up the pleasures which most women seek."

Others believe that woman's failure to keep pace with male musicians is due not to any inherent inferiority but solely to discrimination against them. The professional world of music, it is claimed, is largely a world of men which does not welcome the intrusion of women. At the same time, audiences (including ladies' cultural clubs) seem to show a preference for male artists. Thus, the "veto" power of environment over talent in women may be continuing to assert itself.

In the vocal field, there is no such suppression of musicality in women, for operas and musical presentations of all kinds demand their equal representation. But nevertheless among singers of both sexes the negative effects of environment appear to be much greater than among instrumentalists. As we saw clearly in our tables, training among the singers is dependent upon what happens to their voices during puberty. Regardless of talent or ability, the singer is

SINGING VOICES—PARENTS AND OFFSPRING

Are voice *types* inherited? While not a direct part of the talent study, an effort was made to throw light on the inheritance of voice types by questioning members of the Metropolitan Opera Company and, in addition, about 100 members of the celebrated Schola Cantorum of New York City. The data regarding the voices of these artists and of members of their families, are tabulated below. As can be seen, a general correlation between voices of children and parents is indicated. Where both parents had high voices, most of the children were in the high range. The 26 tenor fathers listed produced no bass sons and only 2 contralto daughters; but fathers with bass voices, and contralto mothers, had a considerable proportion of low-voiced children. (A question mark indicates "singing voice of parent unknown.")

| Number of Matings | PARENTS | | CHILDREN | | | | | |
| | FATHERS | MOTHERS | DAUGHTERS | | | SONS | | |
			Sopr.	Mezz.	Contr.	Ten.	Barit.	Bass
27	Barit. ×	Sopr.	28	14	2	19	17	2
12	Barit. ×	Mezz.	12	13	2	3	8	4
7	Barit. ×	Contr.	6	3	3	3	4	
12	Barit. ×	?	6	7	4	4	3	3
10	Tenor ×	Sopr.	16			5	2	
10	Tenor ×	Mezz.	3	4	2	12	10	
1	Tenor ×	Contr.	1			1		
5	Tenor ×	?	3	2		6	1	
7	Bass ×	Sopr.	6	2	4	2	7	2
1	Bass ×	Mezz.	2					2
2	Bass ×	Contr.				1		2
3	Bass ×	?	2			3	1	
19	? ×	Sopr.	21	3	3	14	7	2
8	? ×	Mezz.	5	2	4	5	8	
7	? ×	Contr.	3	1	6	4	5	
131	(Total matings)		114	51	30	82	73	17

(Total offspring—367)

continually at the mercy of his or her physical equipment. One can buy a violin if it breaks, but one can't buy another set of vocal cords.

"I don't think you can consider a talent for singing in the same way you would a talent for music, as such," Richard Bonelli (one of the Metropolitan stars) said to us. "Altogether aside from the talent for music which a singer should—and usually does—have, there is the question of physical fitness and the very peculiar mental aptitude toward vocal technique which are necessary to make real singers. Consequently, you find thousands of people with fine musical talent who can't sing a lick, and you also find plenty of people with at best an indifferent musical talent, yet who make wonderful singers, simply because they happen to combine the physical and mental qualities necessary."

Without doubt, physical appearance and personality are more important to the vocalists than they are to the instrumentalists. But while these factors may sometimes lift singers to an eminence unmerited by their true talents, their careers are all too often unjustly cut short by age, public fickleness or professional difficulties. To a much less extent is this true among the instrumental artists. Rarely is the career of a great pianist, violinist or conductor terminated by anything but voluntary retirement or death.

However, granted that environment, in the form of early influences, educational opportunities and chance are important in any human career, one more question remains:

To what extent are the achievements of our great musicians and singers to be credited to heredity, and to what extent to environment?

This is of course a rhetorical question to which no scientific answer can be given. But it has been asked so many times, often by the artists themselves and innumerable times by persons who have called on them for judgment and advice, that we thought it worth while to secure their opinions once again. For this question we "polled" only the two senior groups. The answers showed some marked differences of opinion. (See Table VIII.) The largest number took the conservative view that inherited talent and training are both equally important or that no opinion could be given. Those that thought talent more important were almost equally balanced by those who thought training more important. (Note, however, that a majority of the men singers believed training played the biggest rôle in their careers.)

The general views of the artists in both groups, as expressed to us, are reflected in the following selections from their comments:

Sergei Rachmaninoff: "I am inclined to believe that heredity and training are inseparable and indispensable in any art achievement. I consider that capacity for hard work is also a talent and that only those few artists who have inherited both musical and working talents attain the highest peak of their profession."

Alexander Brailowsky: "Genuine talent is the basic requirement and is bound to manifest itself sooner or later; training is an indispensable accessory."

Eugene Goossens: "Heredity unquestionably lays the solid foundation for musical achievement. Proper training lies principally in early apprenticeship to the profession."

MUSIC TABLE VIII

WHICH IS MORE IMPORTANT IN MUSICAL ACHIEVEMENT . . INHERITED TALENT OR TRAINING?

(Opinions of the artists)

	Instrumental Virtuosi	Metropolitan Singers	Totals
Both Equally Important..........	16	12 (10 women 2 men)	28
Talent More Important...........	6	10 (5 women 5 men)	16
Training More Important........	6	11 (2 women 9 men)	17
Uncertain or No Opinion........	8	3 (women)	11
Total Answers.................	36	36	72

Fritz Kreisler: "Heredity and training contribute probably in equal measure."

Nathan Milstein: "Talent is, in my opinion, inborn and independent of training and home influence. But however great, it will remain futile without real training, which is the means and the only one of developing it and making it productive."

Jan Smeterlin: "Heredity without training would not go far, but training without heredity would not go anywhere."

Artur Rodzinski: "Training and above all *luck*."

Grace Moore: "I had a voice even when very young, and all my natural emotional expression was toward music. I only felt completely myself when I sang. *That* I call inheritance of a special spirit and emotional values. The rest was training."

Lily Pons: "One must first be born with a voice, and next the musical background during youth is important. But training makes the difference between the person who just sings and the one who becomes a truly fine singer."

Lotte Lehmann: "Everybody with a fine voice can be trained to become a good singer, but to be a real artist you must have inborn or inherited talent. Nobody can ever learn that."

Lauritz Melchior: "By heredity came intelligence, ear and love of music—the qualities that make an artist and which no teacher can give you."

Mario Chamlee: "Training plays a greater part. With extraordinary vocal equipment and no training singers seldom develop. With little natural voice but consistent effort and training voices have developed to great extents."

Jan Kiepura: "Heredity counts only physically. I received my voice as though given a violin. Training did for me what learning to play would do for a violinist."

Lawrence Tibbett: "I believe heredity may have played some part in my singing ability, but so far as achievement goes, I attribute the greater part of it to training."

Reviewing all the data and opinions in this study of ours, we feel justified in leaving you with the conclusion that some unusual hereditary endowment is essential for great musical achievement.

That opportunity and training are also essentials need hardly be debated, but the important fact is that the talent must be there first before it can be cultivated.

How does this apply to you? If you happen to be an average person in whose life virtuoso talent hasn't entered, the question of your "musicality" must have come up at one time or another.

So our study suggests that if you have tried to play or sing and just haven't been able to, or if you do play and sing but have "never gotten anywhere with it," the fault may not have been in your background, efforts or training, but in your genes. In which case, it is as idle to blame yourself for your musical shortcomings as to blame yourself for not being as tall as you'd like to be.

It suggests that if you have a child and that child shows little or no response to music, you must not try to force musical training upon it.

It suggests that with musical talent having a constitutional basis, often independent of intelligence, it is unfair to penalize children in school for backwardness in music, or to average in "music" marks with those for other studies.

It suggests that when parents are both highly musical they should not frown on a child of theirs who shows no musicality, and that when parents are not at all musical, they should nevertheless keep an eye open for the possibility that a child of theirs may be talented, and give it every opportunity to develop. (The possibility that a talented child will be produced by average non-musical parents is, however, ever so much more remote than is indicated by the "neither-parent-talented" matings in our study. The fact that the latter matings had already produced an exceptional child was proof that the parents carried hidden "talent" genes, whereas average non-musical parents are unknown quantities.)

With awareness of the basis of musical talent there should be a wiser understanding of which children to train intensively and which ones to teach music to only casually, or not at all. Many a tragedy might have been averted if parents had not tried to turn a Jimmy into a Jascha.

All of which brings to mind the pleasant remembrance of a visit which we had with Professor Leopold Auer, one of the greatest violinists of his time, and in later years one of the most famous of music teachers. (As every one in the musical world knows, he was a vital force in the careers of many of our present violin virtuosi, who were trained by him at the Imperial Conservatory at St. Petersburg, now Leningrad.)

When we saw Professor Auer it was in 1926, a few years before his death. A tiny little man, past eighty, he was then established in a big stone house off Riverside Drive, New York, which pupils, friends and a grateful public had provided after the post-war upheaval had driven him from abroad.

Chatting about his celebrated pupils, we happened to bring up the "coincidence" that various of them had given names ending in "cha"—Jascha Heifetz, Toscha Seidel, Mischa Elman, etc. These, Professor Auer explained, were his affectionate Russian diminutives for their real names, Jacob, Thomas, Michael, etc., which he had applied to them in special recognition of their talents, and which they later adopted professionally.

"Ah," we sighed, "now we know why we could not become a great violinist. Our name should have been 'Amscha.'"

The little man's eyes twinkled. "Perhaps," he answered with laughter in his tinkling voice. *"But don't forget that these others had the talent before they got the name."*

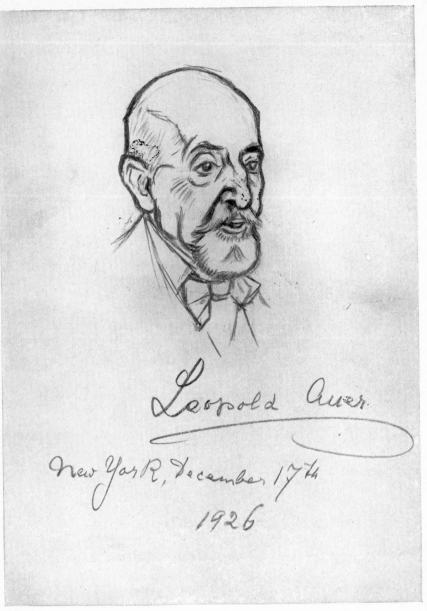

Leopold Auer

New York, December 17th
1926

PROFESSOR AUER
As sketched by the author on the occasion mentioned in the text.

CHAPTER XXXIII

FROM APTITUDE TO GENIUS

IF there is a hereditary basis for musical talent, a logical inference would be that heredity plays a part in other specialized talents and aptitudes.

There is every reason to believe that this is so, but, unfortunately, genetic exploring in other fields is not nearly so easy as it is in music. You will understand why when you recall that our music-talent studies were confined to *performing* or *interpretive* ability— the rendering of set pieces of music whereby individuals of all ages and nationalities can be measured by the same standards. But only in music is this possible, and only in interpretive music. Had we ventured into the field of composing we would have been beset with difficulties. For composing is *creative* art, the very essence of which is individuality; and individuality cannot be measured by any yardstick. That is why we did not include composers in our study, unless by coincidence they also happened to be outstanding performers.

The difficulty of evaluating creative achievement impedes genetic study similarly in the other arts—painting, sculpture, literature, etc. —with the added difficulty that in these fields there is no interpretive art as there is in music. Moreover, where in interpretive music great achievement, with attendant recognition, may come in childhood, in the creative arts talent requires many years to ripen, and recognition may not come until long after—if ever. In all history, we are not aware of a single important piece of creative work done by a pre-adolescent child.

Many composers, artists and writers did give early evidence of potential creative talent, but innumerable others were nothing to brag about as children. Of course, the talent may have been latent and unrevealed for the lack of aptitude tests. It is to remedy this

279

that many special tests have been and are now being devised which seek to measure aptitude in other arts and fields (including business, mechanical pursuits, science, etc.) as the Seashore tests do in music.

Although the heredity of other specific artistic talents may be harder to discover, if we consider them all together, a trend toward artistry in general does seem to run in given families. One member might become a musician, another a writer, another an actress or dancer, etc. We have many instances of this, suggesting that all the arts have certain "genes" in common. In music, writing, painting, sculpture, drama, architecture or esthetic dancing, one encounters the same basic principles of composition, tempo, rhythm, form, tonality or shading. In each field, however, there are certain special requirements: In writing, a knowledge of and "feeling" for language; in painting, a sense of color; in music, an "ear," etc.

If we think, then, of all the various artistic elements as being correlated with genes, we can easily see why, although two persons in a family may each carry many of the same "artistry" genes, a difference between them in a single "key" gene may send them off into different channels. An individual with many "artistry" genes who yet lacks the "color" gene may become an etcher or a black-and-white artist. A child of musical parents, failing to get the "musical-ear" genes, may become a painter, sculptor or writer. Or one lacking genes for manual facility may become an actor, or dancer. But of course, this is still theory.

Whatever the genetic explanation, the relationship of the various arts is clearly shown by the fact that so many persons talented in one field are also talented in other fields. To cite only living examples, Deems Taylor is a composer, writer and skilled cabinet-maker. George M. Cohan and Noel Coward write, compose, act. John Held, Jr., the cartoonist and writer, is also an accomplished musician. Professor John Erskine, educator and author, also appears as a concert pianist. John Barrymore, the actor, began his career as an artist, and Paul Muni might have ended up as a violinist. The writers, Joseph Hergesheimer and Somerset Maugham, started out as painters, while Hendrik Willem van Loon, E. E. Cummings and John Dos Passos are among many who continue to "double" in both fields of writing and art. Sinclair Lewis, Nobel-Prize-winning author, is one of our most gifted mimics. Angna Enters, mime and dancer, also paints and writes. These are but a handful of instances that come to our mind. As we think further, it is almost a rule that a person greatly talented in one of the arts should also show talent for some other art. (Of course, the greatest of all exemplars of versatility was Leonardo da Vinci, of whom we shall speak later.)

Not to be overlooked as an outstanding factor in the development of any creative artist is our old friend, Environment. A talent may be all dressed up with no place to go. If a talent for art crops out in an environment where no one wants art, it may die a-borning. Again, under modern conditions, with insistence on specialization, a person with various talents is forced to decide early which talent to cultivate. The wrong choice may lead him to failure where the cultivation of an alternative talent might have led to success. Few question that environment has stifled many more talents than have ever come to fruition.

Where there is no true talent or aptitude for a given pursuit, but conditioning has created an "imitation" of it, the results may be as unfortunate as the stifling of talent. Thus, the child of a musician, writer, artist or actor—or of a doctor, lawyer, engineer or business man—may, through precept and training, *acquire* tendencies which are eagerly seized on as symptoms of his being a "chip of the old block." Yet he may lack the inherent factors necessary for achievement. This may explain in part why so many sons who attempt to follow in the footsteps of illustrious fathers come to grief. A clear understanding of the required basic aptitudes and talents would greatly reduce the many sad failures who fill the arts and professions.

Here is where the aptitude tests in all fields may prove of great value. Six hundred American colleges which offer pre-medical courses now give aptitude tests to candidates for admission. Many dental colleges also give tests for prospective dentists. Tests for almost every profession are being given by the "Human Engineering Laboratories," the one at the Stevens Institute of Technology, Hoboken, N. J., the other in Boston. Some 20,000 adults and children over eleven years of age have been tested in the past few years for their capacities, with the purpose of directing them into the proper channels.

In the fields outside of the arts, such as law, medicine, business, trades, etc., we have reason to believe that environment or training, rather than inherent capacities, have heretofore been chiefly responsible for sending individuals into specific channels. On this premise the fact that there are families of doctors, lawyers, clergymen, business men, etc., might have no more genetic significance than that there are families of house-painters, railroad men or plumbers. Caution must be used in speaking of this or that family, group or race as inheriting specialized tendencies. One hears it said that Jews have "business" minds, Germans "technical" minds, Frenchmen "artistic" minds, etc. This is no more valid than saying, from what we see in the United States, that the Chinese have "laundering" or "chop suey restaurant" minds, the Greeks "shoe-shining" minds, the Armenians "rug-peddling" minds, the Irish "police" minds, etc.

Genetics emphasizes constantly the danger of generalizing and the necessity of thinking in terms of individuals and individual characteristics. For instance, let us say that *one* of the requisites for achievement in science, engineering or business is a "head for figures." By isolating the single unit factor of "mathematical" talent (if there is one!) we could look for its appearance in given families. Thus, college records have revealed a correlation between the standings in mathematics of fathers and sons, and also of brothers, which has led to the belief that mathematical talent has a hereditary basis. (Some authorities go so far as to ascribe it to a dominant gene.) If a few more unit factors which play a part in business achievement are found to run in families, we might then, but only then, be justified in saying that "business ability" is inherited.

Some investigators have also reported an apparent correlation between mathematical and musical talent, pointing out that musicians must have a "feeling" for numerical ratios. We might then expect that some mathematicians (granted that they also had a few of the required "music" genes) would be able to play. A few isolated examples prove nothing, but it is interesting to point to

Prof. Albert Einstein, and perhaps to former Vice-President Charles Dawes, a banker, as men with "heads for figures" who are both accomplished violinists.

Also considered closely allied with mathematical ability is virtuosity in chess. That there may be a hereditary basis for chess virtuosity seems indicated by the several instances where chess talent cropped out at an early age, notably in Jose Capablanca, former world chess champion; Paul Morphy of New Orleans, another chess expert; and, most strikingly, in the present chess champion of the United States, Samuel Reshevsky.

As many may recall, Reshevsky (now twenty-six) burst upon our chess horizon when, at the age of eight, he came from Poland with his father and made a spectacular tour of the United States, playing matches sometimes with as many as twenty or thirty players *simultaneously*. At one of the cities he visited, we were sent (in our reportorial capacity) to a private home, where he was being boarded, to interview the prodigy. Loud outcries greeted us from the rear yard. Investigation revealed a frail, undersized youngster shouting at some neighbor lads, in language unintelligible to them, that he was the great chess player. (His adversaries seemed totally unimpressed, and only a timely rescue prevented *lèse-majesté* from being committed.)

In other words, the prodigy appeared to be no different from any other small boy. Yet that night we saw this frail, undersized child suavely and single-handed engaging a roomful of adult and expert chess players, moving with bewildering swiftness from board to board and in short order defeating all but two, who were declared tied because little Sammy was getting sleepy.

The "something uncanny" which people associate with prodigies might be nothing more than the premature development of certain "unit" characteristics of the mind. An exceptional development of the power of memory might of itself produce prodigy qualities in a child. One prodigy of our acquaintance, a young miss whose IQ at twelve was one of the highest on record, had not only a remarkable memory, but the ability to "see in chunks" (as she put it)—to read not by word or phrase but by whole paragraphs at a time. The two gifts in combination enabled her to take her studies in kangaroo leaps. In most other respects, however, she was no different than other children of twelve, and at last reports she has grown up to be a bright, but not outstanding, young married woman.

The foregoing case, and that of Reshevsky, illustrate the fact that in many prodigies only *part* of a child's mentality may be prematurely developed. It may very well be that certain genes, or perhaps environmental factors, have acted to stimulate an early growth of such mental characteristics, in the same way that there are genes or factors which may force the premature arrival of puberty. The mistake, however, is to assume that the *entire* mental process has been advanced, and also to overlook the rôle of experience in producing maturity. By therefore confusing precocity in only limited respects with adult mentality, and forcing prodigies into adult levels to which they were not adjusted, much grief has been caused them in the past.

The tendency now is to recognize unusual brilliance in a child as merely a "unit" manifestation, in the same way that children may have unusual athletic ability or musical talent and yet be quite average in other respects. Accordingly, advanced school systems are now providing extra outlets for the mental energies of superior children, the while keeping them at average class levels and in association with other children of their age.

Talent, aptitude and creative ability reach their fullest expression in those most remarkable of all human phenomena—the true geniuses, whose intellectual and creative powers carry them to such heights that long after they are gone humanity continues to be illumined by their achievements. Think a moment of Leonardo da Vinci, whose talents ran a bewildering gamut—art, architecture, poetry, music, engineering, anatomy, biology, invention, city planning—with outstanding contributions in each field. How are we to account for him? Or for such other geniuses, less versatile, but no less great, as Shakespeare, Michelangelo, Plato, Sophocles, Spinoza, Newton and the few score others of similar caliber in all history?

Because geniuses seem to arise spontaneously, with apparently no relationship to their family, background or training, they were formerly looked upon as divine, supernatural and inexplicable

Kubli photo

HEREDITY OR TRAINING?

Samuel Reshevsky, later to be United States' chess champion, is here shown, at the age of eight, on the occasion referred to in the text when he played thirty opponents simultaneously.

human phenomena. Geneticists now incline toward a more prosaic explanation: That great geniuses were, or are, merely the result of rare and unusual combinations of "superior" genes, interacting with the necessary environmental conditions. The very fact that such men have arisen from every type of background, sometimes in the face of extreme adversity, and all sorts of handicaps, rules out the theory that it is environment which produces genius. Nothing in the background or training of a Shakespeare, Leonardo, Lincoln or Edison was any more unusual than that of countless others who never rose beyond mediocrity.

A gene hypothesis similar to that which we advanced for the inheritance of musical talent might be elaborated to explain the derivation of genius of any kind. Naturally, for different types of geniuses, different gene combinations would be required, and the rarer the genius, the rarer and more complex the combination of genes would have to be. (Mind you, we are speaking theoretically.)

Taking Shakespeare as an example, if we tried to "break down" the components of his genius, we might say that they must have included an extraordinary intelligence, an unusual memory, intense emotional feeling, an extreme sensitivity to "sound effects" in words, remarkable powers of imagination, a sense of harmony, composition and rhythm, a response to color, etc.; and coupled with all that, an unusual "drive" which enabled him to produce his masterpieces in so short a time. Each of these attributes of his may have been due to one or many genes, and every single one of these genes would have been required to make the *potential* Shakespeare. The absence of just one "key" gene might have reduced the whole combination to mediocrity.

We can thus see (again theoretically) why Shakespeare's parents as individuals were nonentities in spite of the fact that they might have carried a large number of the precious genes; and why, with only half of his genes passed on to any child, Shakespeare's genius never again repeated itself in his descendants. So with Lincoln, Wagner, or any other genius in history. It would then be little wonder that there is no record of *two* truly great geniuses following each other in the same family.

Again it should be emphasized that the mere presence of the requisite combination of superior genes would not insure the flowering of a genius. We have no way of telling how many equally great or perhaps even greater *potential* geniuses than those on record were suppressed by some unfavorable circumstance. Especially does this suggest itself with regard to the failure of women to keep pace with men in achieving greatness. Everything we have learned in genetics (as we pointed out in the preceding chapter) proves conclusively that any combination of "superior" genes that could occur in a man could also occur in a woman; in fact, that as women carry more genes, the combination would be even likelier to occur. We must therefore conclude that (a) our social environment, in which women have always been kept subordinate to men, is responsible for suppressing their potentialities, or (b) that something constitutional—possibly hormonal, or such factors as motherhood—acts as an inhibitory influence. As to the latter, we have seen that in hardly more than a generation since women have been given comparative freedom in careers, but not yet equality, they have produced many notable persons. Until they are given *full* equality and full opportunity we cannot conclude that there is something inherent in women which prevents their being geniuses.

One other question that is bound to come up in any discussion of genius:

Is it true that geniuses are always a little "queer" mentally or physically?

The belief that such is the case has been and still is widespread. Back about 50 A.D. Seneca said, "There is no great genius without a tincture of madness." In the seventeenth century John Dryden wrote,

> *"Great wits are sure to madness near allied,*
> *And thin partitions do their bounds divide."*

And capping mere adages with weighty scientific thought, Lombroso, a generation ago, brought forth reams of data to prove that genius was akin to insanity. Others have followed with added testimony that many great men were "queer" or physically warped.

Reported as epileptics were Mohammed, Paul of Tarsus, Julius

Caesar, Francis of Assisi, Alfred the Great, Peter the Great, Napoleon I, Dostoeffsky. Listed as emotionally unstable or of a "hysterical" temperament were Bismarck, Poe, Goethe, Kant, Pascal, Rousseau, Baudelaire, Wagner, Schopenhauer, Tolstoy, etc. Insanity —or suicide—ended the careers of Schumann, Nietzsche, Van Gogh and many others. This and that man was sexually abnormal. So we could continue to fill pages.

The implication from all this, taken at face value, is that genius carries with it an evil destiny, or that genius can only flower in unhealthy soil. This is far from a universal fact. While it is quite true that many great men were mentally or physically abnormal, many more great men were apparently not physically or mentally abnormal. The records of the great men of our own country or of our own time will bear this out. We have only to think of Washington, Franklin, Jefferson, and Lincoln, of Mark Twain, Emerson, Henry James and of George Bernard Shaw, Toscanini, Sibelius; Einstein, Darwin; Justices Oliver Wendell Holmes and Brandeis. Neither insanity, nor morbidity, so far as we know, characterized or characterizes any of these men.

Why, then, has genius always been linked with madness or some pathological condition? Perhaps the first reason, as various authorities suggest, is what may be bluntly termed the "sour grapes" attitude of more ordinary mortals—the wish to explain achievement far beyond them as due to something undesirable. Many early scientists were looked upon as sorcerers and many great men were hounded or even executed because their words or talents were believed to have an evil source.

If a large number of geniuses or other celebrated figures were "queer," so have been innumerable persons who weren't great. With regard to insanity or nervous disorders, also, we know that the incidence in the general population is high enough to explain why a fair percentage of great men should also be so afflicted. And when we get right down to it, how many of us who aren't geniuses could prove that we are at *all times,* and under all conditions, fully sane?

Because the records of great men were carefully kept, and their lives subjected to close scrutiny, it should be expected that their "abnormalities" would loom up out of all proportion to those in the general population. Nevertheless, it is also possible that the strain, the responsibilities and the abnormal social environment surrounding great men and geniuses might have tended to make them eccentric, or to undermine their health.

"I wouldn't want my child to be a genius!" is something that you yourself might have said. There may be a sound basis for this, not because of any evidence that geniuses are doomed to unhappiness by something inherent in them, but because the world isn't fully prepared for geniuses. As was brought out earlier, steps are now being taken to make the development and adjustment of superior children easier. In the opinion of genetic authorities the genes requisite for genius abound throughout the world in all classes and among all peoples. Not an "unhealthy" soil, but a healthy social environment, they believe, will eventually result in the bumper crop of geniuses that may lift all humanity to new and far higher levels.

CHAPTER XXXIV

PERSONALITY

IF people in real life were like characters in the movies and the comic strips, we could make these definite assertions:

All fat people are good-natured, frank and easily moved to laughter or tears.

All blond women are dumb and frivolous, or else are cold, calculating and morally loose.

All black-haired men with swarthy skins and sharp noses are villains.

All red-heads are passionate; all men with high foreheads are intellectual; all men with receding chins are timid.

The list could be extended indefinitely to include the various features and looks that are supposed to indicate jealousy, meanness, criminality, aristocracy, treachery, affectionate disposition, etc.

But is there actually such a correlation? If there were, then knowing that heredity influences one's appearance, we might go further and ask whether heredity does not also *make a person act the way he looks?*

Much attention has been given recently by scientists to these very points. As in other studies, we begin with the lower animals. Here we do find indications of what the scientists call inherited "behavior patterns," which characterize not merely the different species, but subdivisions of the same species. It is well known that various types of birds build their nests in various ways, that different breeds of dogs behave differently—fox-terriers being nervous and aggressive, St. Bernards calm, bulldogs persistent, etc. Is there a parallel in different strains of men?

Approaching the subject objectively, scientists now say that our behavior may have a genetic basis just as well-founded as that in the lower animals. As Professor James Gray of Cambridge expresses it: ". . . I do not believe we can put our finger on any of our mental powers and say, 'Herein are we a race apart, elevated above the rest of the animal world.' " To illustrate, Professor Gray reports his discovery that even the lowly fish have not merely automatic movements but powers of forming associations between events, of memory in carrying out highly complicated excursions, and also power to display emotion.

On a physical basis, all such activity in the fish is explained as being the result of a series of "reflexes." If a fireman is awakened in the middle of the night by a gong he automatically jumps out of bed, pulls on his trousers, shirt, socks, shoes, slides down the brass pole, etc. This sequence of acts, initiated by the gong and one act giving rise to the next, might also be thought of as "reflexes." Further, were such a pattern of actions "inherited," we might expect that a fireman's child, hearing a gong for the first time, would go through the same procedure (assuming that the clothing, pole, etc., were at hand).

Strangely enough, scientists believe that not too dissimilar patterns of behavior can be inherited among the lower animals. In the fish, a certain stimulus produces a certain reflex, etc., the chain of events often resulting in highly complex actions. These reflexes may be provoked or conditioned by environment and by imitation of others. Nevertheless, widely separated individuals among fish as well as other lower animals often act in the same way, so on the whole the various behavior patterns which are characteristic of the different species with respect to sex or food-gathering, or nest-building among birds, dam-building among beavers, honeycomb-building among bees, etc., may be considered as due to something inherited rather than acquired.

All this, and studies of humans themselves, have led to the belief that there may be laws of inheritance which apply to human behavior just as there are laws of inheritance that apply to our physical structure. Or, in other words, *that there are genes which govern our temperament, disposition and behavior* in the same way that there are genes for other characteristics.

It is when we try to isolate and identify these "behavior" genes in the light of our present limited knowledge that we encounter difficulties. Much more than in the case of mentality, human behavior is influenced and modified by training and environment, and any comparison between humans and lower animals falls short if it does not take this into account. As just one factor, our young remain helpless and dependent for a much longer time than do the young of any other animals. This long formative period of itself offers great opportunity in humans for shaping and perhaps distorting whatever inherited behavior patterns we may have.

A girl is blond, blue-eyed, beautiful. Does a certain kind of temperament, character, behavior, go with that combination? Or does beauty in a girl produce a certain kind of environment about her which in turn molds her temperament and behavior? Here is where we must consider two kinds of environment—the *external* environment which one encounters in any society, and the *internal* environment which a person himself or herself *creates*.

If a girl is beautiful as a child, she evokes quite different responses and attitudes toward her than does the homely girl, and it would be strange indeed if her character were not affected. As she carries her beauty into maturity its effect on others—family, friends, masculine admirers, employers—increases and reacts again on herself. To the extent that these experiences and effects are similar in all beautiful girls, it may be said that beauty is accompanied by a certain type of personality. The mistake would lie in assuming that the *genes* which tended to produce beauty also produced this temperament.

Consider the case of the *very tall girl*. If her growth comes early, she must begin dressing as a grown-up before her classmates do. The discrepancies between her mature appearance and her immaturity of experience may tend to produce in her a sense of maladjustment. Finally, the man problem comes along. The tall girl encounters difficulty in finding dancing partners, boy friends or mates. Often forced to be with herself a great deal, the tall girl may turn to reading and reflection, and become more sober and serious.

The *very fat girl,* always a target for pleasantries, may build up a defense by being the first to laugh at herself in order to disarm others. You may have observed that at costume parties big, fat girls often dress in "kiddy" costumes, to expose fully the plumpness of their arms and legs, just as do the fat ladies in the circus. Never feeling themselves quite at ease, it would not be surprising if fat girls as a class are emotionally not too well balanced.

Similarly, *very short girls* appear in children's costumes (those of little boys or little girls). In buying clothes they must patronize the junior-misses' or even children's departments. Men good-naturedly toss the little girls about, bigger girls baby them, people constantly jest about their size. These and other factors may make the small girl hypersensitive, high-spirited, high-strung.

The effects of extreme *homeliness* on a girl should be obvious. The lack of welcome she receives, the indifference of men, the greater difficulty in finding jobs and in making a place for herself in society, the many unpleasant experiences she encounters, could well explain certain aspects of her temperament; and yet most people confuse the resentfulness, the anti-social attitude often displayed by homely girls with something basic in their make-up.

A psychologist would extend this type of analysis to every other kind of person. In men, very short men, like very small girls, tend to be sensitive and eager to dominate; handsome men, to whom many things come too easy, may often be ne'er-do-wells. So too, great physical strength on the one hand or sickliness on the other may each be correlated with a type of personality.

Now all of these cases (which may conjure up pictures of some of your friends, and perhaps even of yourself) are important because they illustrate the fact that appearance can influence personality and behavior. If, then, appearance in turn is due to certain genes, we might conclude that a child who inherited genes which make him *look* like his father would automatically grow up to *act* like his father. In other words, that people who looked the same would act the same. But this is not necessarily true.

A person with one type of "personality" in one environment might have developed into quite a different person in another environment. Consider our girl types again: If our tall girl found herself in a society of uniformly tall people, she would no longer be maladjusted; nor would the short girl be exceptional in a society of very short women, nor the fat girl in a country of fat women. The blonde with the streamlined, hipless figure who may be so popular in New York society might quickly develop an inferiority complex in a Turkish outpost where plump women are preferred.

So much for certain kinds of *looks* that alter actions. But there are also certain kinds of *actions* that alter *looks*. In fact, human appearance is much more plastic than is generally imagined.

As every one knows, habits of occupation and of living may produce marked differences not merely in behavior but in physical appearance and facial expression. Scientists now have a term, "muscle tone," which they apply to the degree of contraction of a muscle, or in other words to the manner in which it works. The "tone" of a muscle results from the way in which one habitually uses it. The face is a network of innumerable muscles, large and small, governing every movement of the features. Through use and habit starting from infancy, every facial muscle develops its "tone," its peculiar way of working, or relaxing. A person's facial expression in repose or in action, therefore, would be the sum of his facial-muscle "tones." Similarly, all acquired mannerisms of walking, moving the hands, posture, etc., would be due to the "tones" of the muscles involved.

When we add to the muscle tones the effects of other living-habits —diet, sleep, work, etc.—we can see why persons in the same occupation, farmers, policemen, firemen, teachers, clerks, etc.—may develop certain similarities of appearance. Even more emphatically, persons in the same country or locality with similar habits and conditions may develop characteristics—of moving the hands, talking, walking, etc.—which are erroneously assumed to be basic and hereditary.[1]

To hark back now to the habit of associating a certain kind of appearance with a certain kind of personality, we find that interpretations may vary markedly with the locality or country. Why are villains depicted among us as dark-haired men with swarthy skins, sharp noses and heavy black eyebrows? Probably because in Amer-

[1] The interesting theory has been advanced that eating habits among various peoples or individuals may be influenced by inherited variations in the sense of taste. In support of this theory are findings (by Dr. A. F. Blakeslee and Prof. L. H. Snyder among others) that certain chemicals or substances taste differently to various individuals and that these taste reactions are apparently inherited. We have not stressed this point because there are as yet no data regarding the heredity of taste reactions to any common foods—for instance, spinach.

ica, and perhaps in England, the type was that of the foreigner who differed radically from the prevailing native stock. It is human to view strangers with suspicion; and we dare say that among many black-haired, dark-skinned people, the villains would be depicted as blond and light-skinned.

There is also a tendency, in associating appearance with personality, to resort to allegorical interpretation. "Black" connotes mystery, death, tragedy, and sinister influences; it is easy to see why villains would be depicted as "dark." And similarly why the Little Evas and the innocent heroines would be depicted as blond, blue-eyed and white-skinned.

A radio psychologist recently made the assertion that all pop-eyed persons are talkative, and all people with deep-set eyes are reticent. This theory does not conform to fact. The "pop-eye" correlation is based on the idea that goiter or thyroid conditions frequently cause pop-eyes, and that often the "hyper-thyroid" person is given to verbosity. But this far from implies that *all* people who are hyper-thyroid types or all persons with goiter are talkative, or that all persons with pop-eyes produced by other causes are also talkative.

The idea that protruding eyes mean "protruding" personality or vocal assertiveness, may have as its converse the idea that deep-set, receding eyes connote reticence or "receding" personality. A similar notion is that receding chins indicate a "receding" or weak character, while a protruding jaw indicates pugnaciousness and bravery. Science, however, offers nothing to substantiate this. Surely, there is no evidence that peoples with more receding chins, such as American Indians and Chinese, are inherently less brave than big-jawed Europeans.

Although countless detailed studies have been made and are in process of being made, we are not yet able to point to any particular type of body, face, head or skeletal structure in normal individuals as definitely correlated with any given type of behavior. The German psychiatrist, Ernst Kretschmer, some years ago presented evidence that dementia praecox cases were most frequently found among long and thin persons of the "asthenic" type, and that manic-depressives were most frequently of the short and rounded "pyknic" physiques. But his claims of other correlations, in non-pathological cases, between physical structure and behavior have not stood up.

Glandular disturbances or nerve and mental disorders obviously can result in abnormal behavior. It is therefore logical to suppose that inasmuch as the glands, through their hormones, are known to influence greatly both physical development and emotional states among all individuals, the degree in which "gland" genes might vary among even normal persons would have some bearing on their differences in behavior. This implies not that "gland" genes directly determine personality, but that they are important influences in its production.

According to Professor Gordon W. Allport, Harvard psychologist, a newborn infant can be considered as lacking personality, for personality must be thought of as developing from birth onward. But the child is by no means a mass of clay in this respect, to be molded solely by the forces of environment, as the extreme "behaviorists" formerly maintained. Forces inside every child—implanted by heredity—work together from the very beginning with forces from the outside to develop its personality.

Psychologists may be adding nothing to what mothers know when they report that one can detect distinct differences in personality among the youngest infants. Alertness, dulness, restlessness placidity, enterprise, laziness, fretfulness, calmness, responsiveness to people about them or indifference—these and many other traits in varying degrees may be noted among infants whose environments are approximately the same. In fact, in these early manifestations some authorities see portents of the child's future personality.

However, whatever inner "personality" factors there are can be considered only as related to potentialities. That is, one must consider each individual as having from the beginning not a definite personality but the potentialities for a wide range of personalities— the form which his personality will take depending upon the circumstances encountered. Nor can we consider that the personality will take any fixed form. A moment's thought will make clear that one's personality is never constant and may undergo continuous changes. But again, when we remember that there are "time" genes which do not come into play until given stages in a person's life are reached —genes acting at puberty, maturity or old age, such as those for baldness, mental defects, many diseases, etc.—it may readily be gathered that heredity as well as environment acts throughout life to effect such personality changes.

(An interesting note in passing is the observation by Prof. Jennings that the personalities of dull persons may be influenced more by heredity than those of bright individuals, because the latter are more responsive to their environments.)

As for the rôle of environment, the most significant evidence we have is provided by our study of identical twins. If there are differences in personality between identical twins, with exactly the same genes, these differences must be directly attributed to environment. Especially illuminating, then, would be a study of *five* individuals with the same genes. So we turn again to those invaluable little aides of science, the Dionne quintuplets.

After two years of careful observation, Drs. W. E. Blatz and D. A. Millichamp, psychologists of the University of Toronto, report that the quintuplets show variations in behavior, personality and temperament, even greater than they do with regard to their physical make-up and mentality. However, it is the physical differences, as we saw, that form the point of departure for their other differences.

The personality studies of the Dionnes were made along the most approved scientific lines. The quintuplets were compared in their social behavior both with the standards for average children of their own age and in relation to one another. The observers noted every action and incident which had a social significance— that is, which threw some light on the attitude of any one of the quintuplets toward others in the group, and their responses in turn toward her. If any child did something to attract the attention of the others, or if she showed more interest in one sister than in another, this was carefully recorded. And these were the findings:

Yvonne is the most popular one within the group. Although the most advanced in general development, she is nevertheless the least socially aggressive, quite good-naturedly letting the others take the initiative in play. So distinct is her personality that she has been dubbed by the psychologists "The Matriarch."

Annette is the most aggressive. She clamors for attention and is watched the most by the others. This attention that she receives, say the psychologists, stimulates her to "further aggressive social behavior in order to satisfy the developed need of an audience."

Emilie is a happy-go-lucky little individual, not caring much "who starts what or does which," and is the most self-sufficient of the five.

Cecile is set down as the "unknown quantity," her behavior with regard to the others being the most variable and most unpredictable.

And finally we have little Marie—Fortune's Stepchild of the quintuplets. Starting off with physical handicaps, these led to handicaps in mentality and achievement, and these in turn now conspire against her socially. The baby of the group, she is the least skilled in manipulating materials, in play and in enterprise. Poor little Marie! She tries so hard to initiate contacts, but only motherly Yvonne pays much attention to her.

Let us stop a minute. We have almost forgotten that we are dealing with "identical" quintuplets who look so much alike in the pictures that we cannot tell them apart. And yet here are these striking differences in personality among them—Yvonne at one extreme, Marie at the other—*despite the fact that all five carry exactly the same types of whatever genes there are for behavior, personality and temperament.*

Is it any wonder that we have such difficulty in determining how much of an ordinary individual's personality is inherited or "basic," and how much is due to environment?

What, for instance, would we call the "basic" personality of the Dionnes, even if we considered them all together as a group? What has been the effect upon them of their training, their association with good Dr. Dafoe and their nurses, their consciousness of being watched, and all the other unusual influences in their "hothouse" environment? The psychologists cannot help wondering what the personalities of the quintuplets would be now (a) had they all been separated at the beginning and reared in different environments, (b) had they been kept together, but reared in free association with other children, or (c) had they been left with Papa and Mama Dionne, to be reared any which way with the large brood of older brothers and sisters.

Of this there seems to be no doubt, that the personalities of the quintuplets will always be distinct from one another, the differences probably increasing with the years, and that *they would have been different and distinct under any circumstances.* In short, that the environment can never be exactly the same for any two individuals, and that even with exactly the same genes present, the slightest environmental changes can produce differences in personality.

On the other hand, emphasis must also be placed on the evidence, provided by many other twin studies, of the effects of heredity. After long and detailed study of large numbers of twins, Professor Newman has reported:

Identical twins do show marked similarity in behavior and personality which cannot be entirely explained on the ground of similar environment.

Even when reared apart, identical twins, although differing in many ways, are nevertheless *more alike than fraternal twins reared together,* tending to prove that there is a genetic basis for "personality."

At the same time, the resemblance in personality between any two identical twins—whether reared together or apart—is much less than their similarity in physical characteristics. Or, to sum up Prof. Newman's conclusions, on the basis of the twin studies, it appears that *physical characteristics are affected least by environment; intelligence more; education and achievement still more; and personality and temperament the most.*

Among psychologists in general the belief prevails that of the various factors involved in producing personality, the likelihoods of their being influenced by heredity are as follows:

Most likely to be influenced by heredity: Basic abilities, such as intelligence, speed of reaction, motor skills, sensory discrimination, etc.

Less likely to be influenced by heredity: Temperamental traits, such as emotionality, alternation or evenness of mood, activity or lethargy, and other characteristics in which gland activity is conceivably involved.

Least likely to be influenced by heredity (if at all): Attitudes,

THE DIONNE QUINTUPLETS

YVONNE	MARIE	CECILE	ANNETTE	EMILIE
Ht., 39½ in.	39 in.	39½ in.	39½ in.	39¼ in.
Wt., 40½ lbs.	36¼ lbs.	39¾ lbs.	41 lbs.	38¾ lbs.

The early differences among the five, due to differences in pre-natal environment are here shown to have persisted. The photograph was taken in August, 1938, some months after their fourth birthday. Note the marked contrast between Yvonne, "matriarch" of the group, and Marie, the "baby"; also the fact that Marie and Emilie, the "twinned" pair, are still closest in measurements.

stylistic traits, beliefs, values and other such characteristics in which training or conditioning are clearly major factors.

To sum up this chapter, every trail of scientific evidence and reasoning points to the existence of genes which influence behavior, temperament and personality. Where, within the same family, under a similar environment, great differences in personality appear among the children, we may ascribe these differences in some degree to different combinations of genes. We can also assume that some of the similarity in personality between parents and their children is produced by genes. But we are still unable to identify any of these genes, or to gage the extent of their effects, or to hazard any predictions as to what the personality of a given child will be on the basis of what we know about its parents. What is fully clear is that such genes as may be involved in molding personality are highly susceptible to outside influences. We can therefore hardly consider them as producing such distinct effects as do the genes for many physical traits which we have noted, or as charting a definite course for an individual's personality.

Nor do we know of any other influences that can chart a fixed course for one's personality. There are many myths and superstitions, and not a few pseudo-scientific theories, regarding the influence of the stars, planets, atmospheric conditions and various cosmic factors on the behavior, temperaments and achievements of individuals—all implying that a person born at certain times, under certain conditions, will have such and such a personality. Regarding these we can only say that science offers no corroborative evidence whatsoever. To discuss these "influences" at greater length would be like setting up stuffed dummies for the sole purpose of promptly knocking them down again.

Neither through the genes, then, nor through other influences, are we prepared to say that any normal human being is "predestined" to act in any certain way. This still leaves open the question of "abnormal" behavior—such as *criminality,* which we consider next.

CHAPTER XXXV

ENTER THE VILLAIN

TIGERS and wolves are "killers." Jackals and buzzards are scavengers. Magpies and cuckoos are thieves. Leeches are parasites. If these and hosts of other animals were judged by human standards, we would say that they were all of them congenitally "anti-social."

But we do not hold the lower animals strictly to account for what they do because we do not credit them with the same sort of intelligence that we have, or with any will or conscience. We ascribe their acts to "instincts," to uncontrollable impulses; we say "they were born that way." On the other hand, what the human animal does we like to think of as dictated by intelligence and reasoning powers. On this assumption, that what *we* do is done wilfully, are based all our existing codes of law and morality, of responsibility for our acts, with punishment for "bad" behavior and reward for "good" behavior.

Are we entirely right? Disquieting theories have been advanced that many human criminals are no more responsible for their acts than are the lower animals; that they, too, are impelled by uncontrollable impulses and inherited anti-social instincts. If this were so, it would be highly important for geneticists to ascertain the genes responsible for criminal behavior, so that these could be listed prominently among the "black" genes.

Long before the mechanics of heredity was revealed, the belief was prevalent that the tendency to commit murder or crimes of every kind "ran as a taint" in certain families. Toward the end of the nineteenth century, the Italian criminologist, Cesare Lombroso, startled the world with his theory that there was a definite correlation between criminality and bodily constitution, and that various kinds of criminals were of specified physical types. Back of this

300

lay the thought that one could be born *predestined* to a life of crime.

Lombroso's theory did not stand up well under an onslaught of contradictory evidence, and was abandoned by most criminologists and psychologists. Recently, however, some of the principles have been revived. One of our own prominent scientists, Professor Ernest Hooton, says his personal studies of criminals suggest that there is an unduly large proportion of very short fat men among sex offenders and an excess of tall, slender men among murderers. Others, pointing to the fact that there is every type represented among criminals and murderers, look skeptically at the "predestination" theories.

Most closely approaching factual evidence are the studies that have been made of criminality in twins. Professor J. Lange, who studied twins in German prisons, reported that in almost every instance where one member of a pair of identical twins had taken to crime, the other had also become a criminal. What was more, the types of crime committed by the twins were the same, or closely related. Among fraternal twins (who had different hereditary factors) he did not find a corresponding similarity. All this would tend to indicate that heredity played an overwhelming part in criminality and that *the criminal twins had an inborn tendency to a life of crime.*

Lange's work, which was based on a limited number of cases, inspired further study of criminality in twins, including studies in the United States. These later studies with many more cases recorded modify somewhat Lange's findings. They do indicate a much greater likelihood that identical twins will both become criminals than that fraternal twins or any two ordinary brothers will both become criminals. But also, many cases are revealed where *only one* member of a pair of identical twins went astray, and where the other, with exactly the same heredity, did not. This rules out the possibility that crime is *invariably* predestined, and suggests that slight differences in environment may make one twin a criminal while the other goes straight. It also suggests that in many instances where *both* twins become criminals, a similarity in their

HOMICIDES* — UNITED STATES AND OTHER COUNTRIES

Number of persons
Killed in years stated,
per 100,000 population:

1　2　3　4　5　6　7　8

United States ('35)

Roumania ('33)

Hungary ('34)

Czecho-Slovakia ('35)

Italy ('34)

Switzerland ('35)
Belgium ('34)

Canada ('35), Germany ('34)
N. Ireland ('35)

Sweden ('33)
Japan ('34)

Holland ('34)
Denmark ('35)
Norway ('33)

England, Wales
and Scotland ('35)

*Homicides include not only murders
but justifiable, excusable or unin-
tentional killings.

The year stated for each country
was the latest for which a report
was obtainable.

environment, and their close association with each other, may be
responsible.

While the evidence as to the rôle of heredity in crime is meager,
there is no such uncertainty regarding the influence of environment. Consider the most serious of crimes, murder:

The murder rate in the United States is far above that of any
large European country. For homicides (which include manslaugh-
ter) the rate per 100,000 population in large American cities is
almost *twenty times higher* than in England and Wales and about

three to four times higher than in Germany or Italy, with the rates for other countries somewhere in between.

Knowing that the hereditary factors of the people of the United States can be no different than that of their European progenitors, we are forced to conclude that *there is something in the environment of this country which produces more murders*. This becomes even clearer as we examine comparative murder statistics within the United States itself:

In 1936 there were *no* murders in such fair-sized cities as Davenport, Iowa, Lynn, Massachusetts, and Berkeley, California; only 9 murders each in Boston and Milwaukee; and *118 murders* in Atlanta, and 70 in Birmingham, Alabama, each of these last two cities with about one-third the population of Boston. Certainly an uneven distribution!

Almost uniformly, the homicide rate in southern cities is overwhelmingly greater than in our cities elsewhere—including *Chicago* and *New York*. (None of the ten largest cities of the country, in fact, are in the list of the thirty with the highest murder rate.) The high murder rate among Negroes in the South has a bearing on the situation, but by no means accounts for all of it, because the murder rate among southern Whites is also far higher than among Whites elsewhere.

Thus once more, as no one would claim that the Whites of the South have a much more "murderous" heredity than those of the North, or that, comparing cities elsewhere, the people of Denver, Colorado (with a murder rate of 10 per 100,000), are by heredity five or six times as murderous as those of Boston and Milwaukee, we must look for an explanation to environmental differences. And we can readily find it. Wherever living conditions, poverty and ignorance are the worst, politics most corrupt, graft most rampant, the police most inefficient and the courts most lax, there the murder and crime rate will be the highest.

Perhaps you remember this story:

In a "hell-roaring" mining town of Wild West days, there was a commotion one evening. An old "Forty-niner" stuck his head out of a barroom and saw his son being led to jail by the sheriff.

"Hey!" he called out. "What's my Willy done?"

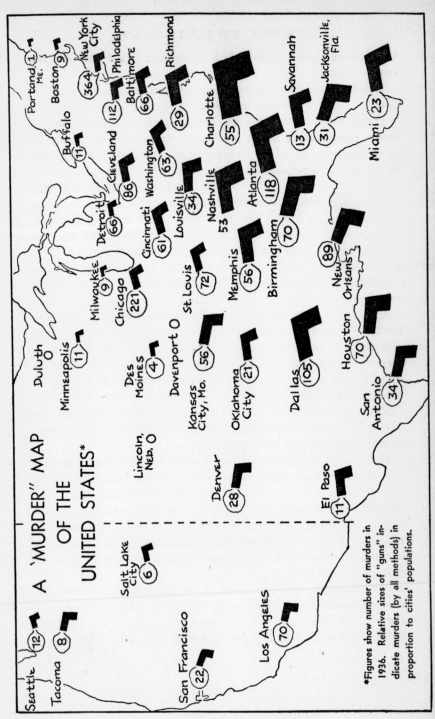

A "MURDER" MAP OF THE UNITED STATES*

Seattle (12)
Tacoma (8)
San Francisco (22)
Los Angeles (70)
Salt Lake City (6)
Denver (28)
El Paso (11)
San Antonio (34)
Houston (70)
New Orleans (89)
Dallas (105)
Oklahoma City (21)
Kansas City, Mo. (56)
Davenport O
Des Moines (4)
Lincoln, Neb. O
Minneapolis (11)
Duluth O
Milwaukee (9)
Chicago (221)
St. Louis (72)
Memphis (56)
Birmingham (70)
Atlanta (118)
Nashville (53)
Louisville (34)
Cincinnati (61)
Detroit (66)
Cleveland (86)
Buffalo (11)
Washington (63)
Richmond (29)
Charlotte (55)
Savannah (13)
Jacksonville, Fla. (31)
Miami (23)
Baltimore (66)
Philadelphia (112)
New York City (364)
Boston (9)
Portland, Me. (1)

*Figures show number of murders in 1936. Relative sizes of "guns" indicate murders (by all methods) in proportion to cities' populations.

The sheriff yelled back, "He got mad and killed one of them Eastern dudes!"

"Shucks," said the old-timer, going back to his tippling. "I thought mebbe Willy'd stole a horse."

This is not so far-fetched. Horse-stealing was a hanging offense in the frontier days, when a murder was often looked upon as an indiscretion. A not too dissimilar easy atttitude toward murder on the part of juries today, coupled with lack of restriction against "totin' a gun," has a lot to do with high murder rates, not only in individual sections of the country but in the United States as a whole compared with European countries. No one doubts, for instance, that the tendency of our chivalric juries to all but pin a medal on fair murderesses, after they have dutifully recited ". . . He struck me . . . then everything went dark" has acted as a "go ahead" signal for many whose husbands or lovers prove annoying.

Although it might appear obvious that environment is to blame for differences in murder rates between one group of Americans and another, or between Americans in general and Europeans, there is nevertheless an undercurrent of belief that differences in murder rates *among various nationalities* in our midst are due to *heredity*. This belief was one of the important reasons for checking immigration and fixing quotas, it being felt that many of the immigrant peoples (especially those from southern Europe) were *by nature predisposed* to criminality.

How true is it, for instance, that Italians are more "hot-blooded," and therefore more easily moved to murder or crime in general than other people? Statistics do show that in certain large cities there is a higher percentage of murders by Italians than by *native* Whites of British or German descent. But further investigation will show that the comparison is unfair, because the mass of Italians in these cities live under conditions far more unfavorable than do most of these others.

We also might find that many of the murders by Italians here were committed by members of the old Mafia or Black Hand who came to our shores and who had no more in common with other Italians than some of our native gangsters have with other Americans. As a final commentary, an elaborate study of Italian convicts in western Pennsylvania prisons has resulted in these conclusions: That crimes of violence are *not* a racial trend of the Italians; that the crime rate among second-generation Italians is not notably greater than among other native Whites; that the Italians in the area covered by the survey were not professional, but rather accidental, criminals, their crimes being the result of factors that generally are conducive to crime—want, unemployment, low mentality, etc.

Negroes, too, are popularly thought of as more "hot-blooded" and inherently criminal than Whites, but it is now being shown that where their crime rate is high, one should look first to environment instead of blaming heredity. If bad conditions can explain high crime rates among Whites, the immeasurably worse conditions under which Negroes live can explain a far greater degree of criminality. In Birmingham, Alabama, where illiteracy among Negroes was decreased one-half, the murder rate was also decreased one-half.

The whole question of crime in relation to our foreign-born was thoroughly investigated by the National Commission on Law Observance and Enforcement, in 1931. Studying the high delinquency areas, or slums in American cities, the Commission found that while these areas were inhabited largely by the foreign-born, it was not the nationalities of the people, but the conditions surrounding them, that produced the high crime rates. Although the nationalities of the people in these areas changed almost completely over a period of twenty years, the rate of delinquency in these areas remained about the same. Furthermore, when the older national groups moved to more favorable sections, the delinquency among their children consistently declined.

Coming back to murder, we are led to the conclusion that no group of people in the United States is by nature more murderous than any other, but that bad environment increases the murder rate in *any group*. This still leaves open the possibility that among *individuals* in the same bad environment, under the same conditions, there are some who will kill, while others will not, because of an inherited *tendency* toward murder. (Or, as some suggest, because of emotional instability or warped intelligence.) The difficulty, however, in finding the genetic basis for any such "murder instinct" is the same as that we encountered with regard to cancer.

The motivations for, and types of, murder are of every conceivable kind, just as are cancers. The fact that there was a murderer in several successive generations of the same family proves nothing. One might have killed in revenge, another for love, another in self-defense, and another while insane. In different circumstances none of these murders might have been committed. Only when murder is linked with certain violent forms of insanity (paranoid psychosis) does it appear to have a definitely inherent basis; that is to say, a demented individual may be impelled to kill for fancied slights or injuries.

Back of the theory that there is a "killer" instinct in people, lurks the more ominous thought that war is a wholesale expression of that instinct and is therefore inevitable. But yet entire generations have grown up and passed on in many countries, such as Holland, Switzerland, Iceland, Norway and Sweden, without ever having gone to war. We can hardly imply that the present inhabitants of these countries have lost any possible "fighting" genes that their ancestors might have had. For peaceful as the Dutch, Swiss and Scandinavians may now appear to be, we know that in former times they were as warlike as any. In fact, not a nation, race or people anywhere in the world would be surviving today were it not that in previous times it had battled for its existence.

War, too, if considered as a form of "mass" murder, may be set down as depending for its expression on environment. Likewise, the "inevitability" of war must remain open to doubt until it can be proved that there is an inherited "murder" or "fighting" instinct in human beings. That there *is not* is the belief of more than 90 percent of several hundred American psychologists who were recently polled on the question.

Regarding other forms of crime or wrongdoing—burglary, theft, embezzlement, suicide, prostitution, sex-crimes, drunkenness, etc.—the rôle of heredity is being similarly minimized, the rôle of environment emphasized.

Crimes in the *theft* category are obviously correlated with economic factors. While the "stealing point" in some people is lower than in others, if there is a "theft" instinct almost all of us can be said to have it in some degree. (Will all those kindly step forward who never stole fruit, flowers or candy when they were young? Who never filched a sign or gadget for their college room? Who never absconded with an ash-tray or hotel towel, or a Chinese soup-spoon from a chop-suey restaurant? Or who never, *never* beat the government out of any income tax?) There are, of course, thefts, swindles, and financial breaches of every kind, "harmless" and "serious," "impulsive" and "deliberate," but until we can accurately weigh all types in our moral scale we will be hard put to identify "genes" for thievery.

Prostitution, because it takes toll of so many millions of women throughout the world, has been thoroughly investigated everywhere. The most recent of the studies is that made by Dr. Tage Kemp in Copenhagen, where all common prostitutes must be registered. He found, as investigators have found almost everywhere, including the United States, that many of the prostitutes are mentally defective, some of them psychopathic; that most of them had been brought up in the very worst surroundings; and that many had had drunken fathers and some, mothers or sisters who were prostitutes. In a number of cases, however, the women came from fairly good homes, so bad upbringing cannot be considered as sufficient in itself to explain their delinquency. And in many cases, also, prostitutes are of high intelligence. In New York City, in fact, Dr. Walter Bromberg, criminal court psychiatrist, reports that he has found prostitutes no different mentally or psychotically from the average run of women.

As Dr. Kemp points out, his information relates principally to the poorer type of prostitute, as the "higher type," who does not ply her trade openly, is not registered. On the whole, his studies bear out previous conclusions that prostitution is largely the product of bad environment. But again we must keep in mind that not all women in the same environment, even those mentally deficient or psychopathic, become prostitutes. There is still the possibility that heredity may produce a weaker will or lower moral resistance which may increase the chance that a woman will turn to prostitution under given conditions. But those conditions have to be there first.

Because this question is frequently asked, it may be said that neither Dr. Kemp's studies, nor any others, show that there is any basic sexual difference between prostitutes and other women. Few of those studied by Dr. Kemp were oversexed or perverted. In fact, many authorities incline to the belief that prostitutes are more often *undersexed* and that their comparative lack of emotion and indifference to sex relations facilitates their taking up and carrying on their pursuit. From this, and the preceding observations, it may be concluded that no inherent constitutional basis for the "oldest of professions" has yet been established.

Suicide, included spiritually if not legally among crimes, has also been said to "run" in families. That the suicide of a parent may induce morbidity which might influence a child to take the same step is not hard to see, nor need one dispute the fact that an unbalanced mind (which may be inherited) may lead to the suicide of several individuals in the same family. But that there is any hereditary tendency toward suicide itself is still to be proved. Every available fact, on the contrary, would indicate that the causes of suicide are predominantly environmental. The suicide waves in the United States following the stock-market crashes and in Austria following the Nazi invasions, and the general rise in suicides everywhere in recent years, bear sad testimony to this. In "normal" times suicide (in the words of one writer) is "a phenomenon of social isolation." The highest rate is among divorced persons, with next in order those who have never married.

The attitude toward suicide, as toward murder, may also be considered a factor in its frequency. Where the concept of suicide as a serious crime is prevalent, suicides are at a minimum. The recent rise in suicides both here and abroad, often explained as being due to increased tension of modern life, may be equally ascribed to growing "individualism" and a modification of the attitude toward self-destruction.

This brings us to the point that "anti-social" acts of human beings in general may be motivated less by any inherent tendencies than by the atmosphere in which people are reared. The whole subject of "right" and "wrong-doing" rests on the shifting sands of prevailing social viewpoints. Murder may at one time and place be condemned and in another time and place be extolled as a noble deed—as, for instance, the assassination of Premier Dollfuss of Austria. Prostitution has been and still is considered among some peoples a "respectable," or even a noble calling. Suicide was looked upon as an honorable deed in earlier civilizations, and is still thought of as such among the Japanese. Theft is a virtue among certain Bedouins. There is probably not a crime, social breach or type of dereliction on our police registers that in certain localities in the world, or among certain groups within our own country, is not considered quite proper.

To sum up: Genetic studies of the possible rôle of heredity in human wrong-doing bog down because of our inability to disentangle any inherent crime tendencies from the environmental factors in which they are enmeshed. We have no proof of a direct correlation between any specific crime and any given type of body structure, physical characteristic, mental state or racial identity. On the other hand, it seems to be clear that an atmosphere of degradation, ignorance and poverty will breed crime and that lax prosecution or public indifference to any type of crime will foster its development.

So, where the hereditary factors are so vague, and the environmental factors so clear, it would seem that if we want to do anything about crime we should worry less about what is inside of people and more about what is *outside* of them.

CHAPTER XXXVI

SEXUAL BEHAVIOR

No phase of human behavior is more important than that of sex, and none presents greater difficulties when we try to find the hereditary basis for such of its various manifestations as are considered "abnormal" or "anti-social."

From what we have already learned, there is every reason to believe that basic patterns of sex behavior are inherited by human beings just as they obviously are by the lower animals. But on the other hand, human sex behavior is so highly variable and so strongly influenced by training, laws, taboos, regional customs, habits, etc., that it is extremely difficult to ascertain what may be due to inborn tendencies and what to environmental influences. Nevertheless, advances have been made in clarifying many phases of the subject.

Like any other characteristic, sexual behavior in either men or women can be judged only in relation to accepted standards. Almost immediately, then, we are confronted with the fact that *there are no scientifically determined standards for "normal" human sexual behavior*. There is not even a real definition available for what constitutes "masculine" and what "feminine" behavior, or what is "manly" and what "womanly." Look up these words in your dictionary and you will find that "manly" and "masculine" are defined approximately as "having the characteristics of a man," and "womanly" and "feminine" as "having the characteristics becoming to woman." But the views as to what these characteristics might be have changed from age to age and continue to vary with each country and each locality. As Margaret Mead showed in her studies of primitive peoples, many of our accepted patterns for masculine and feminine behavior are completely reversed among certain tribes. And within our own United States, and in our own time, we have

Whether You Are a Man or a Woman

—YOU ARE CONSIDERED "MASCULINE"	—YOU ARE CONSIDERED "FEMININE"
IN THE DEGREE THAT YOU ARE INTERESTED IN:	IN THE DEGREE THAT YOU ARE INTERESTED IN:
Exploit and adventure Outdoor activity and physically strenuous occupations Machinery and tools Science, physical phenomena and inventions Business and commerce	Domestic affairs Art, literature, music Sedentary and indoor occupations Ministering to the helpless and distressed "Moral" activities
—AND TO THE EXTENT THAT YOU ARE:	—AND TO THE EXTENT THAT YOU ARE:
Self-assertive Aggressive Hardy Fearless Rugged Blunt of manner and speech	Compassionate Timid Sympathetic Fastidious Emotional Sentimental and affectionate

seen radical changes not only in the views regarding sex, but in sexual behavior itself.

It was clear that before any progress could be made in studying the subject there would have to be some standards to follow. So, as sequels to the "intelligence" tests and the "personality" and various other behavior tests, a series of "masculinity-femininity" ("M-F") tests were recently devised by Prof. Lewis M. Terman and Catherine Cox Miles of California for measuring degrees of human sexuality. These "M-F" tests comprise a series of questions (the same for both men and women) to each of which an individual can give either a response considered "masculine," or one considered "feminine." Thus, an answer indicating physical callousness might be set down as "masculine," one indicating tenderness as "feminine."

THE "INK-BLOT" TESTS for "MASCULINITY" and "FEMININITY"*

What do these pictures suggest? Check the word you
think most descriptive of each:

A
1. ax
2. boat
3. chopper
4. moon

F
1. bow
2. chain
3. footprints
4. tie

B
1. brush
2. centipede
3. comb
4. teeth

G
1. baby
2. buoy
3. lady
4. valve

C
1. flame
2. flower
3. snake
4. worm

H
1. chimney
2. coil
3. smoke
4. thread

D
1. baby
2. bell
3. idol
4. incense

I
1. funnel
2. horn
3. jack
4. vase

E
1. boat
2. door
3. hat
4. stump

J
1. couch
2. cow
3. deer
4. horse

HERE IS HOW THE ANSWERS ARE SCORED:

PICTURE:	A	B	C	D	E	F	G	H	I	J
Masculine:	1, 2, 4	1, 2	2	1, 2	1, 3, 4	2, 3	1, 2, 4	2	3, 4	2
Feminine:	3	3, 4	1, 3, 4	3, 4	2	1, 4	3	1, 3, 4	1, 2	1, 3, 4

* From "Sex and Personality", by Terman and Miles

For every "masculine" response the individual is given a "+1" mark; for every "feminine" response a "—1" mark.

Testing 4,000 individuals, Terman and Miles found that the "M-F" scores of male adults range from "+200" to "—100" (for inverts), with an average of "+52"; while female adults score from "+100" to "—200," with an average of "—70." In other words, the difference in "M-F" response between an *average* man and woman is quite great, revealing the expected distinction between them in sexual personality. But in individual cases, *some men* (with the high "minus" scores) *are revealed as being more "feminine"* in their responses than a good many women, and *some women* (with the high "plus" scores) *as being more "masculine" than many men.*

Classifying men and women into various groups, we see some striking differences. The *most "masculine" men*—but remember, only on the basis of the Terman tests!—*are college athletes and engineers; the least "masculine" men are artists and clergymen.* And much to our surprise we find that policemen and firemen have the lowest "masculinity" scores in the occupational classes! The Terman-Miles study indicates that this is in line with the "feminizing" influence of social-welfare work, but also suggests that policemen and firemen are likely to be drawn from the ranks of men who are by nature lacking in marked mechanical interests and financial objectives, who are seeking job security and who are amenable to discipline (all considered "feminine" characteristics). In other words, the "M-F" tests would lead us to believe that our proud wearers of civic uniforms may really be sheep in wolves' clothing!

Among women, the most "feminine" are domestics, the least "feminine" are the superior female athletes. (Scores for all classes are given in the diagram opposite.) Thus, in both men and women, athletic pursuits are correlated with "masculinity." But one should be careful not to confuse external appearance with personality, for various authorities have pointed out that the appearance of roughness or ruggedness presented by either a rawboned, swaggering male or by a heavy-set, homely female, may mask a soft, feminine nature; and that a delicate-appearing man, equally

"MASCULINITY" AND "FEMININITY"

(How various classifications of men and women rank according to average scores in the "M-F" tests)

MASCULINITY
(Degrees shown by "plus" signs)

FEMININITY
(Degrees shown by "minus" sign)

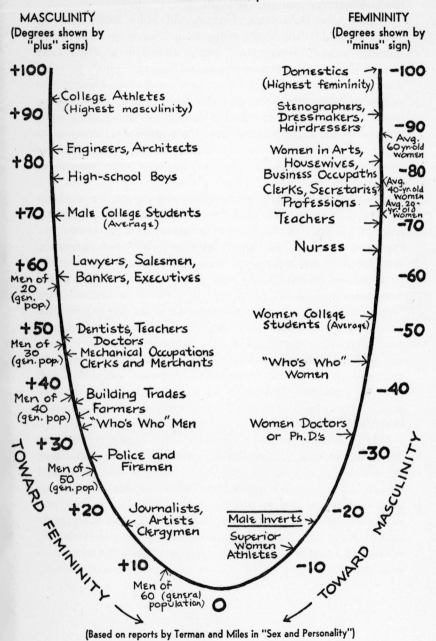

+100

+90 ←College Athletes (Highest masculinity)

+80 ← Engineers, Architects
← High-school Boys

+70 ← Male College Students (Average)

+60 Lawyers, Salesmen,
Men of ← Bankers, Executives
20 →
(gen. pop.)

+50 Dentists, Teachers
Men of → Doctors
30 ← Mechanical Occupations
(gen. pop.) Clerks and Merchants

+40 Building Trades
Men of → Farmers
40 ← "Who's Who" Men
(gen. pop.)

+30 ← Police and
Men of → Firemen
50
(gen. pop.)

+20 Journalists,
← Artists
Clergymen

+10
Men of
60 (general
population) O

TOWARD FEMININITY

Domestics →
(Highest femininity) -100

Stenographers,
Dressmakers,
Hairdressers → -90
← Avg. 60 yr.old women

Women in Arts,
Housewives,
Business Occupat'ns -80
Clerks, Secretaries? ← Avg. 40-yr.old women
Professions → ← Avg. 20-yr. old women
Teachers → -70

Nurses →

-60

Women College →
Students (Average) -50

"Who's Who" →
Women

-40

Women Doctors →
or Ph.D.'s

-30

Male Inverts → -20
Superior
Women →
Athletes

-10

TOWARD MASCULINITY

(Based on reports by Terman and Miles in "Sex and Personality") with a pretty and petite girl, may sometimes be at heart as relentless and daring as the steeliest soldier.

Generally, however, physical factors do seem to play a part in molding sexual personality, and this is especially true of age. Studying their records, Terman and Miles report that *both men and women tend to become more "feminine" as they grow older*. At the age of 20, males average "M-F" scores of "+58," but at 70 the average has gone down to "+3," that is, 55 points in the direction of "femininity." In part, this is ascribed to the "feminizing" effect of marriage and domestication. In females the change is not nearly so marked, the scores for females at 20 averaging "—75," and at the age of 60, "—89," only 14 points of "femininity" greater.

These tests are interesting, but it must be kept in mind that they record "masculinity" and "femininity" from an arbitrary point of view, influenced or conditioned by general standards. For instance, "courage" and "hardihood" are popularly linked with physical activity. And yet the supposedly "feminine" artists, writers or musicians as a group are often required, in pursuing their careers, to cope with privation, insecurity and professional hazards that would intimidate many an average "masculine" man. A shy little "—100" dressmaker, casting herself adrift in marriage with some comparatively unknown man, may be proving more adventuresome than an Arctic explorer. The habitual "wallflower" going doggedly to a dance to face masculine slights, the stammerer getting up to make a public speech, the clergyman who takes issue with his "big-wig" deacons, these and many others may be constantly displaying on the social battlefield courage of the highest sort, which ordinary standards of "masculinity" may disregard.

Like the intelligence tests, the "M-F" tests are the same for both males and females, also disregarding the fact that boys and girls are trained from infancy to act differently, and that throughout life males and females have radically different environments. Thus, these tests do not gage *basic* sexual personality, as is clearly shown by the fact that the "M-F" scores, especially of men, change radically with age. Nor do the tests attempt to measure the *sex impulse* of the individual—the functional aspect of sex which concerns society the most.

The assumption has always persisted that degrees of intensity of the sex impulse have a hereditary basis. Some individuals (and some "races") are popularly thought of as inherently more strongly sexed than others. Also, where there are unusual types of sex behavior, these too are spoken of as "running" in families. To the extent that sex-functioning is motivated by organs, glands and constitutional factors, it is not illogical to suppose that heredity may play a part in its various manifestations. But only where there is some easily recognized "abnormality"—that is, some marked deviation from what we consider "normal" sexual behavior—are we able to look for a hereditary basis.

In devising the mechanism of sex, it has long been assumed that Nature had only one objective—to provide a means for propagation of the species. Among most lower animals, sex-function and reproduction are in fact synonymous. That this should also be so among humans has been the widely held belief in civilized society. Any manifestation of sex, or any exercise of the sex functions that adversely affects or prevents reproduction has therefore been considered anti-social and often, from the religious point of view, immoral. And most strongly has condemnation been directed toward that form of sexual behavior known as *homosexuality,* which swerves individuals away from relations with members of the opposite sex and inclines them toward relations with those of their own sex.

The subject of homosexuality is not a happy one to discuss. Conditioned as most persons have been to avoid open mention of it—just as venereal disease was not discussed in polite society until recent years—they prefer to think of homosexuality as something far removed from their own lives. These facts—gleaned from leading authorities—will therefore come as somewhat shocking:

From 3 percent to 5 percent of all males everywhere are believed to be homosexual. (Active, or "overt," homosexuality is implied in the case of men in the large cities. Elsewhere the percentage of "overt" homosexuals may not be so great.)

In one of the largest American universities the medical staff reports that 4 percent of the students have homosexual tendencies. (By this is probably meant, also, homosexual interests.)

In the population at large, it is estimated that an average of one man in every thirty is strongly enough inclined to homosexuality to find relationship with the opposite sex difficult.

It might be added that while the number of female homosexuals is also considered far greater than is generally supposed, no definite estimates can be made for them because homosexuality in women is much harder to trace than it is in men.

With the revelation of this rather large proportion of individuals who would be considered by society as seriously "abnormal," it becomes important to determine the basis for the condition.

From a moral point of view, homosexuality has often been pointed out as the product of a degenerate civilization, a concomitant or a portent of the collapse of a nation. However that might be, we find undisputed evidence that it exists in regions where civilization has never penetrated, at widely scattered points throughout the world, and that, in fact, among many peoples it is a social institution as well recognized as marriage. When we link this with evidence that homosexuality is also found among the lower animals we must begin to look for other than merely environmental factors.

As the first step in their studies, authorities point out that there are two kinds of homosexuals—the "active" and the "passive." In either sex it is the "active" homosexual who plays the part of the male, the "passive" one the part of the female. Thus the "active" male homosexual, even though he prefers the company of males, may be outwardly no different from other men; he may, in fact (as Prof. Terman's studies have shown), be actually more "masculine" than the average man. Similarly the "passive" female homosexual, who plays the part of the female in relations with other women, is often intensely feminine in her behavior. Both "active" male homosexuals and "passive" females may therefore outwardly show no sign of abnormality and are difficult to recognize.

It is the "passive" male, who acts like a female, and the "active" female, who often looks and acts like a male, whom we usually have in mind when we think of homosexuals. As we saw in the chapter on "The Twilight Sexes," where a man looks and acts like a female, and a female looks and acts like a male, there is ground for believing that some glandular disturbance, or some other physical factor, is responsible. What is significant, then, is that many authorities today look upon *all cases* of homosexuality, whether "active" or "passive," and regardless of outward appearance—so long as persons show a sexual preference for those of their own sex—as likewise having a *constitutional basis which might conceivably have been inherited.*

Searching for evidence to bear out this latter theory, some investigators (Hirschfeld, Van Romer, Walter Wolf, et al.) reported that 35 percent of the homosexuals they studied came from families in which the trait had made its appearance in other members, often a brother and sister both being homosexual.

But even more significant might seem the studies made of *homosexuality in twins* (if we can consider the limited number studied as fair evidence). Where one member of a pair of identical twins was a homosexual, in almost every instance the other twin was also a homosexual. This same correlation was not found to exist among fraternal twins, for where one was homosexual, the other usually was not. Dr. J. Sanders, Director of the Dutch Institute for Human Genetics, who recently summarized the reports on this subject, believes that they prove heredity to be an important factor in this condition.

"Direct" inheritance of homosexuality hardly seems possible. What is usually implied is the inheritance of a *tendency* toward homosexuality which depends for its expression on certain environmental or psychological factors. Among both men and women, for instance, the lack of available members of the opposite sex, or for one reason or another any acquired aversion to relations with members of the opposite sex, would favor the expression of such a tendency.

As for the homosexual tendency itself, the most probable basis, in the opinion of authorities, appears to be some glandular disorder which upsets the hormonal balance of the individual. In the lower animals we can readily prove by experiment that maleness and femaleness of behavior are biochemically determined. We have already seen how secondary physical characteristics in the sexes can be changed. Sexual behavior, too, can be radically altered by sex-gland operations, especially if performed at an early age. Even after maturity hens can be made not only to look but to *act* like roosters; and pigeons, mice, guinea-pigs and other animals of one sex can have their sexual behavior radically changed or turned into that of the opposite sex. All this has been done in laboratories time and again.

Naturally, no such deliberate experiments have been performed on humans, but some not too dissimilar results have been noted from sex-gland operations performed through necessity, or from some pathological condition which altered the individual's glands or hormonal balance. Also, the failure of the sex organs to develop properly, preventing normal sexual relations, has been cited as a motivating cause of abnormal behavior. Thus, with a constitutional basis indicated, it is believed that an individual might sometimes or often be *born* with the conditions which would predispose him or her to homosexuality or to some other deviation from "normal" sexual behavior.

Summarized (according to prevailing views) the possible causes of abnormal sexual behavior would be these:

1. Tendencies *inherited* through "abnormal" genes.[1]

2. Pre-natal factors: *Possibly* infiltration of mother's hormones (in a male); failure of some necessary elements for developing the glands to reach the embryo; some intra-uterine accident affecting development of the sex organs, etc.

3. Some glandular or other upset after birth (probably during puberty) due to either internal or external causes, and impeding the proper development of the sex organs.

4. Inversion through necessity—lack of available persons of the opposite sex.

5. Psychic causes: Shock; adverse early conditioning; "fixations" and "complexes"; an instilled impression that sex relationships are immoral; fear in women of pregnancy or in men of fathering a child; ugliness in a woman, or homeliness or "unmanly" appearance

---

[1] Prof. Richard Goldschmidt has suggested that, based on his findings in certain lower animals, it is possible that homosexuality may result from an unbalance in the sex-determining genes, which may swerve a female toward "maleness" or a male toward "femaleness."

in a male, prompting avoidance of those of the opposite sex; some mental derangement; etc.

Psychoanalysts and psychiatrists are inclined to psychic explanations for most cases of abnormal sexual behavior. While undue stress is often placed on psychological factors, it is not at all impossible for some experience or chain of experiences to so act upon the nervous system, and through it in turn upon the glands, as to produce the same effects which might come through direct physical action or change. Mental or nervous influences of this kind, which lead to physical disturbances, are called *"psychogenic"* factors, and have been known to produce a wide variety of conditions, ranging from eye symptoms to (in women) symptoms of pregnancy. Farfetched as it might seem, it would therefore be conceivable that some early psychological disturbance in a boy and its corresponding psychogenic effect on his glands, might lead not merely to his acting like a girl, but to his *looking* like a girl, at least with regard to certain secondary sexual characteristics. Similarly, a girl might conceivably get to act and look like a boy.

All this is, of course, still theory. Some authorities, notably Dr. George W. Henry of New York, report that homosexual patients may show deviations from the average in certain secondary sexual characteristics. In homosexual males, he observes, there may be the "feminine carrying angle of the arm, narrow hips, deficient hair on face, chest and back, feminine distribution of pubic hair, high-pitched voice, excess of fat on shoulders, etc." In homosexual females, conversely, there may be characteristics usually associated with males, "firm adipose tissue, deficient fat in shoulders, firm muscles, excess hair on face and chest, tendency to masculine distribution of pubic hair, underdevelopment of breasts, low-pitched voice, etc." However, not all authorities have found this to be generally so, and certainly, the facts do not apply to all homosexuals, many of whom, as we have pointed out, are more masculine looking than average men, and if women, extremely feminine in appearance.

But whether or not abnormal physical factors are present, and regardless of how they originated (particularly with or without some hereditary basis), it appears clear that the expression or

development of any abnormal sexual tendency is largely conditioned by environment.

The most recent views on the subject have been expressed by
Dr. Henry, who is at this writing engaged in a study of both
male and female homosexuals. Here are some of his conclusions:

"Personality forces and human interrelations contributing to a
homosexual development cannot be traced to their ultimate sources,
but it appears that the more closely a relative or friend is associated,
especially in childhood, the more direct and decisive is the influence
exerted. This means that the parents are in most instances chiefly
responsible for the homosexual developments in their children. Not
uncommonly a nursemaid, a brother or sister, a cousin, an uncle
or an aunt may be involved in the distortion of a child's psychosex-
ual development. It appears, also, that boarding and non-coeduca-
tional schools are more likely to favor a homosexual development.
It is generally recognized that any segregation of the sexes is likely
to bring about overt expression of latent homosexual desires.

"Whatever these external influences may be, the majority of
persons do not succumb to them and the minority who do succumb
appear to be fundamentally predisposed. Some of this predisposi-
tion may be inherited through the germ plasm, but in the cases
studied thus far it is rare to find overt homosexuals in more than
one generation. The tendency may nevertheless be inherited, because the difference between latent and overt homosexuality is
often very slight. Undoubtedly there are many instances of overt
homosexuality in the family of which the informants are unaware."

So finally we come to this question: Assuming that an individual
does reveal "abnormal" sexual tendencies, either in childhood or
later, what can be done about it?

Where the condition is considered chiefly psychological or environmental, it might perhaps be best treated by a psychiatrist. Where
morphological, due to a defect in the sex organs making "normal"
relations difficult, an operation might help. If the tendency is
revealed as having a glandular or hormonal basis, there is a possibility that its expression (in the future) may be repressed by hormonal treatment, just as diabetes can be curbed through insulin.
Indeed, many scientists are now at work identifying, isolating and

even artificially producing the various hormones concerned with sexuality. But while hormonal treatments at this writing are being given to some homosexuals, it is still too early to report any positive results.

All this is predicated on the assumption that homosexuality

SEX CHARACTERISTICS IN LIMBS

ARMS		LOWER LIMBS	
FEMALES	MALES	FEMALES	MALES
Angle, corresponding to knock-knees	Straight	Slightly knock-kneed	Straight

ANGLE

STRAIGHT

should be cured and eliminated, an assumption well justified by the fact that in our present society this condition seriously militates against an individual's adjustment and happiness. We need hardly enlarge on this phase of the subject. But at the same time, if it should be proved that this form of sexual behavior is a *natural* one with many individuals—that they have either inherited the tendency or acquired it without any volition—and that nothing can be done—or possibly even should be done—about it, the question arises as to whether the attitude of society should not be changed.

Viewed from any standpoint, the subject calls for more sympathy and understanding than is now being given it by the public and by the law. In the light of what little we already know, the hounding of homosexuals as criminals, classifying them with degenerates, drug-fiends and insane, exhibiting them on the stage as freaks and subjecting them to scorn, ridicule and ostracism, seems hardly in keeping with a supposedly enlightened age.

CHAPTER XXXVII

EVOLUTION: CHICKEN OR EGG?

THINKING back over the many odd and various human character-istics that we have been discussing, you undoubtedly have won-dered, "How did they all originate? Where did all the different kinds of people there are in this world come from?"

Some eighty years ago Charles Darwin, claiming to have the answer for those very questions, threw a bombshell into thinking society with his theories of *evolution*. The resulting explosion set thundering against him avalanches of wrath from many quarters, which still echo as stray rocks of denunciation come rumbling down.

The most violent of the reactions, as every one knows, was occasioned by Darwin's implied assault on the Biblical story of creation. Darwin dismissed the idea that man was dropped into the world ready-made, and, on the contrary, advanced the belief that man was the end result of a step-by-step development from the most elemental living things through fish, reptiles, lower mammals, up to apes and then, by some "missing link," to primitive man.

All this may seem like an old story, but the fact is that the Darwinian theories are very much alive and are constantly being tested by scientists. The mass of evidence has now established most of Darwin's theories as accepted fact. But in one conclusion it appears that he was most certainly wrong. And this involves the hoary old enigma:

"Which came first, the chicken or the egg?"

Or, from the standpoint of evolution, and thinking of chickens as symbolical of various species: Did a new kind of chicken arise, which then produced a new kind of egg?

WHICH CAME FIRST...?

ACCORDING TO DARWIN:

1. **First there was a certain kind of bird,**

2. It laid and hatched eggs,

3. **Which produced offspring similar to itself.** *But—*

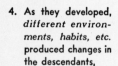

4. As they developed, *different environments, habits, etc.* produced changes in the descendants,

5. Which ACQUIRED changes were communicated and PASSED ON THROUGH THEIR EGGS

6. Until, with many such changes in successive generations added together, eventually there resulted THE CHICKEN

7. Which then produced the characteristic CHICKEN EGG

So by this reasoning THE CHICKEN CAME FIRST.

—BUT ACCORDING TO MODERN GENETICS:

1. **First there was a certain kind of egg.**

2. Which produced a characteristic kind of bird,

3. But in some of these birds something happened to produce MUTATIONS

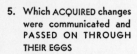

4. Which resulted in their laying eggs with certain CHANGED GENES

5. Which produced birds differing from their parents. And as mutations continued,

6. In the course of ages there resulted A NEW KIND OF EGG WITH NEW GENES

7. Which produced THE CHICKEN

Thus, as science now indicates, THE EGG CAME FIRST.

Or did a *new kind of egg* originate, which then produced a new kind of chicken?

Darwin held with the first theory. He took it for granted, as did almost every scientist until the gene mechanism was revealed (long after his death), that heredity, and with it "upward evolution," was a *blending* process. By such a process the improvements or changes that each generation made in itself would be added to and *blended* in with those of the preceding one and the combination passed along to the next generation. Thus:

1. Giraffes got their long necks by stretching higher and higher for choice leaves on trees, each generation benefiting by the stretching done by their parents.

2. Apes developed their brains and muscles by the effort of keeping up with their respective Joneses, and passed on their accomplishments to their offspring.

3. And, conversely, in various species, organs became atrophied or lost through disuse, the classic example being that of the fish who swam into dark caves and by staying there generation after generation eventually gave rise to a race of blind fish.

All this summarizes the *theory of the inheritance of acquired characteristics,* which as we said at the very beginning of the book, has been completely discredited. Darwin, however, believed it, and so did most of his contemporaries. But then some of them began to think about it. Why hadn't the principle worked with regard to the binding of feet by the Chinese, circumcision by the Jews, tattooing by the savages, and the many other changes made by people in their bodies, through customs, habits, etc., for generation after generation—*with no effect on their offspring?* Skeptics among the scientists began to experiment. August Weismann (in 1880) gravely cut off the tails of mice for *twenty successive generations,* but in the last litter—just as he expected—the mice showed not the slightest shortening of their tails as compared with their ancestors.

The "cave-blindness" theory was tested by keeping flies in pitch-blackness for fifty successive generations; and at the end, once again, the last batch of offspring, when born into the light, had just as normal eyes as ordinary fruit-flies.

What about accomplishments in mentality and behavior? Innumerable experiments have since been performed by geneticists in training successive generations of animals to do certain things or act in certain ways; and yet no effect of this training shows in their offspring. (Pavlov thought at first that he had produced hereditary "reflex" improvements in mice by training, but later discovered that his conclusions were erroneous. In experiments of this kind, very often, it is not that the animals become more responsive but that the investigators become more adept in training them.)

Could a child *inherit* the habit of drunkenness from a drunkard father? Geneticists kept generations of mice, rabbits, guinea-pigs and poultry virtually stupefied with alcohol. There wasn't the slightest evidence that such alcoholization produced any changes in the genes, although, true enough, when the mother was alcoholized, some of her weaker offspring were killed off in embryo, so that successive generations were in some cases *actually stronger*.

The experiments made along these lines run into many hundreds. Finally, as perhaps the best evidence, geneticists stopped to reason: Recessive genes, paired with dominants, may be carried hidden for generations in bodies of persons with entirely different characteristics than those which the recessives tend to produce, and yet these genes are never affected. The blue-eye gene isn't changed if coupled with a brown-eye gene and made to live for a lifetime in brown eyes. No "normal" gene of any kind is affected by living in an "abnormal" body; and no "abnormal" gene is "normalized" by living in a normal body. This in itself is held *prima facie* evidence that the internal environment of an individual cannot change his genes.

As Prof. Thomas Hunt Morgan has summed it up, *the belief in the inheritance of acquired characteristics is not based on scientific evidence, but on the very human desire to pass on one's acquisitions to one's children.*

If, then, the material for evolution was not provided by acquired characteristics, from where *did* it come? It probably came—almost all geneticists are now agreed—through spontaneous changes in chromosomes which we have already referred to as mutations.

Darwin himself was not unaware that new characteristics inexplicably cropped out in living things. But he did not believe that these happened often, and not knowing anything about genes, he attached little importance to them. Today, however, *the entire concept of evolution centers about mutations.*

As geneticists look back, they see that mutated genes must have been responsible for innumerable new characteristics in all kinds of animals and plants within the last few hundred years. In 1791 a Massachusetts farmer found in his flock a peculiar lamb with a long sagging back and very short legs. It offered to him a distinct advantage: It couldn't jump the fences and get away. So from this single mutant (of course he didn't think of it as such) he bred the strain of sheep known as Ancon, which was so popular for many years and is still extant.

In 1889 a hornless Hereford calf appeared in a Kansas herd, and from this has been bred the present "polled" (hornless) Hereford cattle, valued because they suffer fewer injuries than horned cattle.

The list of comparatively recent mutations recorded among all sorts of animals could be greatly extended. Vastly more numerous are those that have been observed in the plant kingdom even within our own time. Many of these have given rise to unusual new types of flowers or of highly desirable fruits, vegetables and grains. Geneticists believe, also, that mutations of various kinds have taken place in human beings in our own times and are still taking place. Especially interesting is the recent theory that the gene for hemophilia which Queen Victoria passed on to her descendants *arose in her through mutation.*

But what causes gene mutations? They happen so rarely under natural conditions that geneticists had little opportunity to find out. Even among the carefully watched Drosophilæ, tens of thousands of flies had to be counted for every mutation that was found—usually of an almost imperceptible kind. One had to sit and wait for a mutation to happen, and there wasn't a clue as to when or how.

Then, in 1927, came the epochal discovery by Prof. Herman J. Muller that *if flies were exposed to X-rays, the mutations would occur about 150 times as often.* Immediately, under X-ray bombardment, mutations in the Drosophila began coming thick and fast. Thus Prof. Muller's discovery led to the speculation that perhaps some sort of *natural* emanations or atmospheric disturbances—for instance, *cosmic rays*—produced the mutations in nature. Flies were taken up into different altitudes, or into mines or regions where natural radiations were known to be more intense, and, true enough, it was found that the rate of mutations *was* speeded up. In a recent balloon ascension into the stratosphere, flies were taken to a height of over thirteen miles, and it was shown that the mutation rate was accelerated to five times its pace at sea level.

Seizing on the "cosmic-ray" theory, H. G. Wells, in his unusual book, "Star-Begotten," projected the fanciful idea that inhabitants of Mars, presumably far advanced beyond us earthlings, have perfected a method of bombarding us with rays which cause "superior" mutations, and in turn "superior" humans. Assuming that there is a grain of truth in all this, you might ask, "Do we have to wait for the inhabitants of Mars to bombard us with rays? Couldn't we ourselves use X-rays on people to produce mutations in their germ cells?" We probably could, but the weakness of the idea (which also applies to the Wellsian concept) lies in the fact that rays are random shots in the dark, which hit genes indiscriminately. There is no way of predicting which gene will be hit, or what the mutation will be. Most mutations are so slight as to be hardly noticeable—a minute change in eye color, a slight change in form. But whatever the effect, in the *vast majority of cases it is harmful.* Only once in many times does a mutation produce any change that could be considered beneficial.

Knowing now that rays of some kind, X-ray or cosmic, can cause a gene to mutate, we have some clue as to what happens. The gene, in the opinion of many geneticists, is a molecule of living stuff made up of many atoms held together. The number of atoms in each gene, and the way they are arranged, is believed to determine its behavior. Suppose now there is a sudden shock, caused by a ray. The arrangement of the atoms might be changed, or some of them might be knocked out. And there would be a "mutated" gene, with a different kind of behavior!

Applying this principle to the theory of evolution we could start, back in some infinite past, with a single gene. (*We make no attempt to explain whence it came.*) The single gene gives rise to many genes like itself, and each forms a simple cell functioning in the same simple way. Possibly in some of the cells, a few of the genes cling together. Then in a flash, something happens to make one of the genes mutate. Now we have a cell with two kinds of genes, able to do something the others can't do. If what it does is advantageous, this cell reproduces itself more prolifically than the simple ones until there are many two-gene cells. Before long there is another mutation, and another variety of gene is created, which chance links together with the other two genes. More and different genes are created, and the work they can do in cooperation grows in complexity as they utilize new and different materials. *And all the time the chains of genes grow longer, forming the chromosomes.*

With more and more "mutated" genes being created and linking together, the chromosomes become longer and longer. Now, as they lash about in their cell activities, in "crack-the-whip" fashion the chromosomes may break into two, each half forming a separate and distinct chromosome. With further mutations, any number and kind of chromosomes can result. So here the mechanism is at hand for producing an endless variety of genes and chromosomes, and through these, of animals more and more complex and differentiated.

Thus, starting with a single gene, we can theoretically account for all the changes and processes by which the innumerable types and species of living things, including man, were evolved. (All this would have had to take millions of years, but why not? Nature had an infinity of time behind and ahead of her, and needn't have been in any hurry.) Generally speaking, the higher types of animals seem to have more genes, but the number of chromosomes in which these are arranged has little significance. Where one animal has more chromosomes than another, it may mean merely that it has *fewer genes* to a chromosome.

Through the mutations of genes and their arrangement, combination and recombination in sets of chromosomes, we have therefore the raw materials provided by nature for the evolution of man. But these raw materials were not in themselves sufficient. They had to be *used,* and first they had to be selected and tested, for they weren't ordered in response to the needs of any individual (most often, in fact, quite the contrary). They popped up from nowhere at irregular and unexpected times. Each species found the materials for its evolution dumped on its doorstep, so to speak, the good with the bad. And from this point on Darwin's theories as to *how* evolution proceeded have been greatly strengthened by the recent findings in genetics.

We know, unquestionably, that under natural conditions nature spawns an infinitely greater number of individuals for each species than there could possibly be room for. There must therefore be a constant battle between the individuals and their environment, or between the individuals themselves, for survival. So we have Darwin's theories of the *struggle for existence* and the *survival of the fittest.*

These theories now call for some modifications. As we have noted, the vast majority of mutations are harmful, in reality caused by an *injury* to a gene. Where these produced serious functional defects in an individual, he usually perished. But in some cases the mutations produced merely adverse reactions to certain degrees of temperature, or moisture, or nutrition. In other cases they were minor physical variations. Where these characteristics were disadvantageous only in a certain environment or under certain conditions, the individual was frequently able to move to another environment, or, in man's case, to change the conditions. Often, in fact, what in one environment had been a serious defect in another became a decided advantage. (And many times, as in the case of the dinosaurs and other extinct species, what made them supreme in one environment made it impossible for them to survive as conditions changed.)

However, among the many mutations produced, there were some that proved highly useful to the individual. Such improvements—stronger and better organs, keener eyesight, better teeth, more flexible muscles, keener intelligence, etc.—also enabled him to excel, and perhaps eliminate, the weaker members of his species, and so (according to Darwin) would tend to promote the gradual *upward* trend of evolution.

For back of all this lies the thought that evolution *was a process upward,* always toward some higher objective. The weak were weeded out, the fittest survived. But, one might ask, the *fittest for what?* Sometimes those that survived might have perished in another environment; sometimes those that perished might have flourished in a different environment. The survival of the fittest, categorically stated, would imply that certain individuals were predestined to survive *even before the environment which their descendants were to encounter had been created.*

If we think, from our own viewpoint, of man as the ultimate stage in the evolution of animals, we would have to believe that back in the dim Proterozoic era when all was water and swamp, already changes were taking place in certain primordial creatures which were planned for the millions of years hence, when they would evolve into majestic man. It would mean clearly that some great directing Force was at work, planning and producing mutations for future needs, not as yet apparent, for an environment that was anticipated but not yet in existence. This might also be called the theory of predestination, or *purposive evolution.*

But if we think of all the vast majority of haphazard, harmful mutations that have no rhyme nor reason, and the very few that could possibly be advantageous, we might have to conclude that man was no more foreordained among other animals than Pike's Peak, Lake Winnepesaukee in New Hampshire, or some oasis in the Sahara was foreordained among the earth's physical features. Many scientists believe that man was a biological accident, happily able to survive in the environment in which he found himself. But what if there had been a different environment, if the water had still covered the earth, with only marshes sticking out here and there? Or what if today, through some cosmic cataclysm, there is an upheaval of the earth's surface, if the temperature changes radically, if the chemical composition of the atmosphere is altered, making it impossible for man and other higher vertebrates to survive, while lowly fish and insects might find themselves quite at home? Do we not, in contemplating such a dire possibility, have to revise our ideas of *"fitness"*?

So we add another to the list of arbitrary terms such as "superior," "inferior," "normal" and "abnormal," which we must be careful in using with regard to humans. And most especially must we be careful, as geneticists point out, when we take it for granted that the onward march of time has been synonymous with "upward evolution" and that we are here, and other earlier races of man are not, because of our inherent superiority and greater "fitness." All this may become clearer when we turn from generalities and try to determine by what steps and processes primitive man, once he arrived, gave rise to the specific types of people we now have in the world.

CHAPTER XXXVIII

RACE

THE subject of "race" has an ominous significance today when men are again writing their theories regarding it in blood. The validity of these theories can now be weighed in the light of recent scientific findings.

Our preceding chapter sketched roughly the processes by which the most elemental creatures evolved into the highest types of mammals. All this must have required many millions of years, but how many would be only a guess. The scientist prefers to talk about the vague pristine stretches in terms of eras divided into periods, subdivided again into epochs, and these in turn into ages. Thus, he will tell you that the first primate, or forerunner of man, appeared in an early epoch of an early period of the Cenozoic era. This was at least ten million and possibly fifty million years ago. At any rate, it was exceedingly long ago.

The new creature that arose may have been chiefly distinguished from any other mammal by its slightly more specialized brain. But this first primate was not yet an ape, any more than it was a man. It had a long way to go to develop into either. For if it is any comfort to you, anthropologists now hold that man did not descend from any existing type of ape, but both apes and man descended from a common primate ancestor. The subtle difference is that instead of thinking of ourselves as descendants of the apes we see, we may consider them as merely our remote cousins.

From the same primate (perhaps somewhere in India) it is now believed that the descendants took two main evolutionary routes, one leading "ape-ward" and the other "man-ward." The routes were by no means direct. Any number of "trial and error" variations must have been evolved before anything like an ape resulted along one route, and anything like a man on the other route.

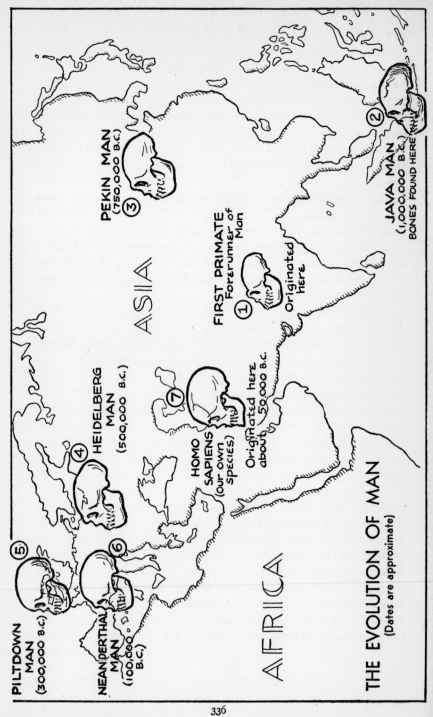

PEKIN MAN
(750,000 B.C.)
③

JAVA MAN
(1,000,000 B.C.)
BONES FOUND HERE
②

FIRST PRIMATE
Forerunner of
Man
①
Originated
here

ASIA

HEIDELBERG
MAN
(500,000 B.C.)
④

HOMO
SAPIENS
(our own
species)
⑦
Originated here
about 50,000 B.C.

PILTDOWN
MAN
(300,000 B.C.)
⑤

NEANDERTHAL
MAN
(100,000
B.C.)
⑥

AFRICA

THE EVOLUTION OF MAN
(Dates are approximate)

Our first glimpse of one of the creatures on the "man" route —a true "missing link" which Darwin had sought in vain—is in the form of fossilized (or petrified) bones, found in Java. To the creature from whom these bones came anthropologists have given the name of *Pithecanthropus erectus,* because, as his skeletal conformations show, he walked not like other mammals on all fours, but almost erect. Popularly he is referred to as the "Java Man," although he was far from being a man in the present sense of the word.

The "Java Man" is believed to have lived about a million years ago. There follow long blank periods in which only here and there have lucky finds brought to light other glimpses of man-creatures—the "Pekin Man" (dated about 750,000 B.C.), the "Heidelberg Man" (about 500,000 B.C.) and the "Piltdown Man" (about 300,000 B.C.). All these creatures had heavy, chinless lower jaws and many apelike traits.

Not until about 100,000 B.C., with the coming of the Ice Age, do the mists of man's past begin really to clear away. Now emerges the "Neanderthal Man," definitely of the genus Homo. We have more than a hundred skeletons to attest the fact that the Neanderthaler was about five feet three inches high, thickset, beetle-browed, long-armed, with a massive jaw, little chin, big teeth, a large aquiline nose and other primitive features. Nevertheless, he could *think.* He fashioned wooden spears and chipped tools of flint (the latter by some process which still eludes us), he used fire and respectfully laid out his dead. It is with this man that our cultural history begins.

The days of the Neanderthaler, however, were numbered. For, beginning with about 50,000 B.C., there was being fashioned in the crucible of evolution a new type of man. To the best of our knowledge this New Man arose in the region of Mesopotamia. Quite likely his ancestors had also been Neanderthalers. But of whatever species of Homo they were, they had stumbled into what was then one of the most favored habitats of the world. It had the best of climates, an abundance of game, fruits, nuts and foods of every kind. Compared to other regions where the scattered hordes of man-creatures battled for existence against great odds, this was a veritable Paradise. Here there was every opportunity for a species to thrive and develop, and by an accumulation of mutations in the course of time to give rise to a new species.

Thus, if you are so inclined, you may think of this region as the Garden of Eden, and of the New Man that arose in its midst as Adam, first of the species *Homo sapiens*.

We must not assume that this Adam (the Hebrew for "man") sprang into being overnight. Various new genes had been arising over a long period, and, proving their worth, had been multiplying and coming together in individuals who supplanted those less favored. Even in this region of abundance there must have been a struggle for existence. But eventually *Homo sapiens* and his descendants reigned supreme—and alone.

For here is our second important point: That *every human being on earth today, civilized or primitive, descended from the same stock and belongs to the same species, Homo sapiens.*

The first point we noted was that mankind descended not *from* apes, but *with* them, from a common primate ancestor. Together, then, the two points controvert earlier evolutionary theories, still cherished by some anthropological die-hards, that different divisions of men stemmed from different types of apes (the inference being, of course, that "superior" humans came from "superior" apes). The evidence to substantiate our new theory of common origin is based principally on the fact that all men, from Nordics to Pigmies, are fertile with one another, and from the genetic findings that the differences in basic traits among them are extremely few. This is not true of the apes, which include a variety of species differing radically in their genes and chromosomes, making some types of monkeys or apes infertile with others. In fact, there are much greater differences between gorillas and some other types of apes than there are between gorillas and men.

To suppose, then, that starting from different species of primates and within a comparatively short evolutionary period the various races of man could have achieved the biologic unity which they possess, is quite inconceivable. We can therefore safely assume that the history of all modern mankind begins with the same single group of the species *Homo sapiens,* clustered, as we believe, at the crossroads of Asia, Europe and Africa.

Favored by environment as this group was, it must have multiplied rapidly. Within five or six hundred years it is not inconceivable that from a single pair of humans (Adam and Eve, if you wish) there could have developed a population of one million. Inevitably, dispersal followed, for in those early days very little was required to set people a-moving. There was no strong sense of fixity in habitat, no dwellings, no cultivated fields, no cattle, nothing to hold people down. Bands of humans roved about, following the hunt or good weather, or dispersed by quarrels, natural forces or enemies. In terms of today, floods, dust-storms and earthquakes, tornadoes and severe cold spells, food shortage, or wars and oppression of minorities, would quickly set large groups of people moving to new territories.

So bands of *Homo sapiens* fared forth among such other species of men as still roved the continents. We cannot say that the New Man was superior to all others, for some isolated species of man wiped out by ill chance might have been superior to *Homo sapiens* both mentally and physically. (Often, in fact, we have reason to wonder how well our species deserves the name "sapiens," which means "wise.") The New Man may have killed off the men from whom he differed radically, or may have blended with those whom he found compatible. Recent evidence (in Palestine) indicates that he did mate with some of the lingering Neanderthalers. But whether *Homo sapiens* exterminated or absorbed other men, before long, as we said, he had the world to himself.

Now came another period of integration. Large groups had drifted far enough apart to become isolated, and for a sufficiently long time (at least many thousands of years) so that various mutations could take place which would differentiate one group from another. Thus there developed in the region of China the "Yellow-Brown" or Mongolian race, in Africa the "Black" or Negro race, at the crossroads of Europe and Asia the "White" or Eurasiatic race, and in the South Pacific the Australoid race, somewhat akin to the Negro, but whose derivation is not certain.

The genetic differences that developed among the races were,

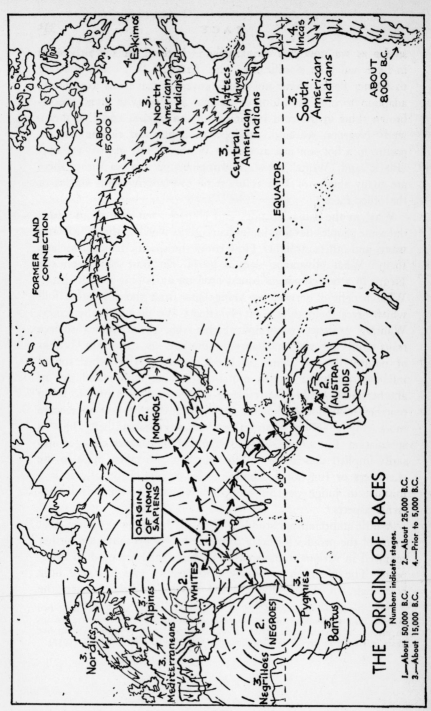

THE ORIGIN OF RACES

Numbers indicate stages.

1—About 50,000 B.C.   2—About 25,000 B.C.
3—About 15,000 B.C.   4—Prior to 5,000 B.C.

ORIGIN OF HOMO SAPIENS

2. (MONGOLS)

2. (WHITES)

2. AUSTRA-LOIDS

3. Nordics

3. Alpines

3. Mediterraneans

2. (NEGROES)

3. Negrilloes

3. Pygmies

3. Bantus

3. North American Indians

4. Eskimos

4. Aztecs

4. Central Mayas American Indians

3. South American Indians

4. Incas

ABOUT 15,000 B.C.

ABOUT 8,000 B.C.

FORMER LAND CONNECTION

EQUATOR

340

so far as we now can see, largely in surface traits which seem to have had little significance. The shades of skin color, contrary to former beliefs, have not been proved to have any correlating adaption to climate. Mongols do just as well with their yellow-brown skins in the cold regions as in the tropics, and "Northern-ized" Negroes, we find, can become sunburned on sudden exposure to a hot sun just as well as Whites.[1] (The terms "Yellow," "Black" and "White" races are misnomers. Within each race there are many shades of skin color, some overlapping with shades of the other races.)

Why, in the same latitudes and climates, but in regions apart, did some peoples develop kinky hair, others woolly, others curly and wavy, and others straight? How could the specific hair forms help them? What advantage does a broad, flat nose confer on the Negro in a hot climate, a round head on an Alpine mountaineer? What benefit is derived by Mongolians from the epicanthic fold which gives them their slant-eye effect? We do not really know. Wanting evidence, we might gather that these various surface traits arose through haphazard mutations as mere idle pranks of nature. Possibly some localized cosmic ray or other special influence produced certain mutations in one region and not in another; and possibly the resulting traits served for a time to bring together individuals who had them, in the belief that they were more closely related than others not so distinguished. This is speculation. But we must not assume that the surface changes necessarily implied that important changes had also taken place in the characters or functional aspects of the peoples. Especially is it a mistake to judge degrees of "primitiveness" in humans by external aspects.

A little unprejudiced study by scientists has shown, in fact, that many of the peoples formerly considered most primitive are farther removed in various traits from the primate than are modern Europeans. The Negro is extremely curly-headed, and has very little body hair, in these respects being much less apelike than the

[1] "The death-rates from the effects of heat throughout the South run from two to more than six times as high among Negroes as among White persons, perhaps on account of greater occupational exposure of the Negro."—From "Twenty-five Years of Health Progress," by Drs. Louis I. Dublin and Alfred J. Lotka. (1937)

White Europeans and aboriginal Australians, who both have straight or wavy hair and considerable body hair. With regard to skin color, the Negro is also farther away from the brown ape than is the European. Again, the full, fleshy lips of the Negro are a highly specialized and advanced human feature, for it is the thin lip that characterizes the ape. To point out, on the other hand, that Europeans may possess certain features less apelike than those of the Negro would have just as little meaning.

With many thousands of genes involved in producing a human being, the proved segregation of a few for surface traits within given groups cannot be considered highly significant. This will become clearer when we follow the further trend of the races.

The clearest trail is that of the Mongols. Beginning with about 15,000 B.C., we can follow their trek up from China, through Siberia and then over by way of Alaska (probably connected at the time with Asia) and into North America. Generation by generation the migration pushed ahead until by about 8,000 B.C. the tip of South America had been reached. Meanwhile, also, groups had strayed off in different directions, giving rise eventually to the Eskimos, the North American Indians, the Aztecs, Incas and other groups. (Here in the Americas, among the Mongol offshoots, we have interesting evidence of how much—or how little—genetic variation can take place in isolated groups of people of common stock within given periods.)

Back in Asia, Mongols had been moving in all directions, but with no such clear paths ahead as had their brethren in America. For the other races had also been on the march. A blending process was beginning. Mongols, Whites, Blacks, and Australoids joined in populating India. South of the Sahara, while the Negroes were branching off into various groups, some of the Eurasiatics from the north and east were blending with them. A mixed stream compounded of Whites, Yellow-Browns and even some Blacks poured into Europe and gave rise, as human puddles collected at various points, to the Nordic, the Alpine and the Mediterranean peoples. These, in turn, mingled with offshoots of each other and of invading hordes from Asia to form still further subdivisions of peoples.

Note that we have said "peoples" and not "races." "Race" signifies a sufficiently long continuity of common ancestry and a uniqueness of hereditary traits to distinguish one group of peoples from another. The primary White, Yellow-Brown and Black races did experience such isolation while leisurely forming in prehistoric times. But their offshoots were developing within a much smaller space of time, and when growing population and culture were bringing men closer and closer together. There were, as there still are, some isolated outposts of mankind, but in the civilized world we have ample evidence that for the last few thousand years the genetic fences among humans have been knocked down in all directions. Today, among civilized peoples, no "pure" races can be said to exist.

So it is that while some still speak of a "Nordic race," "Alpine race," "Mediterranean race," etc., and others go even farther and talk of an "Italian race," "German race," or "English race," leading authorities are now speaking of these as "ethnic groups," or "peoples." They know well that if on the map of Europe one tried to indicate the paths of all the various peoples that went to make up the different nations, the effect would be very much like a confetti shower during the height of a New Year's Eve party.

Here we may pertinently (or perhaps impertinently!) quote from the well-known German treatise on human heredity by Baur, Fischer and Lenz, a standard text in the field of genetics. Wrote Professor Erwin Baur (one of Germany's greatest geneticists):

"What we today term a nation or a people is, biologically considered, a mishmash of the most extraordinarily diversified elements. . . . It cannot be too emphatically insisted that that which is common to the people of one nation, such as the German, the British or the French, and that which unites them as a nation, is not, properly speaking, their 'race,' but first and foremost, a common speech and culture. Racial distinctions, such as the differences between the before-mentioned peoples, are never anything more than relative distinctions, insofar as the quantitative proportions out of which the mixture is made up in the various peoples differ to some extent, some racial elements being more strongly

THE MELTING POTS OF EUROPE

These were the primary sources of your ancestry if your descent is—

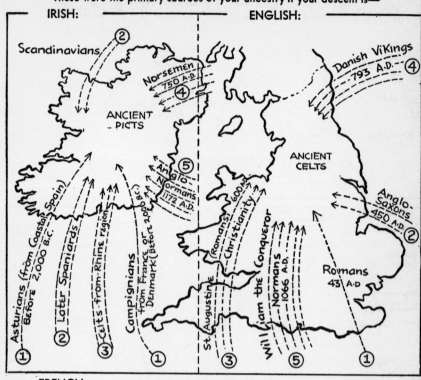

IRISH:

ENGLISH:

Scandinavians ②

Norsemen 750 A.D. ④

ANCIENT - PICTS

Danish Vikings 793 A.D. ④

ANCIENT CELTS

Anglo-Normans 1172 A.D. ⑤

Anglo-Saxons 450 A.D. ②

Romans 600 A.D.

Christianity

Asturians (from Coastal Spain) Before 2,000 B.C. ①

Later Spaniards ②

Celts from Rhine region ③

Campignians from France, of Denmark (before 2,000 B.C.) ①

St. Augustine

Romans ③

William the Conqueror

Normans 1066 A.D. ⑤

Romans 43 A.D. ①

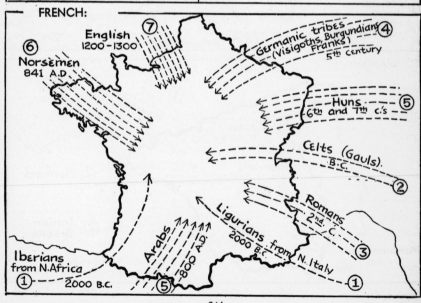

FRENCH:

English 1200-1300 ⑦

Norsemen 841 A.D. ⑥

Germanic tribes (Visigoths, Burgundians, Franks) 5th century ④

Huns 6th and 7th c.'s ⑤

Celts (Gauls) B.C. ②

Romans 2nd. C. ③

Arabs 800 A.D.

Ligurians from N. Italy 2000 B.C. ①

Iberians from N. Africa 2000 B.C. ①

⑤

344

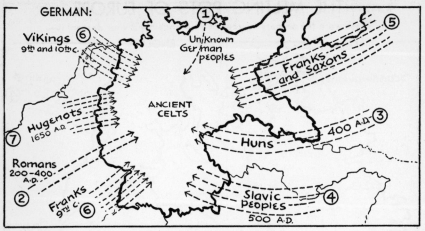

GERMAN:

Vikings ⑥
9th and 10th c.

Unknown
German
peoples ①

Franks
and Saxons ⑤

ANCIENT
CELTS

Hugenots
1650 A.D. ⑦

Franks
and Saxons

Huns 400 A.D. ③

Romans
200-400
A.D. ②

Franks
9th c. ⑥

Slavic
Peoples ④
500 A.D.

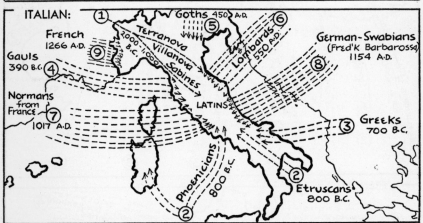

ITALIAN:

French
1266 A.D. ⑨

① Goths 450 A.D. ⑤

Terranova
2000-
1000
B.C.

Villanova

Sabines

Goths ⑥

Lombards
550 A.D.

German-Swabians
(Fred'k Barbarossa)
1154 A.D. ⑧

Gauls
390 B.C. ④

Normans
from
France
1017 A.D. ⑦

LATINS

Greeks
700 B.C. ③

Phoenicians
800 B.C. ②

Etruscans
800 B.C. ②

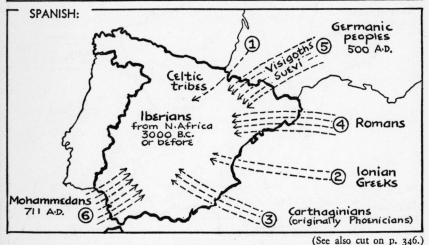

SPANISH:

Germanic
peoples
500 A.D.

Celtic
tribes ①

Visigoths
Suevi ⑤

Iberians
from N. Africa
3000 B.C.
or before

Romans ④

Ionian
Greeks ②

Mohammedans
711 A.D. ⑥

Carthaginians
(originally Phoenicians) ③

(See also cut on p. 346.)

345

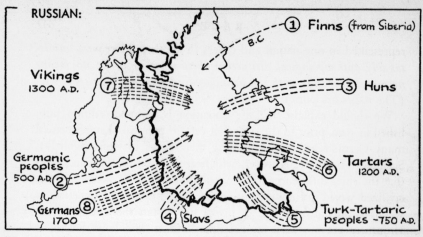

RUSSIAN:

Finns (from Siberia) ①
B.C.
Vikings 1300 A.D. ⑦
Huns ③
Germanic peoples 500 A.D. ②
Tartars 1200 A.D. ⑥
Germans 1700 ⑧
Slavs ④
Turk-Tartaric peoples ~750 A.D. ⑤

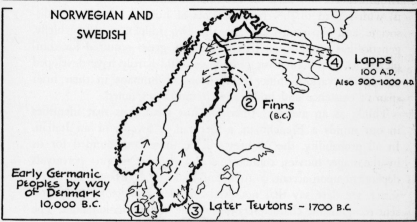

NORWEGIAN AND SWEDISH

Lapps 100 A.D. Also 900-1000 A.D. ④
Finns (B.C.) ②
Early Germanic peoples by way of Denmark 10,000 B.C.
Later Teutons ~ 1700 B.C. ① ③

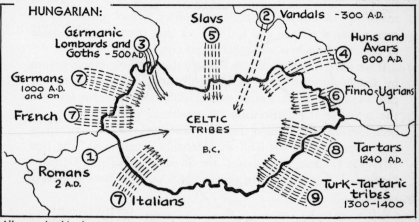

HUNGARIAN:

Slavs ⑤
Vandals ~300 A.D. ②
Germanic Lombards and Goths ~500 A.D. ③
Huns and Avars 800 A.D. ④
Germans 1000 A.D. and on ⑦
Finno-Ugrians ⑥
French ⑦
CELTIC TRIBES B.C.
Tartars 1240 A.D. ⑧
Romans 2 A.D. ①
Italians ⑦
Turk-Tartaric tribes 1300-1400 ⑨

All maps in this chapter were prepared with the aid of Dr. Gene Weltfish, Dept. of Anthropology, Columbia University.

represented in one nation and others in another. Moreover, *unmistakably anthropological distinctions between nations by no means
necessarily coincide with the boundary-lines between folk-speeches.*"
(The italics are ours.)

We should explain that the quotation is from an edition published in 1929, prior to the time that certain political changes caused
many German scientists to modify their views (at least publicly).
Scientists elsewhere, however, will heartily sponsor the conclusion
that the chief differences to be noted among various peoples in the
civilized world are cultural in origin. The findings of genetics, as
we have previously reported, reveal how often the effects of environment are mistaken for hereditary effects, and how difficult it
is, with regard to the complex traits of human behavior, to dissociate and separately appraise the two influences. But chiefly,
genetics has brought out that with many genes required for complex traits, important basic differences could hardly have developed
among the various minor subdivisions of humans in their brief
span of existence and under the circumstances noted.

Think, as an average American, just what it is that identifies
in our minds a Frenchman, a German, a Swede, or an Italian.
In all probability, the pictures will be those compounded for us
by the stage, movies, comic-strips and popular fiction—portrayals
dependent upon accent, costume and make-up. Without such accessories, we dare say that not even our cleverest actors could present recognizable characterizations of the various nationalities. The
problem, moreover, is general. Look at the pictures of "races of
mankind" in any encyclopedia, dictionary, school geography or
even technical treatise and you will see that resort must be made
to costume, hair-dress and other accessories.

If we have such difficulty in distinguishing among ethnic groups
by simple outward traits, it is highly questionable how far we
can ascribe to them temperamental differences so complex that
the genes, or the mechanisms for producing them, have not yet
been identified. We might therefore discount greatly the sweeping
generalizations that the Irish are inherently "pugnacious," the Japs
"sly," the Chinese "inscrutable," the Swedes "stolid," the Germans
"militaristic," or "craving regimentation," etc. We have seen very

clearly in the United States that in a little space of time children of every nationality take on a common American character, to such an extent that when they reach maturity and travel abroad Europeans think of them all as Americans.

Underlying the attempts to prove that there are great basic differences among peoples is the thought that one group (usually that of the speaker or writer) is "superior" to another. Leaving aside the question of what is meant by "superiority," scientists are inclining more and more to the view that such attempts are fruitless and will remain so until we can set up uniform standards of measurement that will apply fairly to all peoples. Geneticists agree that mankind in general is today probably not much different in basic intelligence or capacity from his early ancestors in the New Stone Age. If this is true, and if it is also true that all existing peoples have the same common ancestry, the advance of one and the backwardness of another group might readily be attributed to differences in opportunity and environment.

To retrace our steps, we have evidence that our present civilization had its primary source in the peoples who inhabited Mesopotamia—the "Garden of Eden" to which we referred. Not greater capacity, it is believed, but greater opportunity in the form of abundant resources gave them a "head start" over others. But by no means did they have a monopoly of culture. There is evidence that throughout the world similar ideas, inventions, codes of behavior and other cultural factors arose independently among peoples far apart. This suggests that there may be much the same cultural capacities in all peoples which they may reveal if given full opportunity for development.

We are reminded of the Arctic explorer who was telling about the crude diet of the Eskimos, when a well-meaning but not too bright old lady expressed surprise that Eskimos didn't drink milk.

"Madam," replied the explorer, "have you ever tried to milk a seal?"

There are many things, important to the development of culture, which one cannot "milk" out of an environment where they do not exist. People cannot learn to fashion metals where there are no metal deposits, nor cultivate crops in frozen ground, nor breed cattle where there are only bears and walruses. When we think of their limited resources, it is not surprising that the Eskimos have remained backward in many respects. Far south their more favored cousins, the Aztecs and Incas, did achieve a high degree of civilization. But on the other hand, another set of cousins, some of the American Indians, with great resources at hand, lagged behind. Thus it is not so easy to ascribe reasons for the failure of some peoples to develop culturally.

Too often an entire people is judged by a few gifted members who may not at all reflect the make-up of the mass. Differences between individuals in the same ethnic group are infinitely greater than the *average* difference between any two races or peoples. When we say that one people is superior to another, we generally refer only to its few outstanding individuals. The subsequent idea of attributing to the mass the prowess of these few harks back to the eras when a champion was picked by one tribe to do battle with the champion of another. The qualities of each group were supposed to be transmuted within its representative, and a triumph by the champion "proved" the superiority of his followers. The same concept still permeates undergraduates of rival colleges during a football game. It also hovered in a racial sense over the prizefight between the Negro, Joe Louis, and the German, Max Schmeling.

No more than the last-named contest proved that Negroes as a race are better fighters than Germans, is there proof that a temporary flurry of champions in art, literature, science, invention, commerce or war indicates the inherent superiority of one people over another. Commenting on the claim of "Nordic" supremacy, Professor Lancelot Hogben (himself an Englishman) has pointed out that the Black Moors were highly cultured at the time when the Nordics were little better than barbarians. He quotes a Moorish savant of Toledo as writing of the northern peoples, "They are of cold temperament and never reach maturity; they are of great stature and of a white color. But they lack all sharpness of wit and penetration of intellect." This, as Professor Hogben adds, was at a time when few priests in northern Europe could read or write and when washing the body was still considered a heathen and a dangerous custom.

History reveals many instances where peoples who were on top at one stage were on the bottom at another, and vice versa. The rapidity with which the transitions have occurred has suggested that social and cultural influences were chiefly responsible.

Thus, there is question now as to whether the reign of art among the Athenians, the era of conquest among the Romans, the exploits of the Vikings, the Renaissance among the Italians, and so on, can be considered proof of inherent superiority. Would we say that the present American reign in business proves that Americans carry superior "business" genes? Hardly, for we know very well that favorable conditions gave impetus to American enterprise. And we know also that these or other conditions, and not any hereditary failings, were responsible for what many Europeans long considered the "incapacity" of Americans for response to or expression in the higher forms of culture. Knowing this, we might ask whether many of our own judgments regarding the basic natures or capacities of other peoples are justified.

Are Negroes as a race definitely inferior to Whites in intelligence and cultural capacity? Few authorities today would echo the confident "Yes!" of former times, when Negroes were considered a sub-species of man. Though studies are available which might seem to prove Negro inferiority in some respects, the fairness of these have been challenged on the ground, quite logically, that they have been made by Whites in a White civilization and according to White standards. But even by these standards, and in an environment still prejudicial, the amazing transition of Negroes from a primitive state to one where they are producing writers, scientists, musicians, educators and leaders of high type must be regarded as evidence that their true capacities are far from having been ascertained. As Professor J. B. S. Haldane has observed regarding the question of Negro "inferiority," "Not merely has nothing been proved, but it is going to be exceedingly difficult to prove anything within the next few generations."

We come finally to the race problem that at the moment com-

mands the greatest attention—that which the present rulers of
Germany choose to term "Aryan" versus "Non-Aryan."

Anthropologists tell us that there is not and never was an "Aryan"
race, or even an "Aryan" people. The word "Aryan" was intended
by the philologist [1] who coined the term—Friedrich Max Mueller,
himself a German—to designate a large group of languages, both
European and Asiatic. They include the Celtic, Teutonic, Italic,
Hellenic, Albanian, Armenian, Indo-Iranian and Balto-Slavonic languages. Used in the sense of "race," "Aryan" would have to take
in a wide sweep of the most diverse peoples, ranging from the
Irish to the Vedda Negroes of Ceylon (one of the most primitive tribes in existence).

No more than there is an "Aryan race" is there a "Semitic
race," for "Semitic" also refers to a large family of languages,
among them the Hebrew. However, on the basis of language, the
terms "Hebrew" and "Jewish" are not synonymous. The mass of
Jews, especially in Europe, have little knowledge of Hebrew (using
it only in their religious services, as Catholics use Latin) but
have for centuries employed as their written and spoken language
the Yiddish, a compound largely with an old German base. Judged
by language, then, most Jews would be properly included among
the "Aryans."

The stress laid by Nazi German leaders upon the "Aryan"
issue is one of the attempts to provide standards by which Germans might set themselves apart from other peoples as a "racial
unit." In accordance with what their own authority, Professor
Baur, has pointed out, such attempts are in conflict with fact. Germany includes within its boundaries many ethnic groups—Nordics,
Alpines, Slavs and Mediterraneans—blended, through countless
wars, invasions, and migrations, with the blood of almost every
other people in Europe and Asia. To endow Germans with "racial
unity" and to refer to them as "blood brothers" on the basis of

[1] Prof. Friedrich Max Mueller, noted German philologist, wrote in 1883: "I have
declared again and again if I say Aryan, I mean neither blood nor bones, nor hair,
nor skull; I mean simply those who speak an Aryan language. . . . To me an
ethnologist who speaks of Aryan race, Aryan blood, Aryan eyes and hair, is as great
a sinner as a linguist who speaks of a dolicocephalic [long-headed] dictionary or a
brachycephalic [round-headed] grammar."

a common language and national ties would be equivalent to endowing all citizens of the United States—from *Mayflower* descendants to southern Negroes—with biological unity and "blood brotherhood" because they all speak English.

Bearing further on the Jewish question, it should be clear that the Jews, also, do not constitute a "race" in the sense which we have defined it. While undoubtedly more homogeneous than many other groups, the Jews are none the less compounded of diverse peoples. Originally they were a mixture of Eurasiatics, chiefly Arabian and Mediterranean stocks. However, their troubled history bears witness to the fact that in their wanderings they must have absorbed bloods of every type.

It is not surprising, then, that anthropologists have not been able to find any physical traits which would identify Jews as a people and set them apart biologically from other Whites. While a few characteristics thought of as "Jewish" are found among some Jews, each of these traits is also found among non-Jews; and among Jews in general there is every type of eye, lip, nose, hair form, coloring, head-shape and facial contour common to other Whites. Further, Jews long rooted in different countries differ markedly in appearance, an old-line Spanish Jew looking much more like a Spaniard, and an old-line German Jew much more like a German, than they resemble each other. (This bears out the findings of Professor Boas that environment may do a great deal to alter features.)

As to what, then, constitutes a Jew, there is a growing tendency to look to cultural factors—the effects of common religion, traditions, training, habits and to some extent diet, similarities in social experience, reactions to oppression and other influences. But whether cultural influences alone can explain the story, or as some might term it, the phenomenon, of the Jews, is debatable.

Currently the Jews seem to be the victims of a general movement toward isolation and integration which has been launched in many countries. Illogically, however, some of the nations which are most ardently seeking to cement themselves into "racial units" are also clamoring for expansion. History, physics and genetics all teach that these policies of contraction and expansion are in conflict. Empires cannot be created without sending part of the expanding peoples out into the new territories, and inevitably a mingling of bloods must ensue. It has not infrequently happened that a small body of conquerors has been absorbed by a large body of conquered. In any event, unless a nation welcomes the admixture of foreign blood, history teaches that conquest and expansion are hardly compatible with a policy of "racial integration."

The Negro problem in the United States has aspects somewhat illustrative of the above. Taken into our midst as a conquered and subject people, the Negroes have been gradually intermingling with the Whites until today it is believed that only a fraction of the Negro population is without White blood. It would be folly to assume that all the mixing has been in one direction. Much Negro blood has undoubtedly found its way into the White stream, especially by way of intermarriages with Mexicans, Indians or other peoples who do not too closely draw the "color line." As the Negro population becomes "Whiter" one may wonder how far and for how long the two races can be kept definitely apart.

Everything points to the fact that the possibility of long maintaining any "pure" people in this world of changing humans is exceedingly remote. Taking Germany as an example, even if she drew the most rigid lines about herself, she would be starting out with almost every type of gene known to *Homo sapiens,* including an ample proportion of "Non-Aryan" genes. Supposing again that for a full thousand years she practised the most intensive selection in breeding, casting out the genes she considered undesirable; nevertheless, replicas of many of these genes would be arising through mutation. The evolutionary process, it should always be kept in mind, is still going on. No human force can control it, and to the extent that there are "superior" genes or "inferior" genes, no people can hope to maintain a corner on the one kind or exclude the other. In effect, any people theoretically starting out as "pure" would before long be rendered "impure."

The question then arises, "How important is it to humanity to maintain 'pure races'?" Or, stated in another way, "Is 'race-crossing,' or interbreeding between different peoples, undesirable?"

There is much disagreement on these points. Some have argued that the "purest" peoples have made the greatest advances, and yet, in rebuttal, one need only point to the achievements of the highly mixed population of the United States. From the physical standpoint, some geneticists have claimed that crossing between markedly different peoples may result in misshapen offspring—with big teeth in small jaws, etc. Other authorities dispute these claims on the ground that skeletal parts in humans differ so little that they can freely blend together. The most serious argument against race-crossing is that where peoples of widely diverse type are mated, their differences in temperament, behavior, backgrounds and family connections will make for social conflict that will react unfavorably on their offspring.

We can thus see that all our major "race" problems revolve about the same points: How great are the fundamental differences among various subdivisions of mankind, and to what extent are these differences due to hereditary or to cultural factors? While we have brought out some factual evidence, and a good deal of circumstantial evidence bearing on these points, for the present conclusions must rest on opinion.

As one final commentary, we believe that most leading anthropologists, geneticists and psychologists would agree to this somewhat far-fetched hypothesis:

That if a child fathered by Adolf Hitler were by some whimsy of fate exchanged at birth with the child of a Jewish rabbi, and each were reared unwittingly by the wrong father, in all likelihood Hitler's child would grow up to be "Jewish" in temperament, behavior and social viewpoint, and the rabbi's child would be goose-stepping, storm-trooping and "Heil-Hitlering" with the most rabid of the Aryans.

And we might make similar comparisons in the case of a child of Stalin's reared by Hitler, or an Eskimo child reared by a Hindu, or an Italian child reared by a Swede, or a Turkish child reared by a Boston Cabot. Or, as our photograph proves, of an American child reared by a Chinese.

BIRTH: AMERICAN CULTURE: CHINESE

Fung Kwok Keung, born Joseph Rinehart, of American parents, on Long Island, N. Y., was deserted at the age of 3, and adopted by a Chinese who took him to China. Until he was 19 he was reared among the Chinese as one of their own. Brought back to the United States, he had become so thoroughly Chinese in manner, speech, habit and outlook that he was distinguishable from members of the race only by his features. He is here shown in an "Americanization" class, learning English.

Photo by Acme

CHAPTER XXXIX

ANCESTRY

MR. REGINALD TWOMBLEY DUNN-TWERPP, who is not very bright and weighs 110 pounds—of which a good part is front teeth—likes to boast that he is descended from William the Conqueror, and that the steel-blue blood of ancient warriors flows in his veins. To prove it he will show you his family tree and a beautiful hand-painted crest, prepared by a genealogist in Boston for fifty dollars.

Even in these United States there are still a lot of people like Reginald, who point with pride to some remote ancestor; and, no doubt, others who feel humbled because they haven't any to point to. You yourself may have been among them. We say "may *have* been" because by now you must have gathered that the whole ancestry business has been shaken pretty badly by our genetic findings.

The importance previously attached to ancestry rested on a number of fallacies. First was the pre-genetic concept that heredity was a process of passing on "blood"—the blood of the parents being blended together to form that of the child. No matter how far one traced back, therefore, there was always a little of the blood of any ancestor "flowing" in one's veins. Also, as blood was thought to carry factors that influenced character, the greater the percentage of "blue" or noble blood one carried, the more superior one would be; and the more "common" blood in one's veins, the more inferior one would be. Likewise, touches of genius, of great courage, of brilliance —or taints of criminality, shiftlessness and depravity were thought to be carried in the blood. All that, of course, has been shattered by our knowledge that blood is merely a *product* of each individual's body and that not even a mother and her child have a single drop of blood in common.

Knowing now that all that we inherit are *24 chromosomes* from each parent, ancestry has been reduced to a simple mathematical

OLD CONCEPT OF ANCESTRY

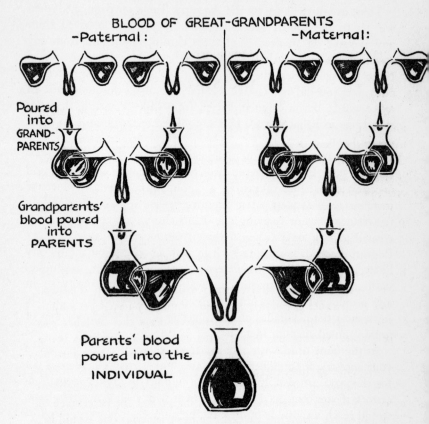

BLOOD OF GREAT-GRANDPARENTS

-Paternal: -Maternal:

Poured into GRAND-PARENTS

Grandparents' blood poured into PARENTS

Parents' blood poured into the INDIVIDUAL

formula: With each generation farther back the *average* number of chromosomes you may have received from any ancestor is reduced by half. Note the qualification "average number." You can be quite certain you received 24 chromosomes from each of your parents, but in the combination from your father, for instance, any number of these 24 may have been derived from *his* father, with the rest from *his* mother. On an *average,* however, you can assume that you received 12 chromosomes from each of your grandparents, that an average of *six* of these came from each great-grandparent, an average of *three* from each great-great-grandparent, and so on, the number from any ancestor being halved with each generation back.

Thus, as you will see by the Ancestry Table on page 358, when we get to the fourth generation you might have received from any ancestor on an average of three chromosomes, and from any specified individual in the preceding generation, either one or two. From that point back, the more remote the ancestor, the greater the odds that you did not receive *a single one* of his chromosomes. In other words, if you claimed descent from Miles Standish, the odds may be 20 to 1 that you are no more related to him than is any one else in town.

That, however, should be qualified. Wherever there was a marriage in your family between two individuals with some common ancestor, the chance of getting a chromosome from that ancestor increased. If *both* your parents claimed descent from Miles Standish, the chance of your carrying one of his chromosomes would be increased to 1 in 10. Further, if there were marriages between other Pilgrim descendants farther back in your ancestry, you might very likely be chock-full of *Mayflower* chromosomes. Thus, in families with considerable inbreeding, such as the European royalty, or in any peoples who have tended to hold together (the Irish, Scotch, Jews, etc.) the possibility of carrying one or more chromosomes of some vaunted ancestor increases.

At the same time, with each marriage between related persons in your ancestry, the number of your ancestors is reduced. Were it not for this, you can readily see that the number of your *potential* ancestors, if you continued to double them with each generation back, would reach impossible figures. As the number of possible ancestors is limited, it has therefore been estimated that all persons of English descent are at least thirtieth cousins; and of course, if we go far back enough, we all have ancestors in common.

Even if one could be certain of carrying one or two chromosomes of some famous ancestor the claim to distinction on that account becomes rather ridiculous when we recall that a full complement of *48 chromosomes* is required to make an individual. Nor is there any guarantee that the one or two vaunted chromosomes which one might have received did not contain the very *worst* of genes.

YOU AND YOUR ANCESTORS

The only possible hereditary link which you can have with any ancestor is through inheritance of one or more chromosomes. This table shows the *average* number of chromosomes which you might have received from any specified ancestor in any generation back, or the odds against having received even a single chromosome.* However, as noted in the text, marriages between relatives in your line of descent intensified your link with any preceding ancestor.

Generation Back	Approx. Year and Generation	No. of "Potential" Ancestors	No. of Chromosomes from Each (Av.)
First (Your parents)		2	24
Second (Grandparents)	1890 (The "Nineties")	4	12
Third (Great g.ps.)	1860 (Generation of Lincoln)	8	6
Fourth (Great-great g.ps.)	1830 (Generation of C. Vanderbilt)	16	3
Fifth (Great-great-great-g.ps.)	1800 (Generation of Napoleon)	32	1 or 2

			Odds Against Having Received Even One Chromosome from Any Given Ancestor
Sixth	1770 (Revolutionary War heroes)	64	4 to 3
Seventh	1740 (Benj. Franklin, etc.)	128	8 to 3
Eighth	1700 (William III)	256	5 to 1
Ninth	1670 (John Bunyan)	512	10 to 1
Tenth	1635 (The Pilgrims)	1,024	21 to 1
Eleventh	1600 (Capt. John Smith)	2,048	42 to 1
Twelfth	1570 (Mary, Queen of Scots)	4,096	85 to 1
Thirteenth	1535 (Martin Luther)	8,192	170 to 1
Fourteenth	1500 (Henry VIII)	16,384	340 to 1
Fifteenth	1470 (Columbus)	32,768	680 to 1

*It is theoretically possible for chromosomes to be passed on in fractions by the process known as "cross-over," but this would not affect the odds or general averages shown.

A second fallacy is that of completely disregarding the unimportant ancestors, and in many families the remoter *women* ancestors. In our first paragraph we mentioned William the Conqueror. While his father was of royal blood, it is seldom pointed out that William's mother was a humble miller's daughter who bore him illegitimately.

In fact, with regard to all family trees the practise has been to lop off the ignoble branches in each generation, so that eventually only the limited few "distinguished" ancestors are left dangling. When a geneticist therefore is confronted with a lineage dating back say, twenty generations, in which at best a selected few hundred out of a possible many thousands are listed, he may be pardoned for not taking it seriously.

A third fallacy in the ancestry field is that of comparing human families to strains of domestic animals—aristocrats to thoroughbreds and ordinary folks to mongrels. True enough, there are genetic aristocracies among horses, dogs, cows and cats; but bear in mind that they were derived only by the closest inbreeding—fathers with daughters, mothers with sons, brothers with sisters—and also by controlling every mating and by discarding those not wanted from every generation or litter. So far as we know, no family of human aristocrats lays claim to having been thus derived. (We're not saying it couldn't or won't be done. No one can predict what certain European dictators may be up to next.) But as matters stand, human breeding has been a haphazard process, and even the bluest of our blue-blooded families are a hodgepodge of unidentifiable genes. To quote the famed biologist, W. Johannsen, "From the point of view of a pure-bred dog, we are all curs."

We cannot deny, however, that there are families which by the consistent achievement of an unduly large percentage of their members do suggest that they carry many "superior" genes. Among such families may be cited the Darwins and the Huxleys in England, and the Adamses, the Edwardses and the Roosevelts in the United States. But it is also clear that even in the greatest of families there are mediocrities who ride along, as in a trailer, pulled by their family influence, opportunity or wealth and who, left to their own power, would get nowhere.

"Ancestry" or "family" has significance only when individuals themselves show clear evidence of continued superiority. But, alas, all our records show that combinations of "superior" genes do not long hold together. Rarely do we find any dynasty of superior humans continuing for as much as four or five generations. (In the Bible we find a suggestion, in another way, that there are limits to the effects of ancestral influence. We are told that "the iniquity of the fathers" is visited "upon the children unto the third and fourth generation . . ." [Ex. 20:5.] This might also be interpreted as applying to ancestral virtues.)

When we turn now to "inferior" ancestry we find that the same fallacies underlie the compilation of "bad" pedigrees as of "superior" ones. The motives, however, are quite different. As we might express it in verse—

> *There was a Bostonese*
> *Who searched out pedigrees*
> *Which she stored in the middle of her forehead;*
> *And when they were good, they were very, very good,*
> *But when they were bad—they were horrid!*

Which is by way of saying that compilers of pedigrees may be motivated by the very human urge to prove extremes. Those who compile genealogies of persons of "superior" stock are out to show how *very good* these people are. In the compilation of pedigrees of "inferior" stock investigators may unconsciously yield to the opposite impulse. Nowhere has this been more clearly illustrated than in those classic horrible examples of yesterday's sociology books—the two distinct clans referred to as the "Kallikaks" and the "Jukes." In case you've forgotten, here are the main facts:

First, the "Kallikaks." In 1898 Dr. H. H. Goddard, then director of an institution for mental defectives in New Jersey, chanced on the strange fact that there were two family groups in the vicinity, distantly related to each other, and yet as different in character as the proverbial night and day. The one branch comprised upright, intelligent, prosperous citizens; the other abounded in degenerates, mental defectives, drunks, paupers, prostitutes and criminals. Struck with the contrast, Dr. Goddard coined for the family the name "Kallikak" (compounded of Greek words meaning "good" and "bad") and after long research into the pedigrees, produced this explanation:

Both clans had stemmed from the same remote ancestor—Martin "Kallikak," a Revolutionary War soldier—*but through two different matings.* Martin Kallikak, himself, it appeared, was of good stock, and after the war had married a worthy young Quakeress by whom he had seven children—progenitors of all the "good" Kallikaks. But—

Before he had married, and while a-soldiering, Martin had met a feeble-minded girl in a tavern, and with her had had an affair. He went his way, and presently the girl bore an illegitimate male child *to whom she gave the name of Martin Kallikak, Jr.* This lad grew up to be so wicked he was known as "Old Horror," and to make matters worse, sired ten worthless offspring. It was from these that Dr. Goddard traced all the several hundred *bad* Kallikaks.

Clearly, looking first at the very, very good Kallikaks, and then at the very, very bad Kallikaks, their differences would seem to have been caused by the two radically different females from whom they descended—the worthy Quakeress and the feeble-minded slattern. For a long time this was held up as a fine illustration of "superior" ancestry and "inferior" ancestry. But, remember, this study was begun in 1898, before there was any science of genetics. Today we can view the situation quite differently.

The comparison rests largely on *the assumption* that the illegitimate child whom the feeble-minded mother chose to call Martin Kallikak, Jr., was indeed the son of the man she designated, which no court would accept as evidence. But supposing that she were correct, a nice point in genetics intrudes itself:

Granted that "Old Horror" (Kallikak, Jr.) was a degenerate because of *bad heredity* (and there is as yet no evidence that "degeneracy" is inherited) by what gene mechanism did he become that way? No *single dominant* gene could produce any such complex condition, nor is there any known gene that can singly produce even feeble-mindedness. *Recessive* genes would have had to be involved. Which means that as such genes must come from *both parents* for the effect to assert itself, no matter how chock-full of "black" genes the feeble-minded mother was, *the worthy Martin Kallikak, Sr.,*

WHAT IS WRONG WITH THIS PICTURE?

In Revolutionary War times there was a soldier named
"MARTIN KALLIKAK"

—after the war he married a worthy young Quakeress

She bore him seven fine, healthy, upright children.

From these came hundreds of the most worthy type of humans, with the best heredity.

While in service he dallied with a feeble-minded tavern girl

She bore a son whom she called "Martin Kallikak, Jr." — later known as "Old Horror."

From "Old Horror" came ten children who spawned hundreds of the lowest humans, with the worst heredity.

362

himself had to be carrying such genes if the condition of his presumptive son, "Old Horror," was due to heredity. And that would mean, in turn, that the "good" Kallikaks also received some of those "black" genes!

Before we go on to a number of other points that any geneticist might raise, let's look into the case of the "Jukes" (also a coined name).

The Jukes family, another unsavory clan abounding in every known type of human riff-raff, was investigated long before the Kallikaks. It was in 1874 that R. L. Dugdale, a New York Prison Association inspector, chanced upon this worthless aggregation, clustered in one locality. Tracing back, he discovered that they all had a common ancestry in two eighteenth-century brothers who had married a pair of disreputable sisters. Intensifying their relationship was the fact that the Jukes were much inbred.

In 1916 the Jukes study was brought up to date with an investigation of the ensuing generations. Degeneracy, immorality and defectiveness were still rampant among the new crop of Jukes, but to a smaller degree. Many of the family, in fact, were honest, hard-working citizens, some even "superior" and prosperous. This improvement was ascribed to reduced inbreeding and the infusion of "good outside" blood.

If we now analyze the Jukes studies, we find them quite as questionable from a genetic standpoint as we found the Kallikak studies. When Dugdale investigated the Jukes, not only was nothing known of the mechanism of heredity, but sociology was in its infancy. Dugdale blandly assumed, as did others at the time, that "pauperism," prostitution and criminality—even the tendency to have illegitimate children—had an hereditary basis. His conclusions were that starting with a bad heredity, the Jukes had created for themselves a bad environment and that this environment had produced bad traits which in turn became hereditary. (Or, in other words, that morals, habits and other *acquired* bad traits are inherited —which, of course, we now know is unfounded.)

We can well suspect that in the original study of the Jukes there were many errors in the dogmatic classification of individuals as "prostitutes," "criminals" or "degenerates" (especially when we con-

sider that some of the individuals classified had been dead for anywhere from 25 to 100 years). But even more strongly can we question the data regarding mental defectiveness, for *at that time there
were not even IQ scores to go by*. Nor were there in the first
studies of the Kallikaks. Moreover, in both studies, the individuals
traced represented only *a part* of all the descendants. This is important, for it is one thing to prove that there are 300 degenerates
out of 600, and another that there are 300 out of 6,000.

With all these reservations, however, there is no gainsaying that
the bad Jukes who were observed, like the bad Kallikaks, were an
unusually undesirable lot. We needn't argue *how* bad or how degenerate they were. What concerns us is the extent to which their
degeneracy and their lowness can be blamed on *bad heredity*.

Let us try to picture one of the Jukes girls, at the time of Dugdale's investigation, in the Seventies:

Mamie Jukes lived in a dark, squalid nest of hovels, with a
drunken, thieving father, a slattern of a mother and a swarm of
untidy, ill-fed brothers and sisters. Mamie didn't go to school, because there was no compulsory education and the district school-
house wouldn't take any of the brood. Decent folks kept away
from the Jukes and whipped their children if they were even seen
talking to Mamie. She was pretty lonely until, when she got to be
about fourteen or fifteen, some men who hung around a pool hall
began to take an interest in her. Mamie was a little bewildered, and
pathetically flattered by this sudden attention. She was too dumb to
understand what was happening, or how it happened, but soon she
became diseased. . . . And one day, months later in a dark corner
where Mamie cowered like a sick animal, another illegitimate, "unfit" child was added to the Jukes clan.

Yes, this is a synthetic picture, but no one who has studied the
records would deny that it is a typical one. Can we still say that
the new Jukes child—or any similar child—starting out life under
such conditions was predestined to inferiority because of "black"
genes? Or could we not equally predict a bad end, *regardless* of the
genes that child carried, on the basis of its "black" environment?

It is because earlier investigators did not quite see this distinction

that their studies are now greatly discounted. To quote Professor
Thomas Hunt Morgan:

"The numerous pedigrees that have been published showing a
long history of social misconduct, crime, alcoholism, debauchery and
venereal diseases, are all open to the same criticism from a genetic
point of view, for it is obvious that these groups of individuals have
lived under demoralizing social conditions that might swamp a
family of average persons. It is not surprising that, once begun,
from whatever cause, the effects may be to a large extent communicated rather than inherited."

And as a *coup de grâce,* we may add this from another famed
geneticist, Professor Lancelot Hogben: "If social biology ever becomes an exact science, the dreary history of the Jukes will be regarded as we now regard alchemy."

CHAPTER XL

THE GIDDY STORK

"We hold these truths to be self-evident, that all men are created equal . . ."

Everything we have learned about human heredity challenges this statement in our Declaration of Independence. While genetics gives no support to the concept of hereditary "superior" or "inferior" classes (to paraphrase Professor Jennings) neither does it support the theory of genetic equality. We have been shown beyond the shadow of doubt that individuals are ushered into the world with every type of *inequality* in body and mind, and when we add to this the obvious inequalities in environment and opportunity, we are forced to conclude that the statement of the Founding Fathers was a flight of poetic fancy (as indeed they may have meant it to be!).

Without inquiring further into the causes of human differences, there is general agreement that we would like to see more of some kind of people in this world than of others. (Which probably means more of "our" kind of people—vague as that might be.) So when we now take a broad view of the population, it is disconcerting to discover—or so we are told—that the kind of people we *do want* are being created not nearly so fast as the kind of people we *don't want.* Here is a new sort of "population fear."

For a long time the fear was that the world would become overrun with human beings. In 1800 all humanity totaled not more than 750 million souls. A phenomenal growth began, due principally to lowered death-rates and improved means of subsistence. Within a few generations the population doubled. (Now it is almost triple.) The specter of a world choking itself to death with overpopulation arose. To meet this came a spread of the Malthusian doctrines that human population growth was a biologically self-regulating process, and that wars, plagues, famines, etc., etc., would automatically step in from time to time to keep the population within bounds.

The Malthusian doctrines, like others we have mentioned, are now being abandoned. For it is becoming apparent that our population growth, in numbers, kind and quality, is controlled not by natural biologic forces but by artificial factors. And again there is alarm, this time that unless we begin *planning* the growth of our population, as we do our crops, we are headed for disaster.

The first fact cited is that not only has the growth of population in this and many other countries slowed down, but that a *decline* is on the point of setting in. "What of it?" you ask, as you view the many unemployed and the many undesirables. "We might be a lot better off with fewer people in this world." That may well be so, but, like the lady in the reducing class, some authorities complain that the decrease is in the wrong quarters.

Viewing the world at large, we find that the populations of our Western countries are being outdistanced by those of Oriental nations. Next, in Europe, the birth-rates in Germany and Italy, under dictatorial stimulus, have begun to go up while the birth-rates in England and France continue to drop. (Which, of course, is cause for alarm only in the democracies.) Finally, coming home, we find that the birth-rate in the United States has declined 25 percent in the last ten years, and that we now have 1,600,000 fewer children under ten than we had only five years ago!

The census figures tell you that our population is still growing, which is true; and it is also true that the birth-rate is still higher than the death-rate. But this is because the great increase in longevity within the past generation has swelled our numbers by millions of middle-aged and old people who would not have been here before. If we thought of our population in terms of an army, a large percentage of veterans have been kept in service far beyond the time when they previously would have been mustered out. Thus, though the number of annual recruits (babies) is rapidly declining, for the time being the army ranks (our total population) appear to be full and even growing. But within twenty years or so the temporary advantage gained by the veterans in the ranks will be overcome, and from then on (about the year 1960) official estimates are that our actual numbers will begin to decline.

In post-Revolutionary War days, American women living through the child-bearing period were producing an average of almost *eight* children each. Today the average is about *two* children. Yet this far from tells the whole story, for it refers to the general average. Actually the birth-rate is unevenly distributed in various levels, being lowest among those in the upper social and economic levels, and highest among those in the lower social and economic levels.

Disregarding for the moment the question of *why* some people are on a lower level than others, as we said at the beginning of this chapter, there cannot be much doubt that certain persons will make better parents than other persons. If we think of those best qualified as "plus" and those least qualified as "minus" we might picture two contrasting types:

The *"Pluses"* are able, willing, intelligent, hard-working, socially-conscious, forward-looking couples who want as many children as they can have.

The *"Minuses"* are the unstable, shiftless, indifferent, unintelligent, unsocially-minded couples, living from hand to mouth in sordid and unhealthy surroundings and looking upon added children as necessary inflictions. By the "Minuses" are further meant not "depression" victims, but those who, even in average times, answer the description given.

So we come to the complaint, which is that the "Pluses" of the United States (and of other countries, too) who want children most and are able to give them the best start in life, are having the smallest families, while the "Minuses" who least desire children and who offer them the worst start in life, are having the largest families. Remember, this is referring to broad averages. It does not imply that all those with small families are "Pluses," and all those with large families are "Minuses." (Our ambassador to England, Joseph P. Kennedy, has a family of nine splendid children and many a good American can boast an equal or an even greater number.)

For the country at large, the highest birth-rates are in the most impoverished rural areas, chiefly of the South and West. In the worst of the areas the population is reproducing rapidly enough to double

THE BIRTH-RATE "DIFFERENTIAL"
(As Viewed by a Population Expert)*

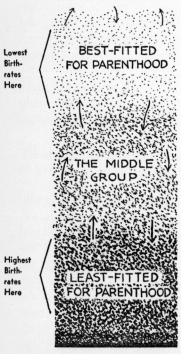

CROSS-SECTION OF
U. S. POPULATION

6% Professional and most-favored groups

Lowest Birth-rates Here

BEST-FITTED FOR PARENTHOOD

30% Intelligent, honest, willing, able, hard-working, dependable, socially-conscious, good citizens of all kinds

THE MIDDLE GROUP

30% The middle group, fluctuating between both extremes, some rising, some dropping

30% Unstable, shiftless, indifferent, unintelligent, unsocially-minded, most unproductive

Highest Birth-rates Here

LEAST-FITTED FOR PARENTHOOD

3% Socially inadequate
½ of 1% Known defectives

* This should be considered as an individual opinion. Other experts might make different estimates of the percentages of "best-fitted" and "least-fitted."

its numbers in one generation. On the other hand, in the more favorable economic areas—which are chiefly urban—fertility is much lower. In some of the large cities fertility is less than 75 percent of that required for replacement, and within the cities proper, the fertility is highest among the poor, the less educated and those in the least favorable circumstances, and lowest among those in the higher income brackets who are engaged in business or professions.

Where the decline in births first took place in the cities, it is now rapidly extending to the rural districts. And here, again, the falling off in births is greatest among the most favorably situated farmers and rural inhabitants. In short, throughout the country, wherever education and standards of living have gone up, with only few exceptions has the birth-rate not gone down.

What are the causes of this disproportion? First and foremost is the growing practise of *birth control,* which is most widespread among those in the "upper" social and economic strata, least common among those in the "lower" strata. Education and improved living standards bring with them the desire to insure better opportunities for children. Which means that the educated and conscientious parents, with the knowledge of birth-control methods at hand, are now regulating the size and spacing of their families to conform with their incomes, health, and opportunities for child-raising. On the other hand, parents in the lowest social and economic levels, who are largely ignorant of birth-control methods or are indifferent to their use, are letting nature take its course.

Comparing city and country, the pressure for limitation of families is not so great in the rural areas. Added children on farms do not mean moving to new quarters with higher rent, as they do in the city. Also, schooling in farm areas is more limited, so that children do not remain dependent for so long; in fact, children on farms are often an economic asset, especially among the most backward, where they are put to work at some task from the earliest years.

Another cause of the disproportion in birth-rates is difference in age at marriage. Persons in the "upper" levels, where education and training are prolonged, marry later; and as the educational requirements for entrance into the professions have steadily increased, the average age at marriage has been pushed forward. A natural result has been a decline in the number of children. Over a period of 80 years it has been found that college graduates have been producing consistently fewer children than their own brothers or cousins who have not attended college.

Among women, the effects of education have been even more acute. Not only may a college education postpone the time when a

YOU AND HEREDITY

By AMRAM SCHEINFELD

Assisted in the Genetic Sections by DR. MORTON D. SCHWEITZER

HERE is a book which, as the authors say, looks from the outside in to one of the most interesting and important subjects in human history. This book tells what the layman wants to know about heredity. And how much that is! Marriage, childbirth, a man's career, the nature of a race, the cause of disease, the progress of civilization, your own personality and physiological characteristics—you cannot be concerned with any of these topics without turning to heredity in the attempt to find an answer, and now the science of heredity is ready to reply to some at least of the questions asked, as definitely as engineering science can say what stresses are involved in the making of a bridge.

Can you forecast the probable appearance and nature of your child, and how? How is sex determined, and can it be artificially determined? Who should marry and who should not marry? Are females less intelligent than males; Negroes less than whites? How long will you live? Can you inherit acquired characteristics, such as education or disease? What does the father give the child? The mother? These are questions answered in this book, and not by generalizing of the moral-popular kind, but by exact statement, and a series of illustrations, maps, and diagrams, which tell much of the story so clearly that the text becomes only a commentary.

There is nothing new here to the scientist abreast with research, and little that is controversial. What we do not know about heredity the authors leave for scientific discussion elsewhere. But we already know so much with certainty that it is possible to give exact statement where the man or woman educated in college courses twenty years ago is still guessing. The process of reproduction, from the nature of the sperm, with its twenty-four elements, and the egg with its twenty-four elements, through conception, the growth of the embryo, and the history of the resulting cells from infancy to death, is now known, so far as heredity is concerned, with almost mathematical certainty. It is not possible to be sure whether you, for example, carry one of the "black" genes that, in combination with others, may spell ruin to your offspring, but the probability can be established and the possible results made clear. It is not known with certainty whether your child will be a superior person, but the probability can be forecast, and the process by which it can inherit superior traits made as clear as the multiplication table. Myth after myth crumbles before the inevitable processes described in this book as the microscope sees them. Much that has been popularly believed about the relation of parent and child and the influence of ancestry proves to be as impossible to believe as that worms are born from mud, or that malaria comes from breathing bad air.

The authors have avoided sensationalism, but much that they write is sensational in itself, because so contrary to common belief. It is, for example, the male who is the weaker sex. More males are conceived than females, for reasons not fully understood. But many more males die in the womb, at birth, and throughout the life cycle. The female is the tougher animal from the moment the sperm bearing the female element penetrates the egg. Again, the unborn child is not dependent upon the mother's blood and nerve system. It is a parasite, drawing from the same nourishment that nourishes her, but by its own system. She can influence it not one whit by what she learns or does during the period of pregnancy, unless, as host of this independent life, she deteriorates in health. A few malignant disease germs have the power to penetrate the wall that separates the child from her organism; but her thoughts, her experiences, her blood stream, make no communication with her child. Nor is the nature of the offspring affected in any way by the age of the parents, provided the mother can bear a healthy child, or by their love or lack of love for each other at the moment of conception. The germ plasm is immortal and operates independently of the history of the body that contains it.

I have written chiefly of parent and child, because so many readers will find in the chapters describing the process of birth interesting additions to their knowledge. But this book is as broadly based as it is lucidly written, and goes afield into the dozens of more general questions involving human history where heredity may be a factor. The problem of racism, upon which political philosophies are now being built, is analyzed completely here. No one will have any doubt, after reading *You and Heredity*, as to the real factors which determine "purity" of blood. They are very different from the superstitions and fallacies put forward for political and economic purposes by the Fascist states, and particularly valuable are the discussions of the subtle intertwinings of the influences of environment and heredity, which have led many of us to ascribe to heredity what only environment can do, and vice versa. In fact, I think that the first reaction of most unspecialized readers to this book will be to realize that they did not really know what heredity was. By seeing how it works, they find out in *You and Heredity.*

I can conceive of no one, man, woman, or child above the age of puberty, who should not read, and who will not read with an often fascinated interest, this excellent popularization of a science which touches everywhere the vital questions of human nature. Psychology often has to guess; but heredity, where it applies, *knows.*

HENRY SEIDEL CANBY

BOOK-OF-THE-MONTH CLUB, Inc. .. 385 Madison Ave., New York, N. Y.

PRINTED IN U. S. A.

young woman will marry and begin bearing children, but in many cases it acts to forestall marriage altogether. Alumnae records of our leading women's colleges show a strikingly high proportion of graduates who remain unmarried. Whether it is because college women become more "choosey" about men, or because careers distract them, the fact remains that where there are diplomas there are all too frequently no marriage licenses or birth certificates.

There are "social sterility" factors of many kinds. Not only for women but for men, certain careers, such as writing, art, music and the theater, where the road upward is long and uncertain and earnings precarious, keep many from marrying or from having children when they do marry. Even where money is not at issue psychological or social forces which prevent settling down may inhibit reproduction. A glance back at the notable instrumental musicians represented in our study will show that all thirty-six, of whom only four are under thirty, have produced but *thirty-seven* children. Another study we made with regard to birth-rate, of one hundred married "Who's Who" American authors represented in the collection of books presented by publishers to the White House, showed that all these authors together produced about one hundred and fifty children. Eleven of these authors were women, and their total number of children was twelve. With about three children to a couple being required for population replacement it will be seen that the birth-rate among all these gifted individuals is well under par.

Several exceptions should be noted to the rule that the "higher up" one goes, the fewer the number of children. Studies at Yale and Harvard showed that among the most successful of the graduates, and among the faculty, those with the highest standing had the largest families. More recently another study of graduates of Brown University of the class of '24 showed that the "high" men produced substantially more offspring than the "low" men, and solely because they married earlier and in larger proportions. It is apparent, however, within the ranks of college men as among socially awakened persons in general, that lower incomes mean fewer children.

Apart from the social factors cited (which by no means constitute all the socio-economic factors involved) it is estimated that one couple in every ten is childless largely because of physical reasons. The sterility, as might be expected, is usually in the woman, but there is a considerable incidence of complete or partial sterility in men. (Further facts on this subject will be given in the chapter on "Program for Tomorrow.")

Most serious among the physical factors affecting the birth-rate are abortions, both spontaneous and induced. Dr. Frederick Taussig, who has made an exhaustive study of the subject, has recently reported that there must be close to 700,000 abortions in the United States annually—or one abortion to every three confinements. From 25 to 30 percent of the abortions are therapeutic—medically sanctioned as necessitated by the mother's condition. (In all countries *nephritis*—kidney disease—in a pregnant mother is legal ground for abortion.) However, 60 to 65 percent of the abortions are illegally induced, only half of these being performed by physicians; and it is the illegal abortions that are largely responsible for the annual death toll of 8,000 women from such operations.

Of significance with regard to the birth-rate is the fact that almost 90 percent of the abortions (according to Dr. Taussig) now occur among married women, most of them between 25 and 35 years of age, and especially where they have had several children. Further, among married women in the cities, there are proportionately twice as many abortions as among women in the country districts, who have less reason to fear the advent of an extra child.

All this again confronts us with the paradox that children are being forced upon many people who do not want them, or should not have them, and are being kept from many people who do want them, and should have them.

The Stork, it seems, has no sense of direction. What shall we do to steer it right?

EUGENICS: NEGATIVE

Not so many years ago the word "eugenics" conjured up a picture of an athletic young man in a leopard skin being mated to a robust young woman in a bathing suit while over them, in an inset signifying "The Future" hovered a large brood of youngsters posed athletically (in their birthday suits) to show the effects of good heredity and a diet of cracked wheat and vegetables.

Later on the picture changed to one of determined reformers shooing the Stork away from slums and hovels while shouting their war-cry, "Sterilize! Sterilize!"

Whatever "eugenics" may now suggest to the popular mind, we dare say that it is still viewed as "just another of those reform movements." If so, the blame attaches to the earlier "eugenists" who got it off to a bad start. And this is unfortunate, for eugenics, properly interpreted, may be one of the great forces for good on our social horizon.

"Eugenics" (based on the Greek word "eugenes"—"well-born") was the term used by Sir Francis Galton in 1883 to designate his movement for improving the human race by scientific breeding. However, as the mechanism of heredity had not yet been discovered, Galton and his followers were motivated by many of the fallacious ideas about ancestry which we previously mentioned. They believed quite strongly that those on top were there largely because of "superior" heredity, while those at the bottom were there because of "inferior" ancestry. Accordingly, they drew strong support from the aristocracy and the "old-line families," in both England and the United States, and at the same time aroused the resentment of the more democratically minded.

When the Mendelian findings did come out, and an array of "black" genes in humans was revealed, the eugenists seized on this as confirmation of their belief that most of the major ills in the world were due to bad heredity. The quickest way, and the only way, to improve the world, they argued, was by breeding better humans. This was violently contested by the "environmentalists" and "behaviorists," who insisted that heredity was of little account and that education, hygiene and social improvements alone could produce a more perfect humanity. Today, as the smoke of battle begins to clear, we find both sides ready to compromise.

Recognizing that heredity and environment are inter-operating forces that cannot be considered apart, the "hereditarians" have come to realize that many defects previously attributed to bad heredity are due primarily to outside influences, and no matter how greatly we can improve our heredity, our efforts will be of little avail unless we can also improve our environment. The "environmentalists," on the other hand, faced with proof that many ills and undesirable characteristics are directly due to or influenced by heredity, must concede that no plan for human betterment can ignore the importance of improving our genetic make-up.

Thus has been formulated this two-fold "eugenics program" in which both environmental and genetic measures are included:

Negative Eugenics, embodying all measures that might reduce the proportion of "unfit" individuals.

Positive Eugenics, embodying all measures that might increase the proportion of "fit" individuals.

Not to give the impression that a definite platform has been drawn up (as by a party convention), we may say at once that the eugenics "program" we are presenting is merely a summary of all the various proposals made for improvement of the human stock. Some of these measures are already being carried out in this or other countries, some are still nebulous proposals, some meet with general approval and others are being hotly debated. All will be discussed impartially.

First, "negative" eugenics: The obvious way to reduce the proportion of "unfit" children is to reduce the birth-rate among "unfit" parents. The cause of their unfitness, as previously explained, is here set aside. No one need deny that couples who are insane, or morons, or deaf mutes, or who are horribly diseased or malformed, or who are criminal or degenerate, can hardly be "fit" parents. (At least under average conditions.) Nor need we deny that a husband and wife who are poverty-stricken, uneducated, living in squalor and already with several children for whom they are unable to provide properly, cannot give a fair start to more children. Yet these parents produce an unduly large number of offspring, chiefly because, through ignorance or indifference—and often against their will—they let nature take its course.

To combat this situation, eugenists favor the spread of *birth-control* information. As has been shown, the more educated and in many instances the more desirable individuals in our population are fully informed on the subject and are widely practising birth-control methods. Only by placing the same information and facilities at the disposal of the more backward persons in our population (the contention is) can we prevent our population growth from becoming adversely one-sided.

"Planned parenthood" is a better term than "birth control" to characterize the eugenic objectives. In many instances what is sought is not a reduction in the size of families, but the proper "spacing" of children, so that they will come when the mother, the home and the family budget are best prepared for their advent into the world. Children, like any guest in a home, it is felt, should arrive only when they are *welcome*.

But what about persons who are considered unfit to have *any* children? For these, the extreme form of birth control is proposed— that of *sterilization*.

Sterilization, as you probably know, is not an *unsexing* operation. It in no way inhibits sex desires or interferes with normal sex-functioning. In men, sterilization is the simple process of cutting and tying up the *vas deferens,* the tube through which the sperms must issue. In women, sterilization is more serious. Here the operation consists of making an abdominal incision and tying the *fallopian* tubes down which the eggs must travel. (See page 32.) While conception is rendered impossible, the ovaries are in no way affected (any more than sterilization affects the testes in men).

Sterilization for eugenic reasons is not new. In the United States it dates back forty years, when a prison doctor in Indiana first began performing such operations on habitual criminals (with their consent). Before long sterilization began to be advocated for mental defectives and in 1907 the first sterilization laws were passed in Indiana and California. Twenty-six other states have since followed suit. To date some 27,000 persons (60 percent females) have been sterilized in the United States, nearly half of these in California alone.

What has been accomplished, and what can be accomplished by sterilization?

The first thought was that it would be a quick and easy method of wiping out all serious hereditary conditions. Let us assume (but with great reservations to be noted later) that the persons sterilized to date did carry serious "black" genes and that thereby the birth of many defective children has already been prevented. But this is the merest beginning. Suppose from now on that we have a free hand so that we can sterilize anybody and everybody, those in institutions and outside, who may be carrying serious hereditary defects. Which ones are sufficiently grave to warrant sterilization?

We can confine ourselves to the more acute mental defects, the severe organic disorders and various malformations or loathsome conditions which make impossible a normal or happy existence. But at the very outset, when we seek to eliminate any given "black" gene, we must consider the gene mechanism involved—dominant, recessive, sex-linked, etc.—for in each case the problem is distinctly different.

The simplest gene mechanism is that of the dominant gene which singly produces its effect. Every person with a dominant condition will transmit it to one in every two children. Sterilize every dominant "black" gene victim and we could *almost* wipe these conditions from the earth within a single generation. We say "almost," because here and there the condition may arise through mutation, but chiefly because, in such maladies as that of Huntington's chorea, or glaucoma, the individual may marry and have children before the condition asserts itself. Where this factor is not involved, the serious dominant conditions that we could eliminate immediately (ear-nerve tumor, complete absence of iris, optic atrophy, etc.) are all so rare as to be of little significance.

Our next category comprises sex-linked genes, conditions such as the classic hemophilia, where a single gene produces the effect in *males only*, with two such genes required to make a female defective. Here our problem becomes complicated. In hemophilia, it is dangerous to try to sterilize the victims (all males) because being "bleeders," any operation might prove fatal to them. This isn't too important, as few hemophiliacs survive to maturity, and those that do today would hardly venture to have children. Few pedigrees of hemophilia run for more than two or three generations. Mutations, it is believed, are responsible for keeping up the supply of "hemophilia" genes, as well as those for a number of other serious defects.

In other sex-linked conditions such as juvenile glaucoma, absence of sweat glands, retinitis pigmentosa, adult Leber's disease, eye-muscle paralysis, peroneal muscular atrophy, etc., where the bleeding factor is not involved, sterilization could of course reduce the circulation of the genes by both male victims, carrying one gene, and female victims, with two.

But in all the above conditions—including hemophilia—we would still have with us the much larger number of women carrying the single hidden "black" genes. How are we to identify these women when they are in themselves perfectly normal? Remember in Queen Victoria's case that only until hemophilia appeared among her descendants was it known that she was a "carrier." (It might be interesting to speculate what would have happened to history had Queen Victoria been forced to undergo sterilization!)

The problem of what to do about "carriers," or suspected "carriers" of serious "black" genes comes upon us with full force when we turn to the *recessives*. Almost all the serious hereditary ills—diabetes, rheumatic fever, certain types of mental defect, etc.—are in the recessive or multiple gene category. And it is these conditions, where at least two genes are required, that constitute our greatest menace and confront us with our principal eugenic predicament.

Consider the hereditary mental defectives. The most serious types —absolute idiots and imbeciles—are either sterile or, being institutionalized, do not reproduce. Our problem is with the morons, or feeble-minded. The estimates as to their number vary from ½ of 1 percent of our population to as high as 5 percent (which latter must surely include those who are merely retarded, rather than defective) and do not differentiate between those whose condition might be due to heredity, or those defective through environment.

Confining ourselves to the hereditary cases, let us assume that we have as many as 500,000 feeble-minded whose condition is due to "black" genes. But this would mean, as geneticists have figured out, that there are at least *ten times as many normal persons,* or 5,000,000 in the population, each carrying a hidden one of those genes. Thus, because the "carriers" would still continue to produce their quota, it is pointed out that sterilization of all the mental defectives would cut down the number of them in the next generation by not more than perhaps 10 percent—some say less, some say as high as 30 percent.

In the next generation sterilization could pick off only the defective children of normal parents who were carriers. Perhaps, through law or voluntary action, these parents themselves would be sterilized as soon as a defective child appeared, preventing further spread of the genes. Nevertheless, with each successive generation the effects of sterilization would be reduced. To thus make any sizeable dent in the hereditary feeble-minded population might take a thousand years, but *never* could the genes involved be *completely* eliminated.

All this applies to every other recessive condition caused by "black" genes, with various additional complications occurring wherever environmental influences are concerned. In manic-depressive insanity and schizophrenia, there is first the uncertainty as to what genes, and how many are responsible; then, as in Huntington's chorea, the appearance of the condition may be long delayed until the victim has already had children; or, again, it may be completely suppressed by favorable environment, so that persons genetically "positive" (with the required genes) for insanity may swell the proportion of normal persons who are "carriers."

In all other conditions that do not assert themselves until after maturity, or that may be suppressed by favorable environment, such as diabetes, glaucoma, childhood rheumatism, certain types of deafness, progressive muscular atrophy, etc., the possibilities in sterilization would be similarly limited. Further, the rarer any gene, the harder it would be to eliminate. Even in so obvious a gene defect as albinism, which shows itself at birth under all conditions, it might

WHAT STERILIZATION COULD ACCOMPLISH

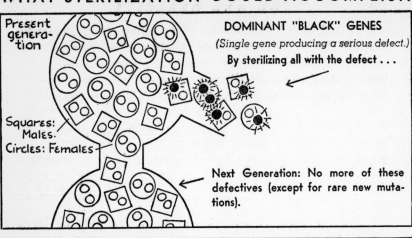

Present generation

Squares: Males.
Circles: Females

DOMINANT "BLACK" GENES
(Single gene producing a serious defect.)
By sterilizing all with the defect . . .

Next Generation: No more of these defectives (except for rare new mutations).

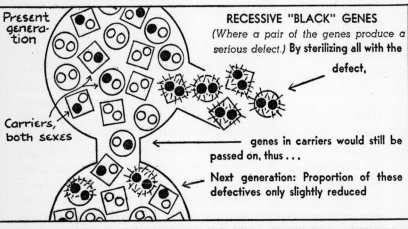

Present generation

Carriers, both sexes

RECESSIVE "BLACK" GENES
(Where a pair of the genes produce a serious defect.) **By sterilizing all with the defect,**

genes in carriers would still be passed on, thus . . .

Next generation: Proportion of these defectives only slightly reduced

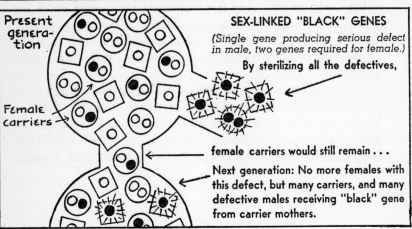

Present generation

Female carriers

SEX-LINKED "BLACK" GENES
(Single gene producing serious defect in male, two genes required for female.)
By sterilizing all the defectives,

female carriers would still remain . . .

Next generation: No more females with this defect, but many carriers, and many defective males receiving "black" gene from carrier mothers.

take two thousand years to reduce the percentage of albinos by one-half. With no recessive defect could sterilization accomplish much in the long run unless all normal persons who were "carriers" could also be sterilized. And that would mean—assuming that "carriers" could be detected, which they can't be as yet—that *almost every one of us would have to be sterilized*.

That the enthusiasm for sterilization might have gone too far was pointed out last year by a committee of the American Neurological Association, headed by Dr. Abraham Myerson of Boston. Special emphasis was placed on the ethical and legal aspects of sterilization, wholesale and peremptory sterilizations being sharply denounced. Sterilization is justified, the committee stated, only in especially selected cases of insanity, feeble-mindedness, epilepsy and a limited number of other conditions we have mentioned, when these show every evidence of being hereditary; and even then, only after careful study of each individual case by experts.

Regarding "carriers" the neurologists reported, "Our knowledge of human genetics has not the precision or amplitude which would warrant the sterilization of people who themselves are normal in order to prevent the appearance (of a condition) in their descendants." A kind word was said for the feeble-minded: "In a world which has much low-grade work to be done, there is still room for the people of low-grade mentality, of good character." Regarding criminals or prison inmates (you will recall that these were the first to be sterilized by law): "There is at present no sound scientific basis for sterilization on account of immorality or character defect." And finally, "Any law concerning sterilization under the present state of our knowledge should be voluntary and regulatory rather than compulsory, and should be applicable not only to public charges but also to those in private institutions or at large in the community."

That sterilization may be invoked recklessly, and perhaps foolishly, was pointed to in the case of a Kansas institution for girls where wholesale sterilizations were carried out in some of the girls merely because—according to official reports—they were obstreperous, incorrigible, fighters or "near degenerates." This was in spite of the fact that the state law specifically lists idiocy and social disease as the only legal grounds for sterilization.

Another *cause célèbre,* at this writing still before the courts, is that of a young woman, daughter of a noted inventor, who is suing her mother for having had her sterilized on the grounds of feeble-mindedness. Here is something to think about: Assuming that the girl was mentally retarded (which has not been proved) might she not also have been carrying valuable "superior" genes of her inventor father? And in such a case, would society be justified in risking the passing on of "feeble-minded" genes in order to conserve the "superior" genes?

As we have now seen, a good deal of cold water has been thrown on the high hopes for the eugenic uses of sterilization. While it can undoubtedly eliminate many defectives, it has serious limitations and many inherent dangers. The situation may be altered somewhat if means are discovered to produce sterilization without an operation, and especially temporary sterilization. Experiments in the latter direction are already being made, with some positive results reported. This would relieve sterilization of much of its drastic significance, would increase the number of those voluntarily allowing themselves to be sterilized, would permit curtailment of reproduction among venereal disease sufferers until they were cured, and would permit "probationary" sterilization of those whose hereditary defectiveness or social undesirability was in doubt. In any event, the final decision as to who should and should not be sterilized, and how that should be accomplished, should be left to competent medical authorities.

Where sterilization falls down with regard to "carriers," eugenics offers as a partial remedy the prohibition of marriages between such persons, that is, if they are suspected of carrying hidden "black" genes for the same condition. Particularly does this apply to marriages between cousins and other closely related individuals. But first let's be clear about this much-misunderstood phase of human heredity.

Cousin marriages, or *inbreeding,* suggests to many persons an array of idiots, imbeciles, monsters, weaklings, blind, deaf and other defective children that are supposed to ensue. To what extent does this accord with fact?

Genetically, the marriage of first cousins means only this: Inasmuch as they have two grandparents in common, *at least one-quarter of their genes, on an average, will be exactly the same.* Thus, if their mutual grandparents were carrying any hidden "black" genes, there will be a much greater than average danger that these will come together in their children. In marriages between second-cousins, the possibility of the same genes coming together is reduced very much, and it continues to decrease as relationship becomes more distant. But wherever there is inbreeding, there is more chance that recessive defects will crop out than there is in marriages between unrelated persons.

Much substantiating evidence is available. Some thirty years ago Alexander Graham Bell made a study of vast numbers of the nation's blind and deaf, and found a high percentage of cousin marriages among their parents. In certain inbred families of Martha's Vineyard there was the abnormally high incidence of 11 percent of deaf-mutism. Where similar inbreeding prevailed, great numbers of feeble-minded were found among the so-called hill-folk of New England, while many dwarfs were found in one of the peninsulas of Chesapeake Bay.

It is estimated that the complete prohibition of first cousin marriages would reduce the incidence of congenital deaf-mutism by 25 percent, juvenile amaurotic idiocy by 15 percent, xeroderma pigmentosum (a fatal skin disease) by nearly 50 percent, and all other types of recessive defects by varying percentages. But we must not conclude from this that a ban on all cousin marriages is justified, or that inbreeding in itself is harmful, sinister or immoral.

Existing laws or scruples against cousin marriages date far back to times when next to nothing was known about the mechanism of heredity. That superstition played a part in compounding these scruples is indicated by this fact: In the Middle Ages the ban on marriages between "related" persons was extended even to *those without any blood tie, who merely had had the same godfather or godmother!*

It is incorrect to assume that there is a deep-rooted or instinctive fear against inbreeding among humans. In Biblical times Jacob wedded his first cousins, Rachel and Leah, while Abraham married his half-sister, and Moses, his aunt. The Egyptian Pharaohs and Ptolemies mated with their sisters wherever possible—Cleopatra having been the offspring of six generations of such brother-sister marriages, while she herself, in turn, was married to her younger brother. The ancient Peruvian rulers also believed that the only bride royal enough for a king was his own sister. The Spartans were highly inbred; there were many cousin marriages among our Puritans; and coming down to the present, the sturdy Pitcairn Islanders are the highly inbred descendants of the famed mutineers of the *Bounty*. *In all the foregoing cases there is no evidence that inbreeding had any harmful effects.*

This brings up the point that where no "black" genes are in circulation, and the family is of unusual stock, cousin marriages or other inbreeding may in fact result in *superior* children. Charles Darwin, married to his first cousin, produced proof of this in his distinguished offspring. Turning to domestic animals, we have ample evidence that constant and intense inbreeding, far from being harmful, has made possible some of our most valuable strains. However, as we noted in the chapter on "Ancestry," the breeder of domestic animals has the privilege of discarding the defectives that crop out and rigorously selecting for matings only the superior animals. If something like this could be done among humans (but we're not saying that it should be done!) cousin marriages would be of immense eugenic value. Thinking in terms of the present, however, we must conclude that unless a family is of unusually high quality, and known to be free of serious hereditary defects, cousin marriages should be discouraged.

But equally, matings between any unrelated two individuals in whose families the same serious hereditary defects occur should also be discouraged. The most direct way of doing this is by encouraging prospective couples to compare the genetic histories of their families before they seek a marriage license. A campaign to popularize such precautions is being carried on in England, by the Eugenics Society, which distributes printed "pedigree" forms, known as "Pre-Marital Health Schedules." These are designed to bring out all facts about the family background or physical state of the individual, which have any eugenic significance.

All this implies voluntary action by parties to a proposed marriage, and can be expected only of the most enlightened and socially minded individuals. Hovering in the background, therefore, is the suggestion that just as venereal disease tests are now required in many states, the filling out of such "pre-marital health schedules" should ultimately be made compulsory; and that when analysis of the facts reveals a strong possibility of defective children ensuing, marriage licenses should be denied.

In this, as in all "negative" eugenic proposals, little account is taken of Cupid. We dare say that any stringent action to greatly hamper Cupid's activities will bring on an uprising in his defense. In fact, when we look back now over all the various "negative" eugenic proposals, it seems pretty clear that whatever is done, at least under democratic rule, to limit the production of "unfit" children will for a long while to come depend largely upon the voluntary action of individuals themselves.

CHAPTER XLII

PROGRAM FOR TOMORROW

EVERY farmer knows that improvement of crops or livestock depends on the two factors, "Seed" and "Feed." These are synonyms for what some biologists call "Nature" and "Nurture" or others call "Heredity" and "Environment."

If the farmer is intelligent and his crops have been running down, he looks first to the "feed"—the soil or his agricultural methods—before he begins bombarding the state farm bureau for new "seed"; and if his cattle and sheep are below par, he looks first to their pasturage and care before he clamors for new animal "seed" (or strains).

So in humans, the program of "Positive Eugenics," which seeks to increase the proportion of the "fit," turns first to "feed," or in other words, environment. We have seen that the reasons for the decline in births among the "fit" were primarily social or economic—late marriages, forced limitation of offspring by limited budgets, etc. To counteract these influences, most eugenic measures proposed for the immediate future are also social or economic. They invite little controversy, because they might be included in almost any program for human betterment.

To illustrate these proposals, let us apply them to two hypothetical young people, John Smith and Mary Jones. Both are as "fit" as can be, healthy and intelligent. John is twenty-three, just out of college, and "breaking into" a profession on a small salary. Mary is two years younger, with a high-school education and is working as a secretary. They're much in love and want to get married, but feel they'd better wait until John can properly support a wife.

Says Eugenics: Don't wait! If money is the problem, this might help:

Marriage grants: Wherever possible, parents should be encouraged to make substantial "setting up" gifts to young people; or provide *dowries* (shades of the Old Country!) Otherwise the state should provide marriage loans or grants. (Already being done abroad.)

Salary increases for married men: Popularize the practise of raising the wages or salaries of men when they marry.

Jobs for married women: Combat prejudices against women continuing to work after marriage, or employers' discrimination against hiring them.

Housing projects: The biggest bugaboo of young couples—high rent—might be shooed away if the government or states would provide "honeymoon" apartments with special rent concessions for the first years of married life.

John Smith and Mary Jones have been induced to wed. They both want a child, but their budget is slim, and they feel they ought to wait until John's salary is large enough to provide for the hospital expenses. So Eugenics suggests:

Lower maternity costs: State grants to maternity hospitals to make possible a cut in bills.

Pre-maternal care: Recognize expectant mothers as the direct concern of the state, establish more pre-maternity clinics and insure that each pregnant woman is given all necessary food and attention.

These measures may relieve the Smiths of some of their worries. But suppose Mrs. Smith can't afford to risk losing her job? Hence:

Maternity leaves for working mothers: Impress employers with the patriotic duty of keeping jobs open for women who take time out to have babies.

Ease burdens of working mothers: Provide diet kitchens, milk services and public laundries (yes, we mean for diapers!). As the babies grow, provide public nurseries and, later, pre-schools to look after them while the mothers are at work.

All these various measures should induce the Smiths not to delay too long about having their first child. But we don't want them to stop there. To encourage larger families:

Rental concessions: Public housing projects with a decreasing scale per room for larger families.

Tax cuts: Larger tax reductions for each child, increasing as the child grows, to keep pace with the added expense.

Educational grants: Relieve parents of the worry about education by providing special scholarships for children from large families.

Let us now look back. Do all the various eugenic proposals seem vague and impractical? Almost every one of them is already in operation either in the United States or in some other country! As an impressive illustration of how effective a "positive" eugenics measure can be—even though it wasn't deliberately planned as such —consider the case of the New York City public-school teachers:

When we were children "teacher" was a synonym for "spinster," and, in truth, school teachers almost invariably were spinsters— because they *had to be.* When women teachers married they lost their jobs. That was the situation in New York City some twenty-odd years ago. But see what has happened:

In 1915, after the issue was fought through the courts, the Board of Education was forced to rescind the ban on married women teachers. *Today, out of some 30,000 women teachers in New York City, between 40 and 45 percent are married.* Of the rest, many more are still young enough to be confidently looking forward to marrying. But teachers couldn't always be so confident. And that is another phase of our story.

At the time the ban on marriages was still in effect, the salaries for New York teachers in the lower grades ranged from $600 to $1,200 a year. By a series of increases it has now been brought to the range of $1,608 to $3,339—with teachers in the upper grades and high schools receiving considerably more. Thus teaching has become one of the most lucrative steady jobs open to women. And presto! Teachers who were once thought of by many men as "queer" or "old maids" by temperament have now become "catches"!

As for their having children, the New York system provides for a maternity leave for teachers with no loss of seniority. The result is that large numbers begin having children in their best years, while many, as soon as their husbands are able to carry on alone, resign to increase the size of their families.

The story of the New York teachers (which is paralleled in many other cities) is emphatic proof of how "social sterility" factors, that have been operating to prevent many eminently qualified individuals from marrying and having children, can be easily eliminated. In New York City alone thousands of women teachers now happily married and mothers of children would have remained spinsters under the old rules. Nor is all this past history, for in many communities the ban on teacher marriages still persists. In fact, as a recent report of the John Dewey Society brought out, some communities still go so far as to enjoin young women teachers, by rule or contract, from even "keeping company" with young men.

Another "social sterility" factor, is that which forces many women to postpone marriage, often until it is too late, in order to care for old or sick parents or younger members of the family. Pensions for aged or sick parents, and educational grants for younger brothers and sisters, would set many of these women free. In fact, when we think of the millions of fine women who are forced to remain unmarried, a great proportion for no justifiable reason whatsoever, we can be very sure that many other "social sterility" factors are at work which should be uncovered and rooted out.

More apparent are the cases of physical sterility. Let us retrace our steps to the young Smiths. Suppose that the economic path has been cleared for parenthood, but that after they wait and wait for several years, the Stork shows no inclination to arrive? This, as we saw, happens with about 10 percent of our couples.

Having cited the Smiths as a "fit" couple, we rule out the possibility of venereal disease, one of the principal causes of sterility. For cases like theirs, then, the widespread establishment of *"sterility clinics"* is recommended. Many of these are already in operation. (In New York City, at the Harlem, Mt. Sinai and Beth Israel hospitals, among others.) The function of such clinics is, first, to look for obvious causes of sterility both in the woman applicant and in her husband. (Not infrequently the seminal fluid of a sexually normal man may be devoid of sperms or may contain all, or a high percentage of, defective sperms.)

Where the sterility is in the man, diseases, accidents or other factors may be responsible, and if the effects of these can be overcome, fertility may be restored. In women, too, where diseases are involved, a cure may restore fertility. However, in normal and healthy women, the cause of sterility is often a minor obstruction in the fallopian tubes. This may usually be remedied by quick and simple treatment. Hormonal and X-ray treatments and even psychological ministrations, have also been reported as useful in overcoming sterility. The clinics claim success in inducing conceptions in about 25 percent of the cases.

We come now to this question: Suppose our fine young Smith couple discover that, through the incapacity of either, or both, they will not be able to have children? To the tens of thousands of couples in that position, the answer is:

Adopt a child, for an adopted child may often be reared to be quite as much like you as a child of your own.

What, by the way, is meant by a child "of one's own"?

We have seen how, with regard to its hereditary factors, every child is a gamble. No one can predict to what extent a child will be genetically like or unlike its parents. True enough, we can make some forecasts about physical characteristics, and here and there about *defects*. But no one can predict the character, disposition, mentality or behavior of any given child of *normal* parentage. These factors are determined or influenced by such a multitude of genes, inter-operating with so many environmental factors that as individuals we can't possibly expect to reproduce *ourselves*. A true "chip of the old block" in humans is a genetic myth.

All this is by way of saying that there may be infants at large, available for adoption, who may have the same kind of genes that a child of your own might be expected to get.

But while the genetic make-up of any child of yours is to a great extent unpredictable, you do have considerable power to control the environment which you will provide for it. Thus, in the opinion of many authorities, if you took a child of genetically normal stock, and raised it carefully, it might in many respects turn out to be as much like you in character and in degrees of *social* resemblance as many a potential child of "your own."

And so, encouragement of more adoptions constitutes another plank in the "Positive Eugenics" platform. But the demand for adoptable infants already exceeds the supply. Where shall we get more of them?

In our previous chapter we spoke of abortions—that one out of every four conceptions in the United States is thwarted by this means. In many cases, undoubtedly, the expectant mother would be happy to give birth to the child if she were properly cared for and were sure the child would have a happy entrance into the world. On this principle a number of private institutions have been established where unmarried mothers can have their babies under the most favorable conditions, and with the knowledge that the infant will be eagerly welcomed by some worthy couple on the institution's waiting list.

Among other proposals to combat sterility are some of a more radical nature, still to have their efficacy tested, and which are certain to evoke widespread dissent. They would involve, in fact, sharp revision in prevailing concepts regarding marriage and sexual morality. We may add that while advanced by eminent authorities, these proposals are not yet incorporated in any formal Eugenics program. Your own judgment must determine how worthy they are of consideration.

First, *artificial insemination* (technically known as eutelegenesis). This is the process of artificially impregnating a female with the sperms of a male without any contact between them. In the breeding of domestic animals it has long passed the experimental stage, and is now being widely used in many countries. Sperms are drawn off, transferred to vials and kept under refrigeration for days, to be used as needed. Thus, in breeding cattle, for instance, the services of a superior bull may be vastly multiplied and carried over wide areas. (Sperms from pedigreed South American bulls have been recently brought to the United States by airplane.) Other advantages of artificial insemination are that females can be impregnated at the most propitious times, that the chances of conception are increased and the possibility of disease transmission greatly reduced.

If we think only of its practical aspects, here is how artificial insemination could be applied to human beings:

1. Where conception in a woman is difficult for organic reasons, the husband's sperms may be artificially inseminated, greatly increasing the chances of conception.

2. Where a husband is sterile but the wife fertile, instead of a couple being forced to adopt a child wholly unrelated to them, the wife could be impregnated with the sperms of some other man with no infraction of the moral code. This has already been done in many instances. (We are reliably informed that there is a private clinic in New York which arranges for "sperm" donors —some of them selected young college men—whose identity remains unknown to the recipient.)

3. Where the husband is not sterile, but where it is feared he may transmit some dangerous hereditary factor; or where husband and wife are fearful that they each carry the same recessive "black" genes (as in first cousins), the sperms from some other man may be used, and a child at least "half their own," genetically, may be produced.

Some biologists hold out high hopes that once the practise of artificial insemination in humans is popularized, the sperms of some eminent or highly desirable man could be used to procreate a vast number of children. Prof. Muller estimates that 50,000 is a reasonable estimate with technical methods now at hand. Going further, he believes that it may be possible in the future to take sperm-tissues from a man and keep the culture going for many years, so that his sperms will be available long after his death. (The recent experiments by Dr. Alexis Carrel, in keeping detached organs alive with the aid of the Lindbergh apparatus, gives encouragement to this theory.)

Artificial insemination also opens up the possibility that we may eventually be able to overcome the shortage of marriageable men by controlling the proportionate birth-rate of the sexes. In our early chapters we discussed the suggestion that this might be done by separating male-bearing from female-bearing sperms. Significant experiments toward this goal have been reported recently, and confidence is expressed that in some not-far-off time, by the artificial insemination of the one or the other kind of sperms, parents will be able to have boys or girls as they desire. There would probably be an overproduction of boys to begin with, but through the well-known law of supply and demand the demand for girls, too, might be expected soon to equalize the ratio.

Back of all the more radical human "breeding" proposals hovers the thought that we may some day be able to breed a race of "superior" humans. Once we have determined the specific genes responsible for the manifold characteristics in human beings, no biologist doubts that, by assembling various combinations of genes in given individuals, we could breed people of specific types, for specific purposes, just as we now breed animals. But that is far from the thought of any democratically-minded eugenist, for it implies the assumption by the state of supreme dictatorial powers over all matings. An unwelcome idea, but not an impossible one. It happened in Sparta long ago, and today we have only to think what has already been done and what can be done in the totalitarian states.

Planned human breeding, carried to the extreme, would demand that the state take charge of all children, virtually from infancy, raising and training each one for special tasks. From the same parents, one child might be selected as the type for a common laborer, another for a scientist. Families as units would no longer exist, until, after many generations of breeding, true genetic families had been achieved, with all the individuals sufficiently alike in mind, temperament, aptitudes and vocation so that the state would see no need of separating them.

Certainly, from our present American viewpoint, any such disregard of the wholesome influence of home environment and the right of individuals to free mating and parenthood would be carrying specialization a bit too far. It brings to mind the story about the old country doctor whose son, studying to be a doctor also, wrote to him, "There's nothing in this general practise, Dad. I've decided to specialize on disorders of the foot." To which his father wrote back, *"Which toe?"*

Finally, for those who cherish the dream of a race of "superior" individuals to be achieved by intensively selective breeding, biologists pose this question: "What do we mean by *'superior'?*" "Superior" in one environment may mean "inferior" in another. We need only point out that the dictators of three European countries, considered as the ultimate of human superiority—almost as demigods—within their own borders, are looked upon by millions elsewhere as the most vicious, anti-social and undesirable of human animals.

For an analogy closer home, consider women. If we had the power to breed women to order, what type would we aim at—leaving it to both men and women to decide? Beauty, delicacy of features, slim figure, tapering wrists and ankles, small, regular teeth, vivaciousness, intelligence but no profundity of intellect—this might perhaps be a general description of feminine desirability. And yet— as our chart (page 394) shows—these characteristics would be quite the opposite of those best suited to motherhood or making for superiority in a woman from a practical point of view.

"Styles" in women and in men change with time and place, and standards of "desirability" or "superiority" in human beings, as in fashion, or art, are far too variable to permit of precise evaluation. Left to the judgment of their contemporaries, some of our greatest men would have been doomed to oblivion (as undoubtedly many unsung prophets must have been). The paintings of Van Gogh, Gaugin, Cézanne, would have been consigned to ash-heaps had the recognized "superior" artists of their day been left to decide. In every one of the other arts as in almost every other important field of human achievement—religion, social reform, invention, science, business—many men who were far in advance of their time were ignored, looked down upon and sometimes persecuted by their contemporaries.

Even among average individuals it is not always so easy to determine which qualities of mind or character are superior, which inferior. The lying child with an overdeveloped imagination may *sometimes* be the forerunner of a gifted writer; the boy who balks at discipline may *sometimes* develop into a blazer of new social trails. Extreme righteousness may often be coupled with intolerance, and bravery may sometimes mean callousness. The requirements for success in many fields may go with such undesirable social qualities as ruthlessness, insensitivity, unscrupulousness and selfishness. As human beings, many obscure little men who never get anywhere may be superior to some of those on top.

DESIRABLE TRAITS IN WOMEN

SOCIALLY:

Beauty first

Delicate features

No "deep" intellect

Vivaciousness

Slim figure

Tiny waist

Small hips

Dainty wrists
and hands

Slender, soft
tapering limbs

Slim ankles

Tiny feet

EUGENICALLY:

Beauty unimportant

Strong features

High intelligence

Seriousness

Sturdy figure

Ample waist

Broad hips

Sturdy wrists,
strong hands

Solid, sturdy
limbs and
ankles; good-
sized feet

So, having sifted the various eugenic proposals, both "positive" and "negative," we may be left with these conclusions:

No radical change in the genetic make-up of human beings can be expected for a long, long time. Nor are we justified, with what little we now know about our genes and their workings, and with our uncertain and short-sighted viewpoint, to plan any drastic change. We can and should try to root out the most serious of the "black" genes which do not appear to have a single point in their favor; we can and should restrain reproduction of individuals who at any stage of civilization would be considered undesirable; and we can and should encourage propagation among those individuals, to be found in all classes and among all peoples, who by every broad rule of human existence can be considered fit and desirable.

In short, modern eugenics places its greatest hope for improvement in the human stock on such changes in the social environment as will bring about the most eugenic distribution of births. Better education, better hygiene, better standards of living, can far more easily and more rapidly reduce the number of "unfit" than can any arbitrary process of breeding. Such genetic improvements as we can effect, short of those possible through the comparatively limited employment of compulsory sterilization, must depend at present on voluntary action. Individuals who are genetically defective must be encouraged to refrain from reproducing, and individuals who are genetically desirable must be awakened to the importance of reproducing themselves. To go much further, and by ban and edict of the state to launch into a program of breeding human beings to order, might bring upon our heads a deluge of evils that might far outweigh the good to be derived.

We were talking about John Smith and Mary Jones at the beginning of this chapter. They signify to us an average desirable American couple. If we can correctly interpret the aims of American eugenics we believe these aims would be to bring to all the Johns and Marys the kind and number of sons and daughters that their own minds and hearts and longings would prescribe for them.

CHAPTER XLIII

YOU AND HEREDITY

This book began, as you may recall, with "Stop and think about yourself."

Now that we reach its end, we hope that you are clearer as to the why and how of yourself and your fellow human beings. But you may rightfully ask, "How can this knowledge be usefully applied to my own life? Of what practical value to me are all these facts about the inheritance of features, diseases, defects, social traits and talents, about race, ancestry, eugenics and so on?"

What can you do with the information concerning the heredity of features and surface details? Yes, it may help to satisfy a natural curiosity about your appearance and the looks of your children. We frankly concede, however, that such knowledge has as yet little practical value to the layman except in doubtful-paternity cases. If you are single, your choice in marriage would hardly be affected by the possibility of your offspring having such or such hair or eyes. And we doubt that you would jilt your sweetheart because you knew that your alliance might result in a child with attached ear-lobes, or even a Hapsburg lip.

But as you will recall, the study of the inheritance of surface traits, initiated by Mendel with his peas, has made possible all our other knowledge about heredity, and leads directly to the understanding of how you may have inherited truly important and vital traits, how your children may inherit them, and what constructive steps can be taken with regard to many problems. This can be best illustrated by considering the hereditary defects and diseases.

Let us assume that some serious "black" gene condition appears in you or runs in your family. (You are indeed fortunate if this is not the case.) What light have our studies thrown on your course of action?

We have previously brought out what society should, might or can do about the "black" genes. But the problem confronting you as an individual when a "black" gene strikes home cannot always be viewed from the broad standpoint of society. To you the problem is not one of tens of thousands of matings with definitely predictable ratios. Everything, in your case, may be staked on a single turn of the wheel of chance. It may give you little comfort to know that the odds are one in four that a defective child will result, for your first child might be that defective one—which would be calamity enough—and the possibility lurks that you might have two in succession.

You must be governed, therefore, by the special circumstances or considerations which apply to your case. Consider the following hypothetical situations:

You yourself are afflicted with some serious hereditary condition. Should you risk having children?

If the condition is a *dominant* one, where a single gene from one parent can cause the damage, you know that there is a straight *fifty-fifty* risk. With the odds so great you must act as if it is almost a certainty that you will have a defective child. Your decision then must be based on the seriousness of the condition, the degree to which it has hampered your own life or impaired your happiness, the willingness of yourself and mate to have a child similarly afflicted and your capacity to compensate it for the handicap. In the few unqualified dominant conditions so serious that many sufferers have said, "I wish I had never been born," your answer could well be "No."

In recessive conditions produced only when two of the same genes come together, the problems are more numerous and more involved, although usually all for the good. That is to say, while the range of odds and circumstances to be considered are much more varied than in the simple dominant conditions, the probability of transmitting a recessive defect is in most cases much less.

Is there insanity in your family?

Then you know that, as all identified hereditary insanities (except for the rare Huntington's chorea) are due to recessive genes, even if you yourself were insane or definitely carry a hidden gene for insanity, *no child of yours could inherit insanity from you alone*. This is true of all recessive defects—feeblemindedness, childhood rheumatism, diabetes, deaf-mutism and others—which constitute numerically the vast proportion of common "black" gene conditions. No one of these defects could be inherited by your child *unless it received exactly the same gene from both you and your mate*.

Here is one of the most far-reaching, important and constructive findings of genetics. How many hapless individuals, parents of a defective child, have had salt poured on their wounds or been scourged by their mates with the words, "You know the child inherited it from you! You know it runs in your family!" What you cannot impress on yourself and others too strongly, therefore, is that wherever there is a child with any recessive defect, the inheritance has stemmed from both parents, and wherever a marriage or conception is being avoided for fear that such a child may result, the family histories on both sides should be considered with equal thoroughness.

The dangerous aspects of recessives lie in the mating of two persons with the same gene. If both you or your mate are normal but "carriers" (which is certain if you each had a parent with the same recessive affliction) then the odds are one-in-four that you will have a child with the defect. If one of you is afflicted, the other a "carrier," the odds are one-in-two. But, most dangerous of all, if you and the person you marry both have the same recessive condition, *every one of your children will inherit it*. For instance, if you have diabetes and you marry a diabetic, *every one of your children will be diabetic*.

So to this problem:

You are in love or engaged, and have just learned that the possibility of having a seriously defective child lurks in your contemplated marriage.

If children are not important to you, the situation can resolve itself easily. But if having children is a primary objective in your marriage, you may have to weigh the "black" gene odds against your affections—even to the point, where the risk is menacing, of considering marriage to some one else. However, as you have learned, in only a small proportion of cases (among them, sometimes, those involving first cousins) need such a predicament arise. Generally, where the risk is not too great, you are justified in being swayed by the redeeming possibilities in your marriage.

We assume next that your problems of mating are far in the past:

Your children have all been ushered into the world and no hereditary defect has yet appeared in any of them. What good will it do to worry about defects appearing later?

The knowledge of what conditions might be expected to develop in a child, and what conditions might not, can do an immense amount of good. Wherever a defect or disease is amenable to treatment and the approximate time of its onset is known, foreknowledge by your doctor of an hereditary tendency may be an invaluable aid to him in preventing its development, arresting its progress or effecting a cure. To cite some specific cases:

—Where diabetic inheritance is suspected, control of diet, abstinence from over-eating, keeping down of excess weight and frequent medical inspection may thwart the development of the disease or greatly impede its progress.

—Where childhood rheumatism lurks in family backgrounds, notably among the poor, its development in many children may be prevented by assuring them plenty of fresh air, proper living-conditions and periodic medical examinations of their hearts and nervous systems.

—In insanity, the foreknowledge of a familial tendency may make possible precautionary steps or early treatment which would save a large proportion of the victims.

—In polyposis of the colon, a cancer-inducing condition, the suspicion of inheritance may be of vital importance in insuring prompt treatment. With regard to common cancer, although the question of its inheritance is still entirely open, specialists tell us that a sharp lookout for and early recognition of its symptoms might save as many as 50 percent of those afflicted.

This brings us to another point. You may have been thinking that all of this searching into ourselves is a wet blanket on romance, that it may take the joy out of life and arouse many fears. In some instances this might be true, but on the whole we believe that genetics analysis can do far more to allay fears than to arouse them.

At the moment that we write this, the newspapers carry the report that a young mother on Long Island has slain her two children (aged two and five) and attempted suicide because she feared that they had inherited cancer from her. Her mother had died of cancer a year before, and the poor woman herself had just undergone an operation for the removal of a growth which she believed, erroneously, was also cancerous. Before the slaying she had sought frantically among her friends for information. We quote from the reports:

". . . She asked the cook all sorts of questions, how long did people live with cancer, and was it hereditary, and did she think the children had inherited it. The cook was unable to answer most of the questions."

Had the distracted mother been aware of the very facts with which you are now acquainted, her children would still be alive. For she would have known that there was no evidence that she had inherited cancer and, in view of its complexity, no chance that she herself could have transmitted it directly to any child.

In innumerable other cases ungrounded fears regarding disease inheritance have wrecked people's lives. Sometimes the fear itself, through *psychogenic* (mentally-induced) effects, may produce symptoms of the condition feared. This is especially true of insanity. Whatever the condition, the truth as to whether it is hereditary or not should usually prove more helpful than harmful to the individual, and is invariably of immense value to the physician, for an essential factor in combating any ailment is the knowledge of how it originates.

To the further credit of genetics as a fear-alleviator, it can be said that a host of conditions formerly thought hereditary have been proved otherwise, and few, if any important conditions not formerly considered hereditary have been added to the list. Fears about the inheritance of syphilis or any other *acquired* condition have been dismissed. Mothers can rest easier as to what they can or cannot do to the child they are carrying. In fact, genetic findings have swept away so many groundless fears that an average couple can today have children with less worry regarding heredity than ever before.

Turning to the social traits, of intelligence, behavior, character, personality, etc., limited as may yet be our genetic knowledge, it is sufficient to also allay a host of longstanding fears. Many of the undesirable social traits in human beings have been indicated as due primarily to environment, and there has been much to challenge prevalent beliefs and suspicions regarding the hereditary "criminality," "immorality," or general "undesirability" of members of this or that group, class or race. These findings, too, may be of use in your own life. If you have had the uneasy feeling that one of the forementioned traits, or some crudity, unpleasant mannerism, inability to "get along" or other social deficiency in you was due to an inherited and incurable "streak," you may see by now that your suspicions were probably unfounded. Again, in marriage, employment, friendship or any other relationship, if any individual you have in mind is personally desirable and of good character, you need not be greatly worried because he is of this or that race or nationality, or be much concerned because a grandfather had a penchant for abducting horses, or a great-aunt was no better than she should have been.

This does not imply that you should ignore the important rôle that genes obviously play in the development of mind, character and personality. But in these complex social characteristics, only where an individual himself shows some markedly adverse trait, or where it consistently appears in his family with no evidence that it is due to environment, can we consider him genetically suspect. Among members of your own family, and your intimates, where there are great differences in behavior and achievement which cannot be traced to environmental influences, you are justified in ascribing them in considerable measure to different gene combinations. Practically applied to your children, such knowledge might lead you to deal more sympathetically with the "black sheep" and to endeavor to make up to them by guidance and training, for inherited deficiencies.

Further, with the strong indication that special talents, capacities and aptitudes are inherited, you may avoid forcing specialized train-

ing on a child not inherently fitted for it, while at the same time
encouraging the child who does reveal such capacities. We may
add that with our knowledge regarding the inheritance of social
traits constantly growing, problems of child guidance and training
and of adapting individuals to the work and life for which they
are best fitted will be increasingly simplified.

So far we have been dealing with the practical application to
your life of *genetic* facts. But, as we have seen, in all major aspects
of our lives we cannot dissociate the effects of heredity from those
of environment. It is of interest to note, therefore, that the technique developed for sifting hereditary factors can be admirably
adapted to the analysis of environmental influences.

In much the same way that our genetic make-up is determined
by *biologic* genes passed on from one generation to another, we
may consider that our social make-up is determined by *"social
genes,"* also passed on from one generation to another. These
"social genes" would include all the factors that go to make for
education, technical knowledge, habits, customs, mannerisms, attitudes, beliefs, etc., and also for the physical effects of our social
environment. Thus, you, like every other person, are the product
of both biologic genes and "social genes," with this difference between them: The biologic genes were passed on to you through
the stream of germ-plasm which has flowed from the dawn of life,
with the only changes made being those produced by mutation.
No human force has ever had the power to change a single one
of these biologic genes; and not even today can we do more than
cast out a limited number of the most defective ones, and that only
by controlling reproduction.

But our "social genes" are no inherent part of our germ-plasm
or of our make-up. They were every one of them *acquired*.

Suppose for a moment that you and your mate were set down,
like another Adam and Eve, on an uncharted island where no
man had ever been before and which no other human could ever
reach. And suppose at the same time, that you were struck by
some force that blotted out completely every thought, every memory, everything you had learned from the moment of birth, and
all consciousness of the past. Would you be able to talk, think,

act or cope with existing conditions any better than did the most primitive Stone Age man? Science, as we have observed, says "No!" For your biologic genes would be hardly different than his, and despoiled of all the "social genes" acquired and accumulated in twenty thousand years, you and your descendants would have to travel the same long road of social evolution that stretched ahead of the Stone Age man. You would have to begin all over again learning the simplest facts by trial and error or accident. Generations and scores of generations would pass before your descendants would learn to build dwellings, plant seeds, fashion the simplest mechanisms and develop a written language.

So if you, or any one of us living today, differ from men of any previous generation in mental development, behavior or other social characteristics, or in the possession of any superior inventions, appliances or objects, it is because we have had passed on to us an accumulation of "social genes" from the past, with their many resulting products. But this does not mean that *all* of the "social genes" of each generation were passed along, or that the best of them were carried over. Each generation has been the heir of all the preceding generations, and from what we know of heirs we have little reason to doubt that in many instances some of the best "social genes" in the successive legacies were lost, destroyed or tossed foolishly away. When we think of all the wars, barbaric invasions and blotting out of whole civilizations, of the whims and judgments of ruling despots that often dictated the course of culture as it is being dictated even today, we have good reason to believe that numerous "social genes" of inestimable value were not passed on, while some of the worst were.

Just as we have identified many biologic "black" genes, we can easily point to "social black genes" linked with or producing poverty, ignorance, social and contagious diseases, injuries from accident, vice, crime, suicide, corruption, strife, conflict and finally war. Look back through our pages and you will find little to suggest that these blights on mankind are inherent in our germ-plasm. Those who point to them as part and parcel of "human nature" ignore the fact that the impulses of the vast majority of people are toward sociality, kindness, peacefulness, tolerance, the desire to be and let be. We have only to think of the sacrifices of parents for their children, of the spontaneity with which we respond to our fellow creatures in time of fire, flood, disaster or distress, of the millions praying each day to be made better and worthier, of countless individuals working throughout the world to uplift others. Back of these impulses we can find many of our superior "social genes."

Herein, then, lies the hope for whatever improvement can be made in mankind, or that you, as an individual, can in your restricted sphere help to make in your children:

1. Through the selection, by regulating and controlling human breeding, of the biologic genes which we pass on.

2. Through the selection, by education, laws or other measures of the "social genes" which we pass on.

As for our biologic genes, we have brought out in preceding chapters what might be accomplished eugenically. By sterilization and birth control we might reduce somewhat the proportion of the "unfit," and by stimulating births in other quarters we might increase somewhat the proportion of the "fit." This is on the basis of our present knowledge of human genetics, which is little compared to what we know about the breeding of plants and domestic animals.

The application of genetic principles to agriculture and livestock breeding has been so sweeping that there is today hardly a fruit, grain or vegetable which you eat, and no egg, poultry or meat from the better farms or ranches, in whose production genetic principles have not been employed. If you have any lingering doubt about the reality of genes and chromosomes, and of the certainty with which they can be identified and combined, we refer you to the yearbooks of the United States Department of Agriculture for 1936 and 1937, the former devoted almost in full and the latter in part, to practical genetics. Here you will find hundreds of pages filled with details regarding the genes and chromosomes of every important cultivated plant and food animal, and with facts which every alert farmer and breeder is applying today.

If the knowledge of human genetics has lagged behind, it is not entirely because of our inability to experiment with human beings.

Also responsible is the fact that the importance of human genetics has not yet been popularly realized and that our all too few trained geneticists have been forced, by practical considerations, to devote themselves chiefly to the problems of crops and livestock in which state or national governments are immediately interested. Once we know proportionately as much about the genetics of humans as we do about the heredity of plants and livestock, there is no predicting what we may be able to do.

However, at the moment we have no need to stake our hopes for an improved mankind on future genetic findings or on radical changes in our biological make-up. We can consider that we have not even begun to tap the genetic resources at our command. We have in our biologic genes now in circulation, scientists tell us, all the potentialities for a race of supermen—*if we can properly direct and control our environment.* In other words, all our studies have led to renewed confidence in "human nature"—in our inherent impulses and capacities—and to the belief that not our biologic genes, but our acquired "social genes," are responsible for most of our social ills.

We noted in the chapter on "Race" that large groups and whole peoples have been praised for the virtues of the few gifted individuals who have raised the general level of those about them.

Similarly, the many have been damned for the excesses of the few. If the advancement of mankind has come through the efforts of a handful, civilization has again and again been hurled back by a few individuals, who, like cancers, have corrupted the rest. We have no more right, therefore, even in these questionable times, to condemn all civilization as hopeless because of some of its evil specimens than we have to consider that all persons are diseased because a few have hemophilia or Huntington's chorea.

Today, evil "social genes" as embodied in the acts of malignant individuals present a greater menace than ever. Mankind has been brought so closely together that it must now be considered as one body. Whatever happens to a group of humans anywhere in the world can sooner or later affect others. *"Il faut cultiver votre jardin"* ("Cultivate your own garden"), said Voltaire. Which was another way of saying, "Look to your own backyard!" But if that was ever

good advice, it is so no longer. We cannot ignore what is happening in the backyards of our neighbors or of our fellow men, be
they ever so far away. We have learned that a malarial swamp on
one man's farm may menace others for vast stretches around, that
a plague in China may reach us here, that a bank crash, a crop
failure, a strike, a financial depression and most certainly a war,
no matter where, may start a chain of effects spreading throughout
the world and ultimately to you. There is no "social black gene"
that might not some day strike at you and yours and no biologic
"black" gene that might not find its way to your children or your
grandchildren.

So, if you are concerned with the practical application of genetic
findings to yourself and to your children, you must think both in
biologic and in social terms, and not only of your own family, but
of others. Biologically, your action is limited by the children you
have or do not have. Socially, even if you are childless, there is no
limit to the influence you can exert. But nothing that is done toward biologic or social improvement can have permanent meaning
if it is confined to one family, one group, or even to one nation.
All that we have learned proves that one section of mankind cannot long maintain a corner on "superior" genes, biologic or "social,"
or rid itself and keep free of the "inferior" genes in circulation.
Only by improving others also can we improve ourselves, and only
by promoting progress on a broad front, throughout mankind, can
we give our own advancement significance or permanency.

That something should and can be done to improve humanity
is the view of many of us who do not consider that this is the
best of all possible worlds and that it can run itself without planning. We have seen and are seeing that the good, the superior, the
"fittest" in genes, persons or doctrines are not automatically being
swept on to survival, and that the bad, the inferior and the most
"unfit" are not automatically swept into the discard. Those of us
who are at the top of the social heap can no longer smugly ascribe
this all to our greater intrinsic worth, diligence and perseverance.
And where as individuals we have failed in what we have set out
to do, if we have not reached the heights in our profession, business or in one of the arts, we cannot so easily blame ourselves. No

one fully aware of the findings of genetics and related sciences can still cling to the old theories of predestination, or, contrariwise, to the belief that the individual is the "master of his fate and the captain of his soul." Knowing that our lives are governed, if not dictated, by both biologic and "social genes," we may look at both the shining successes above us, and at the criminals, the paupers, the drunkards, the misfits at the bottom and well say, "There but for the grace of my genes go I."

But if we today are the products largely of chance, our descendants do not have to be. We have had a long enough spell, all the thousands of years since Homo Sapiens made his appearance, of leaving our destinies to the fates or to the tides of circumstance, largely because we were ignorant of what otherwise to do. But here at last we have the first glimmers of true light as to why we are what we are, and what we can do to make the world better. Genetics and the related sciences have proved beyond question that we can guide, if not control, the destinies of those who follow us by selecting the units of biologic and social inheritance which we pass on to them. To make this selection intelligently, we must first understand ourselves, the sources of the good and the bad in us. It has been the lack of such understanding in individuals, and between one person and another, between man and woman, parent and child, class and class, nation and nation, race and race, that has been responsible for much of the strife, misery and unhappiness in this world. If we are called on to decide what first to include in our legacy to succeeding generations, our wisest choice might well be whatever genes there are, biologic and social, that make for better human understanding.

Appendix

HIGHLIGHTS IN THE HISTORY OF GENETICS

THE following compilation has been abstracted and adapted from the extensive "Chronology of Genetics" prepared by Robert Cook, Editor of *The Journal of Heredity*, and appearing in the Yearbook of the United States Department of Agriculture for 1937.

As Dr. Cook notes, although domestic animals had been bred for many thousands of years, it was not until the end of the seventeenth century that the dark mantle of superstition and gross ignorance about the processes of heredity began to be pierced by the first intelligent experiments and researches. By the latter half of the eighteenth century the foundations of important livestock breeds were already being laid, chiefly in England, through careful inbreeding and selection. With the dawn of the nineteenth century, the march of knowledge leading to our present science of genetics had begun as herewith recorded.

EARLY BACKGROUND

1809 J. B. P. de Lamarck (France) publishes "Philosophie Zoologique," first attempt at a comprehensive theory of evolution.

1820 C. F. Nasse (Germany) suggests law of male sex-linked inheritance, based on study of hemophilia.

1822 John Goss (England) reports but does not interpret dominance and recessiveness, and segregation in peas.

1826 A. Sageret (France) cites unit characters in human eye color, and uses term "dominant."

1841 R. A. von Kölliker (Switzerland) proves spermatozoa arise from parent body and are not parasites as previously believed.

1849 (1) Sir Richard Owen (England) enunciates principle of the continuity of the germ-plasm. This idea culminated in the modern gene theory.

 2) G. Thuret (France), studying seaweed, is first to observe union of sperm cell and egg cell (fertilization) and later shows that egg would not develop without fertilization.

1858 R. Virchow (Germany) enunciates principle that every cell arises from another cell, disposing of theory of spontaneous generation and establishing continuity of all life from remote beginnings.

1859 **Charles Darwin (England) publishes his "Origin of Species" marking turning point in scientific thought and the beginning of the modern experimental approach to biological problems.**

1865 F. Schweigger-Seidel and A. von la Valette St. George (Germany) independently prove that a sperm is a single cell.

1866 **(1) Gregor Mendel (Austria) publishes in the Proceedings of the Brünn Natural History Society his now famous paper, "Versuche über Pflanzen-Hybriden," on inheritance in peas. His paper receives little critical attention and is destined to remain in obscurity for 34 years.**

(2) E. Haeckel (Germany) predicts that the cell nucleus will play a star rôle in heredity.

1875 (1) E. Strasburger (Germany) describes the chromosomes.

(2) Oscar Hertwig (Germany) proves that fertilization consists of union of two parental nuclei contained in the sperm and ovum, demonstrating that sexual reproduction is a process contributed to essentially equally by both sexes.

1883 P. J. van Beneden (Belgium) reports reduction of chromosome number in egg cells to half that in body cells, and draws important conclusion that chromosomes have a genetic continuity throughout the life cycle.

1884-5 Identification of the cell nucleus as the basis of inheritance made independently by Hertwig, Strasburger, Kölliker and A. Weismann (Germany).

1885-7 Weismann publishes a theory of chromosome behavior throwing great light on what happens during cell division and fertilization.

1886 (1) Francis Galton (England) devises correlation table for

applying statistical methods to many biological problems.
(2) Hugo de Vries (Holland) discovers mutations in primrose plants which form basis for his later mutation theory of evolution.

1887 W. Roux (Germany) suggests that longitudinal splitting of chromosomes when dividing means that many different qualities are arranged single file in the chromosome and can by the splitting process all be passed along when the cell multiplies.

1888 Chromosomes named by W. Waldeyer (Germany).

1890 Th. Boveri (Germany) and L. Guignard (France) formulate law of numerical equality of paternal and maternal chromosomes at fertilization.

1892 Weismann promulgates his "germ-plasm" theory, refuting the widely held idea that acquired characteristics can be inherited.

1898 Flemming counts human chromosomes, finding 24 in eye tissue. (Later study is to reveal 24 pairs.)

1899 L. Cuénot (France) working with animals, and Strasburger (Germany) with plants, advance theory that sex is controlled within the germ cell, not by environment.

MODERN GENETICS

1900 Rediscovery and verification of Mendel's principles independently by De Vries (Holland), Correns (Germany), and E. von Tschermak (Austria), marking the beginning of modern genetics.

1902 (1) Bateson and Saunders report identifying 26 paired hereditary factors in various plants and animals. Also suggest that polydactylism (extra finger) in man may be inherited according to Mendelian principles.
(2) De Vries publishes his "Mutation Theory of Evolution."
(3) E. C. McClung offers first clues to the existence of "sex" chromosomes on basis of his studies with insects.
(4) Cuénot first demonstrates Mendelian inheritance in animals (normal and albino mice).

1902-3 W. W. Sutton (United States) shows that body chromosomes are individually recognizable.

1903 W. L. Johannsen (Denmark) advances "pure line" concept and defines difference between "phenotype"—the appearance of an individual, and "genotype"—the genetic make-up.

1904 (1) C. B. Davenport (United States) confirms Mendelian inheritance of polydactylism in man.

(2) Thomas Hunt Morgan becomes professor of zoology at Columbia University, founding the famed "Columbia group" of genetic research workers.

1905 N. M. Stevens and E. B. Wilson (United States) confirm McClung's theory linking sex-determination with the "sex" chromosomes.

1906 (1) The term "genetics" is coined by W. Bateson.

(2) C. W. Woodworth and W. E. Castle (United States) "discover" Drosophila as an invaluable aid in genetic study.

1907 Correns advances theory that there are two kinds of male germ cells—male-determining and female-determining.

1908 Cuénot discovers a lethal factor in mice—that for yellow color—which, if inherited from both parents, kills the embryo early in development. This was the first of the many "killer" genes discovered in animals and man.

1909 The Galton Laboratory at the University of London, the first laboratory devoted to the study of human heredity, is founded with a bequest from Sir Francis Galton.

1910 (1) L. Epstein and R. Ottenberg (United States) point out that human blood groups follow Mendelian principles in inheritance.

(2) Morgan proposes explanation of sex-linked inheritance and publishes report of first gene mutation (white eye) found in Drosophila.

(3) Morgan announces the gene theory and the locating of specific genes at fixed points on Drosophila chromosomes.

1911 W. E. Castle and J. C. Philips (United States) by transplanting ovaries in mice, show that inherited traits transmitted to offspring are not changed by the intra-uterine environment of the mother.

1915 Morgan, A. H. Sturtevant, C. B. Bridges and H. J. Muller (United States) publish "The Mechanism of Mendelian Heredity," an epoch-making book.

1917 W. B. Kirkham, H. L. Ibsen and E. Steigleder (United States) prove the lethal action of the yellow gene in the mouse by embryological studies—an important step in the tracing of gene effects in the earliest possible stages of development.

1918 H. D. King (United States) reports results of inbreeding rats for 25 consecutive generations, showing that close inbreeding need not in itself be harmful if there are no bad hereditary factors in the stock.

1919 Morgan and others publish "The Physical Basis of Heredity," setting forth in detail the gene theory.

1921 Morgan estimates that the gene has a diameter between 20 and 70 microns.

1923 F. A. Crew (Great Britain) finds the first lethal in livestock, that producing the "bulldog" calf, a non-living monster frequently appearing in crosses of Dexter and Kerry cattle.

1927 Mutations are produced artificially through X-rays by Muller, in Drosophila, and by L. J. Stadler, in plants, vastly facilitating genetic studies.

1930-37 Analysis of inheritance in man is greatly enhanced through perfecting of the gene-frequency technique by F. Bernstein (Germany), L. Hogben, J. B. S. Haldane and L. S. Penrose (England), A. S. Wiener and L. S. Snyder (United States).

1931 Wright gives first comprehensive picture of evolution in Mendelian terms, with stress on the balance and interplay between selection intensity, mutation rates, inbreeding, isolation and migration.

1934 Painter discovers that giant salivary gland chromosomes make possible detailed studies of chromosome structure and lead to very exact location of genes.

(Many genetic findings of recent years and those of the last few years are not here listed because sufficient time has not elapsed to definitely establish or fully evaluate them.)

SUGGESTIONS FOR FURTHER READING

WE present here merely a selection of useful references, for our available space would not permit, or the nature of this work justify, a full listing of the several thousand books, papers and articles consulted or drawn upon.

Preference has been given to the latest works, with few exceptions anything published prior to 1930 being omitted in view of the fact that all earlier publications of importance will be found summarized or referred to among the references cited.

In the first classification (GENERAL) which follows, the books *starred* are those least technical and dealing chiefly with human heredity. The others are for the most part textbooks, and unless the titles indicate otherwise, deal with all phases of genetics.

GENERAL

BAUR, E., FISCHER, E., and LENZ, F. *Human Heredity*. Macmillan. '31. (Also revised edition in German—*Menschliche Erblichkeit Lehre und Rassenhygiene*. Lehmann, Munich. '36.)

CASTLE, W. E. *Genetics and Eugenics*. 4th ed. Harvard U. Press. '30.

CONKLIN, E. G. *Heredity and Environment in the Development of Men*. 6th ed. Princeton U. Press. '30.

DUNN, L. C. *Heredity and Variation*. University Society, N. Y. '34.

FASTEN, N. *Principles of Genetics and Eugenics*. Ginn. '35.

GATES, R. R. *Heredity in Man*. Macmillan. '31.

HOGBEN, L. *Nature and Nurture*. Norton. '33.
   Genetic Principles in Medicine and Social Science. Knopf. '31.

JENNINGS, H. S. *Biological Basis of Human Nature*. Norton. '30.
   *Genetics. Norton. '35.

MORGAN, T. H. **Scientific Basis of Evolution*. Norton. '32.
   Theory of the Gene. Yale U. Press. '28.

MULLER, H. J. **Out of the Night: A Biologist's View of the Future*. Vanguard. '35.

NEWMAN, H. H. *Evolution, Genetics and Eugenics.* 3d ed. U. of Chicago Press. '32.

SHULL, A. F. *Heredity.* 3d ed. McGraw-Hill. '38.

SINNOTT, E. W., and DUNN, L. C. *Principles of Genetics.* 2d ed. McGraw-Hill. '32.

SNYDER, L. H. *Principles of Heredity.* Heath. '35.

STOCKARD, C. R. *Physical Basis of Personality.* Norton. '31.

WALTER, H. E. *Genetics.* 4th ed. Macmillan. '38.

WELLS, H. G., et al. **Science of Life.* Doubleday. '31. (Many parts dealing with human heredity scattered throughout.)

SPECIAL TOPICS

For quicker identification, book listings are in larger type than those of papers or articles and are given first.

Pre-Natal Development

DAVENPORT, C. B. *How We Came by Our Bodies.* Holt. '36.

WADDINGTON, C. H. *How Animals Develop.* Norton. '36.

The Human Egg (with Photographs)

LEWIS, W. H. Bulletin, Johns Hopkins Hospital. 48:368. '31.

PINCUS, GREGORY G. Anat. Rec. 69:163. Sept. '25, '37.

Human Chromosomes

EVANS, H. M., and SWEZEY, O. *Chromosomes in Man,* etc. Memoirs, U. of Cal. Press. 9:1-65. '29.

Genes

DEMEREC, M. *What Is a Gene?* J. of Hered. 24:369. '33.

GOLDSCHMIDT, R. B. *Theory of the Gene.* Sci. Monthly, Mar. '38.

(Also see Morgan, T. H., under GENERAL.)

Sex Determination

PARSHLEY, H. M. *Science of Human Reproduction.* Norton. '33. (Also discussed in most text books listed under GENERAL.)

Features

KROGMAN, W. M. *Inheritance of Non-Pathological Physical Traits in Man.* Eug. News, Nov.-Dec. '36.

(Also detailed discussions in Baur, et al., and Gates, listed under GENERAL.)

Twins

NEWMAN, H. H., et al. *Twins, A Study of Heredity and Environment.* U. of Chicago Press. '37.

Dionne Quintuplets

BLATZ, W. E., et al. *Collected Studies of the Dionne Quintuplets.* U. of Toronto Press. '37.

418

APPENDIX

Disease and Defect Inheritance

BLACKER, C. P. *Chances of Morbid Inheritance.* Lewis, London. '34.

COCKAYNE, E. A. *Inherited Abnormalities of the Skin.* H. Milford, London. '33.

MOHR, O. *Heredity and Disease.* Norton. '34.

MUCKERMANN, HERRMANN. *Vererbung und Entwicklung.* Dümmler, Berlin. '37.

GUN, W. Y. J. *Hemophilia in the Royal Caste.* Eug. Rev., Jan. '38.

MACKLIN, MADGE. *The Role of Heredity in Disease.* Medicine. 14:1-75. '35.

WASSINK, W. F. *Heredity of Cancer.* Genetica. 17:103. '35.

Eye Defects

WAARDENBURG, P. J. *Das menschliche Auge und seine Erbanglagen.* The Hague. '32. (Also in Bibliographia Genetica. Vol. VII.)

Mental Defects

HENRY, G. W. *Essentials of Psychopathology.* (Chap. I. on Heredity.) William Wood. '35.

MERRIMAN, W. E. *Psychoses in Identical Twins.* Psychiat. Quart. 7:37-49. '33.

POLLOCK, H. M., et al. *Heredity and Environment in Dementia-Praecox and Manic-Depressive Psychoses.* Psychiat. Quart. Vol. IX, Jan. and Apr. '35; Vol. X, Jan. and June, '36.

ROSANOFF, A. J., et al. *Insanity in Twins.*
(a) Manic-depressive. Am. Jour. Psychiat. 91:247. '34.
(b) Schizophrenia. Am. Jour. Psychiat. 91:724. '35.

SLATER, E. *Inheritance of Mental Disorder.* Eug. Rev., Jan. '37.

Other Defects and Diseases

See *Index Medicus,* Quarterly Cumulative. A. M. A.

Longevity

DUBLIN, L. I., and LOTKA, A. J. *Length of Life.* Ronald Press. '36.

PEARL, R. J. and R. DE W. *Ancestry of the Long-Lived.* Johns Hopkins Press. '34.

MALISOFF, W. M. *Span of Life.* Lippincott. '37.

EATON, O. N. *Summary of Lethal Characters in Animals and Man.* J. of Hered., Sept. '37.

Sexual Abnormalities

GOLDSCHMIDT, R. B. *Die sexuellen Zwischenstufen.* (Intersexes.) J. Springer, Berlin. '31.

YOUNG, HUGH HAMPTON. *Genital Abnormalities, Hermaphroditism and Related Adrenal Diseases.* Williams & Wilkins. '37.

Blood Tests

SNYDER, L. H. *Blood Groupings in Relation to Clinical and Legal Medicine.* Williams & Wilkins. '27.

—— *Present Status of Medicolegal Applications,* etc. Eug. News. 21:45. May-June, '36.

LEVINE, PHILIP. *Application of Blood Groups in Forensic Medicine.* Am. J. Political Science. 3:157. '32.

WIENER, A. S. *Blood Grouping Tests in the N. Y. Courts.* U. S. Law Rev., Dec. '36
—— *Determining Parentage.* Scientific Monthly, Apr. '35.

Intelligence

FREEMAN, F. S. *Individual Differences: The Nature and Causes of Variation in Intelligence and Special Abilities.* Holt. '34.

KLINEBERG, OTTO. *Race Differences.* Harper. '35.

—— *Negro Intelligence.* Columbia U. Press. '35.

SCHWESINGER, G. C. *Heredity and Environment.* (Detailed treatment of intelligence studies, with large bibliography including most references up to 1933.) Macmillan. '33.

TERMAN, L. M., and MERRILL, M. A. *Measuring Intelligence.* (Revised intelligence tests.) Houghton Mifflin. '37.

CATTELL, R. B. *Is National Intelligence Declining?* (British study.) Eug. Rev., Oct. '36.

Papers referred to in text, reporting original studies:

—— LAMSON, E. E., J. of Educ. Psych., Jan. '38.
—— LEAHY, A. M., J. Am. Statist. Assn. 30:281. '35.
—— LITHAUER, DONAH B., and KLINEBERG, O., J. of Genet. Psych. '33.
—— SKEELS, HAROLD M., J. of Consult. Psych., Mar.-Apr. '38.
—— WELLMAN, BETH L., J. of Exper. Educ., Dec. '37; J. of Nat'l. Educ. Assn., Feb. '38; and J. of Consult. Psych., July-Aug. '38.

Musical Talent

MJOEN, JON A. *Die Vererbung der musikalischen Begabung.* Metzner, Berlin. '34.

SEASHORE, CARL E. (Author or Editor). *Studies in the Psychology of Music.* University of Iowa:

—— Vol. II. By HAZEL M. STANTON. *Measurement of Musical Talent.* (With chapter on Inheritance.) '37.

—— Vol. IV. *Objective Analysis of Musical Performance.* '37.

PHILIPTSCHENKO, J. (In Russian.) *Studies on Inheritance of Musical Talent.* Bulletin of the Bureau of Genetics and Plant Breeding, Vol. V. Leningrad. '27.

Genius

ELLIS, HAVELOCK. *A Study of British Genius.* Houghton Mifflin. '26.

HENRY, G. W. *Essentials of Psychiatry.* 350-55. (Discussion of abnormalities in famous persons.) Williams & Wilkins. '38.

TERMAN, L. M., et al. *Studies of 1,000 Gifted Children.* 2nd ed. *Genetic Studies of Genius,* Vol. I. Stanford U. Press.

EAST, E. M. *Insanity and Genius.* J. of Hered., Aug. '38.

Personality

ALLPORT, G. W. *Personality.* Holt. '37.

DOLL, E. A. *A Practical Method for the Measurement of Social Competence.* Eug. Rev., Oct. '37.

MORTON, N. W. *Personality Tendencies and Physique.* J. Abnorm. Soc. Psychol. 30:430. '36.

Sexual Behavior

TERMAN, L. M., and MILES, C. C. *Sex and Personality*. McGraw-Hill. '36.

WESTERMARCK, E. Chapter "Homosexual Love" in *The Making of Man,* edited by V. F. Calverton. Modern Library. '31.

HENRY, G. W. *Psychogenic Factors in Overt Homosexuality.* Amer. J. of Psychiatry. 93:4. Jan. '37.

—— with GALBRAITH, H. M. *Constitutional Factors in Homosexuality.* Amer. J. of Psychiatry, May '34.

SANDERS, J. *Homosexuelle Zwillinge.* Genetica. 16:401. '34.

Crime

HAYNES, F. E. *Criminology*. McGraw-Hill. '35.

LANGE, J. *Crime and Destiny*. A. & C. Boni. '31.

Report of Natl. Com. on Law Observance and Enforcement. U. S. Govt. Printing Office. '31.

HOFFMAN, F. L. *The Homicide Record for 1936.* Spectator, Apr. 29. '37.

ROSANOFF, A. J., et al. *Criminality and Delinquency in Twins.* J. Crim. Law and Criminology. 24:923. '34.

Evolution

HOOTON, E. A. *Up from the Ape.* Macmillan. '31.

HURST, C. C. *Heredity and the Ascent of Man.* Macmillan. '35.

MacCURDY, G. G. (Editor). *Early Man.* (A Symposium.) Lippincott. '37.

REISER, O. L. *Cosmecology: A Theory of Evolution.* J. of Hered., Nov. '37.

Race

BARZUN, JACQUES. *Race: A Study of Modern Superstition.* (Includes an extensive critical bibliography.) Harcourt, Brace. '37.

BOAS, FRANZ. *The Mind of Primitive Man.* rev. ed. Macmillan. '38.

——*Anthropology and Modern Life.* rev. ed. Norton. '32.

—— *Effect of American Environment on Immigrants and Their Descendants.* Science, Dec. 11, '36.

HALDANE, J. B. S. *Heredity and Politics*. Norton. '38.

HERSKOVITS, M. J. *The American Negro, A Study in Race Crossing.* Knopf. '28.

HUXLEY, JULIAN, and HADDON, A. C. *We Europeans.* Harper. '36.

REUTER, E. B. *Race Mixture: Studies in Intermarriage,* etc. McGraw-Hill. '31.

—— (Editor). *Race and Culture Contacts.* McGraw-Hill. '34.

HRDLICKA, ALES. *Reflections Regarding Human Heredity.* Amer. Philos. Soc. Proceedings, 75, No. 4:295. '35

Eugenic Problems

CARR-SAUNDERS, A. M. *World Populations.* Oxford U. Press. '36.

HOLMES, S. J. *Human Genetics and Its Social Import.* McGraw-Hill. '36.

HUNTINGTON, ELLSWORTH. *Tomorrow's Children*. Wiley. '35.

LORIMER, F., and OSBORN, F. *Dynamics of Population*. Macmillan. '34.

POPENOE, P., and JOHNSON, R. S. *Applied Eugenics*. 2d ed. Macmillan. '33.

MYERSON, A., et al. *Eugenical Sterilization*. (Report of Committee, Amer. Neurolog. Assn.) Macmillan. '37.

THOMPSON, WARREN. *Population Problems*. 2d ed. McGraw-Hill. '35.

—— *A Eugenics Program for the U. S.* Eug. Rev. 27:321. Jan. '36.

Pre-Marital Health Schedule. (As used in England, with notes for physicians.) Eug. Rev. 27:306. Jan. '36.

SNYDER, L. H. *Present Trends in the Study of Human Inheritance.* Eugenical News. 23:61. July-Aug. '38.

Fertility and Sterility

CATTELL, R. B. *Sterility in Man*. Oxford U. Press. '37.

MEAKER, S. R. *Human Sterility*. Wood. '34.

WILHELM, S. F. *Sterility in the Male*. Oxford U. Press. '37.

WAGNER-MANSLAU, W. *The Inheritance of Fertility.* Ann. Eugenics. 6:225. '35.

ZUCKERMAN, S. *The Physiology of Fertility in Man and Monkey.* Eug. Rev. 28:37. Apr. '36.

Genetics of Domestic Plants and Animals

Yearbooks, United States Dept. of Agriculture for 1936 and 1937. Superintendent of Documents, Washington, D. C.

(These two massive volumes present in elaborate detail genetic facts about almost every important domesticated plant and animal.)

LEADING PUBLICATIONS DEALING WITH HEREDITY

The following are indispensable sources of information regarding the constant new developments in the field of genetics. Some of these are devoted chiefly to experimental genetics, but all carry many valuable articles on human heredity.

Annals of Eugenics. (A quarterly devoted to statistical studies in genetics and human inheritance.) Galton Laboratory, University College, Gower St., London, W.C. 1.

Eugenical News. Eugenics Research Assn., Cold Spring Harbor, Long Island, N. Y.

Eugenics Review. (Quarterly.) Published in London, Eng. Macmillan & Co., Ltd., St. Martin's St. W.C. 2. (Obtainable free with membership in the American Eugenics Society, 50 W. 50th St., N. Y. C.)

Genetics. Brooklyn Botanic Garden, Brooklyn, N. Y.

Journal of Genetics. (British.) Cambridge U. Press, England.

Journal of Heredity. Published by American Genetic Assn., Victor Bldg., Washington, D. C.

INDEX

(Figures in bold face refer to illustrations.)